THE

NATURAL HISTORY OF SELBORNE

THE WILLOW WREN.

The Natural History

of Selborne

and

The Naturalist's Calendar

BY

GILBERT WHITE

A NEW EDITION

LONDON

BLACKIE & SON, Limited, 50 Old Bailey, E.C.
and Glasgow and Dublin

CONTENTS.

INTRODUCTION.

It would be hard to over-estimate the influence of the "Natural History of Selborne" in promoting the study of Nature; and when it is considered that there is perhaps nothing that yields so pure and simple a delight, or that tends so much to keep the mind fresh and young, as the pursuit of natural science, it will be seen that the author of this delightful book was a benefactor to his race of no secondary or unimportant rank. Indeed, it is not putting Gilbert White on too high a pedestal to say that, among those who have done their best in the humbler and obscurer walks of life to which they have been called, few have left an influence more wide-spread and enduring than he has. No life could emphasize that truth better than his.

Of the details of that life, however, we know little. Nor is it specially necessary that we should, his work, like that of all great men, being his life. To an edition of his "Selborne" published in 1802, his brother John appended a short biographical sketch of the author, and we cannot do better than quote here the particulars he there gave.

"Gilbert White was the eldest son of John White of Selborne, Esq., and of Anne, the daughter of Thomas Holt, rector of Streatham in Surrey. He was born at Selborne on July 18th, 1720; and received his school education at Basingstoke, under the Rev. Thomas Warton, vicar of that place, and father of those two distinguished literary characters, Dr. Joseph Warton, master of Winchester school, and Mr. Thomas Warton, poetry-professor at Oxford. He was admitted at Oriel College, Oxford, in December, 1739, and took his degree of Bachelor of Arts in June, 1743. In March, 1744, he was elected fellow of his college. He became Master of Arts in October, 1746, and was admitted as one of the senior proctors of the University in April, 1752. Being of an unambitious temper, and strongly attached to the charms of rural scenery, he early fixed his residence in his native village, where he spent the greater part of his life in literary occupations, and especially in the study of Nature. This he followed with a patient assiduity, and a mind ever open to the lessons of piety and benevolence, which such a study is so well calculated to afford. Though several occasions offered of settling upon a college living, he could never persuade himself to quit the beloved spot, which was indeed a peculiarly happy situation for an observer. He was much esteemed by a select society of intelligent and worthy friends, to whom he paid occasional visits. Thus his days passed tranquil and serene, with scarcely any other vicissitudes than those of the seasons, till they closed at a mature age on June 26th, 1793."

White was the eldest of a large family, eight of whom grew up. Of these, several of Gilbert's brothers turned their attention to natural history, the same as himself, and aided him considerably in his investigations. One of them, Benjamin, became a publisher, chiefly of works on natural history, and it is probably to his suggestion that we owe the publication of the "Natural History of Selborne". It was certainly first issued by him.

Taking up his residence at Selborne in 1755, while his father was still living, White became the owner of the house in which he was born shortly after the latter's death, which occurred in 1758, and made it his abode for the remainder of his days. He was successively curate of Faringdon, a neighbouring parish, and of Selborne. Subsequently he accepted a living which required no service on his part, the duties being performed by others. The fact is, he had a sufficient income to keep him in ease and comfort; and as he never married, and had no ambition for place or power, he was content to spend his days in the rural village he loved so well, occupying himself with the simple duties that came in his way, and devoting the plentiful leisure which remained to him to the never-wearying study of Nature.

At what time he began his observations is not known, but we may presume that they were commenced soon after his settlement at Selborne, the habit growing and growing, till it became the almost all-absorbing passion that it eventually did. The Letters of which his book consists were probably not originally intended for publication, and it is possibly to that cause that their success must be attributed. They have nothing of the nature of a treatise about them, but are full of the interest and pleasure which the writer takes in his observations and investigations: and therein lies their charm.

The "Natural History of Selborne" was published in 1789, the year of the French Revolution. It has gone through many editions; a German one having been published as early as 1792, a year before White's death, which occurred in June, 1793. Since that time the pleasant Hampshire village, which has become through his labours a synonym for a love of Nature, and the devoted study of her ways, has been as it were a shrine to which students of natural history, and especially admirers of Gilbert White's work, have made loving pilgrimage.

As regards the "Natural History" itself, it must be borne in mind that our knowledge, in respect to the subjects wherein White was specially interested, has greatly advanced since his time; so that in many points his views will be found erroneous, and in some cases his observations not sustained by subsequent research. In some instances these errors have been pointed out in the present edition; but a sparing use has been made of notes, as they tend to distract the attention; and besides it has been thought that, if the book serve its purpose by creating an interest in natural history, and by inculcating habits of observation, the necessary exactness of information as regards contemporary science will easily be obtained from other and more modern works.

One instance in which White inclined to an erroneous view is that regarding the habits of swallows. As will be seen from the letters, he became more and more convinced that they pass the winter in a state of torpidity. Daines Barrington, the correspondent to whom the second series of letters were addressed, was still more positive in favour of that theory as against migration. Yet nothing is now more clearly established than the fact of the annual migration of the hirundines.

Of White's other correspondent, Pennant, it may be as well to say that he was the author of a number of works on natural history, chief among which was his *British Zoology*, which gained him considerable reputation both in England and on the Continent.

For the sake of concentration, some of White's Observations relating to birds, reptiles, and insects, usually printed separately, under the general heading of "Observations on Nature", have been incorporated with the Letters.

THE INVITATION TO SELBORNE.

SEE Selborne spreads her boldest beauties round,
The varied valley, and the mountain ground,
Wildly majestic! what is all the pride
Of flats, with loads of ornament supplied?
Unpleasing, tasteless, impotent expense,
Compared with Nature's rude magnificence.
    Arise, my stranger, to these wild scenes haste;
The unfinish'd farm awaits your forming taste:
Plan the pavilion, airy, light, and true;
Through the high arch call in the length'ning view;
Expand the forest sloping up the hill;
Swell to a lake the scant, penurious rill;
Extend the vista, raise the castle mound
In antique taste with turrets ivy-crown'd;
O'er the gay lawn the flowery shrub dispread,
Or with the blending garden mix the mead;
Bid China's pale, fantastic fence delight;
Or with the mimic statue trap the sight.
    Oft on some evening, sunny, soft, and still,
The Muse shall lead thee to the beech-grown hill,
To spend in tea the cool, refreshing hour,
Where nods in air the pensile, nest-like bower;[1]
Or where the Hermit hangs the straw-clad cell,[2]
Emerging gently from the leafy dell;
By Fancy planned; as once th' inventive maid
Met the hoar sage amid the secret shade;
Romantic spot! from whence in prospect lies
Whate'er of landscape charms our feasting eyes;
The pointed spire, the hall, the pasture-plain,
The russet fallow, or the golden grain,
The breezy lake that sheds a gleaming light,
Till all the fading picture fail the sight.
    Each to his task; all different ways retire;
Cull the dry stick; call forth the seeds of fire;
Deep fix the kettle's props, a forky row,
Or give with fanning hat the breeze to blow.

---

[1] A kind of an arbour on the side of a hill.

[2] A grotesque building, contrived by a young gentleman, who used on occasion to appear in the character of a hermit.

Whence is this taste, the furnish'd hall forgot,
To feast in gardens, or the unhandy grot?
Or novelty with some new charms surprises,
Or from our very shifts some joy arises.
Hark, while below the village-bells ring round,
Echo, sweet nymph, returns the soften'd sound;
But if gusts rise, the rushing forests roar,
Like the tide tumbling on the pebbly shore.

Adown the vale, in lone, sequester'd nook,
Where skirting woods embrown the dimpling brook,
The ruin'd convent lies; here wont to dwell
The lazy canon midst his cloister'd cell;[1]
While papal darkness brooded o'er the land,
Ere Reformation made her glorious stand:
Still oft at eve belated shepherd-swains
See the cowl'd spectre skim the folded plains.

To the high Temple would my stranger go,[2]
The mountain-brow commands the woods below:
In Jewry first this order found a name,
When madding Croisades set the world in flame;
When western climes, urged on by Pope and priest,
Pour'd forth their millions o'er the deluged East:
Luxurious knights, ill suited to defy
To mortal fight Turcéstan chivalry.

Nor be the Parsonage by the muse forgot;
The partial bard admires his native spot;
Smit with its beauties, loved, as yet a child,
(Unconscious why) its scapes grotesque, and wild.
High on a mound th' exalted gardens stand,
Beneath, deep valleys scoop'd by Nature's hand.
A Cobham here, exulting in his art,
Might blend the General's with the Gardener's part;
Might fortify with all the martial trade
Of rampart, bastion, fosse, and palisade;
Might plant the mortar with wide threatening bore,
Or bid the mimic cannon seem to roar.

Now climb the steep, drop now your eye below,
Where round the blooming village orchards grow;
There, like a picture, lies my lowly seat,
A rural, shelter'd, unobserved retreat.

---

[1] The ruins of a priory, founded by Peter de Rupibus, Bishop of Winchester.

[2] The remains of a preceptory of the Knights Templars; at least it was a farm dependent upon some preceptory of that order. I find it was a preceptory called the Preceptory of Sudington; now called Southington.

Me far above the rest Selbornian scenes,
The pendent forests, and the mountain greens
Strike with delight; there spreads the distant view
That gradual fades till sunk in misty blue:
Here Nature hangs her slopy woods to sight,
Rills purl between, and dart a quivering light.

THE NATURAL HISTORY
OF SELBORNE

LETTERS TO THOMAS PENNANT

LETTER I

THE parish of Selborne lies in the extreme eastern corner of the county of Hampshire, bordering on the county of Sussex, and not far from the county of Surrey; is about fifty miles south-west of London, in latitude fifty-one, and near mid-way between the towns of Alton and Petersfield. Being very large and extensive, it abuts on twelve parishes, two of which are in Sussex, viz., Trotton and Rogate. If you begin from the south and proceed westward, the adjacent parishes are Emshot, Newton, Valence, Faringdon, Harteley Mauduit, Great Wardleham, Kingsley, Hedleigh, Bramshot, Trotton, Rogate, Lysse, and Greatham. The soils of this district are almost as various and diversified as the views and aspects. The high part of the south-west consists of a vast hill of chalk, rising three hundred feet above the village, and is divided into a sheep-down, the high wood and a long hanging wood, called the Hanger. The covert of this eminence is altogether *beech*, the most lovely of all forest trees, whether we consider its smooth rind or bark, its glossy foliage, or graceful pendulous boughs. The down, or sheepwalk, is a pleasing park-like spot, of about one mile by half that space, jutting out on the verge of the hill-country, where it begins to break down into the plains, and commanding a very engaging view, being an assemblage of hill, dale, wood-lands, heath, and water. The prospect is bounded to the south-east and east by the vast range of mountains called the Sussex Downs, by Guilddown near Guildford, and by the downs round Dorking, and Ryegate in

Surrey, to the north-east, which altogether, with the country beyond Alton and Farnham, form a noble and extensive outline.

At the foot of this hill, one stage or step from the uplands, lies the village, which consists of one single straggling street, three-quarters of a mile in length, in a sheltered vale, and running parallel with the Hanger. The houses are divided from the hill by a vein of stiff clay (good wheat-land), yet stand on a rock of white stone, little in appearance removed from chalk; but seems so far from being calcareous, that it endures extreme heat. Yet that the freestone still preserves somewhat that is analogous to chalk, is plain from the beeches which descend as low as those rocks extend, and no farther, and thrive as well on them, where the ground is steep, as on the chalks.

The cart-way of the village divides, in a remarkable manner, two very incongruous soils. To the south-west is a rank clay, that requires the labour of years to render it mellow; while the gardens to the north-east, and small enclosures behind, consist of a warm, forward, crumbling mould, called black malm, which seems highly saturated with vegetable and animal manure; and these may perhaps have been the original site of the town; while the woods and coverts might extend down to the opposite bank.

At each end of the village, which runs from south-east to north-west, arises a small rivulet: that at the north-west end frequently fails; but the other is a fine perennial spring, little influenced by drought or wet seasons, called Well-head.[1]

This breaks out of some high grounds joining to Nore Hill, a noble chalk promontory, remarkable for sending forth two streams into two different seas. The one to the south becomes a branch of the Arun, running to Arundel, and so falling into the British Channel; the other to the north. The Selborne stream makes one branch of the Wey; and, meeting the Blackdown stream at Hedleigh, and the Alton and Farnham stream at Tilford-bridge, swells into a considerable river, navigable at Godalming; from whence it passes to Guildford, and so into the Thames at Weybridge; and thus at the Nore into the German Ocean.

Our wells, at an average, run to about sixty-three feet, and

[1] This spring produced, September 10th, 1781, after a severe hot summer, and a preceding dry spring and winter, nine gallons of water in a minute, which is 540 in an hour, and 12,960, or 216 hogsheads, in twenty-four hours, or one natural day. At this time many of the wells failed, and all the ponds in the vale were dry.—W.

when sunk to that depth seldom fail; but produce a fine limpid water, soft to the taste, and much commended by those who drink the pure element, but which does not lather well with soap.

To the north-west, north and east of the village, is a range of fair enclosures, consisting of what is called a white malm, a sort of rotten or rubble stone, which, when turned up to the frost and rain, moulders to pieces, and becomes manure to itself.[1]

Still on to the north-east, and a step lower, is a kind of white land, neither chalk nor clay, neither fit for pasture nor for the plough, yet kindly for hops, which root deep into the freestone, and have their poles and wood for charcoal growing just at hand. The white soil produces the brightest hops.

As the parish still inclines down towards Wolmer Forest, at the juncture of the clays and sand the soil becomes a wet, sandy loam, remarkable for timber, and infamous for roads. The oaks of Temple and Blackmoor stand high in the estimation of purveyors, and have furnished much naval timber; while the trees on the freestone grow large, but are what workmen call shaky, and so brittle as often to fall to pieces in sawing. Beyond the sandy loam the soil becomes a hungry lean sand, till it mingles with the forest; and will produce little without the assistance of lime and turnips.

LETTER II.

In the court of Norton farmhouse, a manor farm to the north-west of the village, on the white malm, stood within these twenty years a broad-leaved elm, or wych hazel, *Ulmus folio latissimo scabro* of Ray,[2] which, though it had lost a considerable leading bough, equal to a moderate tree, in the great storm in the year 1703, yet, when felled, contained eight loads of timber; and, being too bulky for a carriage, was sawn off at seven feet above the butt, where it measured near eight feet in the diameter. This elm I mention to show to what a bulk planted elms may attain; as this tree must certainly have been such from its situation.

In the centre of the village, and near the church, is a square

---

[1] This soil produces good wheat and clover.—W.
[2] *Ulmus montanus.*

piece of ground surrounded by houses, and vulgarly called the Plestor.[1] In the midst of this spot stood, in old times, a vast oak, with a short squat body, and huge horizontal arms extending almost to the extremity of the area. This venerable tree, surrounded with stone steps, and seats above them, was the delight of old and young, and a place of much resort in summer evenings; where the former sat in grave debate, while the latter frolicked and danced before them. Long might it have stood, had not the amazing tempest in 1703 overturned it at once, to the infinite regret of the inhabitants, and the vicar, who bestowed several pounds in setting it in its place again: but all his care could not avail; the tree sprouted for a time, then withered and died. This oak I mention to show to what a bulk planted oaks also may arrive: and planted this tree must certainly have been, as will appear from what will be said farther concerning this area, when we enter on the antiquities of Selborne.

On the Blackmoor estate there is a small wood called Losel's, of a few acres, that was lately furnished with a set of oaks of a peculiar growth and great value; they were tall and taper like firs, but standing near together had very small heads, only a little brush without any large limbs. About twenty years ago the bridge at the Toy, near Hampton Court, being much decayed, some trees were wanted for the repairs that were fifty feet long without bough, and would measure twelve inches diameter, at the little end. Twenty such trees did a purveyor find in this little wood, with this advantage, that many of them answered the description at sixty feet. These trees were sold for twenty pounds apiece.

In the centre of this grove there stood an oak, which, though shapely and tall on the whole, bulged out into a large excrescence about the middle of the stem. On this a pair of ravens had fixed their residence for such a series of years, that the oak was distinguished by the title of the Raven Tree. Many were the attempts of the neighbouring youths to get at this eyry: the difficulty whetted their inclinations, and each was ambitious of surmounting the arduous task. But, when they arrived at the swelling, it jutted out so in their way, and was so far beyond their grasp, that the most daring lads were awed, and acknowledged the undertaking to be too hazardous: so the ravens built on, nest upon nest, in perfect security, till the fatal day arrived in which the wood was to be levelled.

[1] Plestor Saxon *Plegstow*, means playing-place.

It was in the month of February, when these birds usually sit. The saw was applied to the butt, the wedges were inserted into the opening, the woods echoed to the heavy blow of the beetle or mallet, the tree nodded to its fall; but still the dam sat on. At last, when it gave way, the bird was flung from her nest; and, though her parental affection deserved a better fate, was whipped down by the twigs, which brought her dead to the ground.

LETTER III.

The fossil-shells of this district, and sorts of stone, such as have fallen within my observation, must not be passed over in silence. And first I must mention, as a great curiosity, a specimen that was ploughed up in the chalky fields, near the side of the down, and given to me for the singularity of its appearance; which, to an incurious eye, seems like a petrified fish of about four inches long, the *cardo* (or hinge) passing for a head and mouth. It is in reality a bivalve of the Linnæan Genus of *Mytilus*, and the species of *Crista Galli*; called by Lister, *Rastellum*; by Rumphius, *Ostreum plicatum minus*; by D'Argenville, *Auris Porci*, s. *Crista Galli*; and by those who make collections, cock's-comb. Though I applied to several such in London, I never could meet with an entire specimen; nor could I ever find in books any engraving from a perfect one. In the superb museum at Leicester House, permission was given me to examine for this article; and though I was disappointed as to the fossil, I was highly gratified with the sight of several of the shells themselves in high preservation. This bivalve is only known to inhabit the Indian Ocean, where it fixes itself to a zoophyte, known by the name *Gorgonia*. The curious foldings of the suture the one into the other, the alternate flutings or grooves, and the curved form of my specimen are much easier expressed by the pencil than by words.

Cornua Ammonis are very common about this village. As we were cutting an inclining path up the Hanger, the labourers found them frequently on that steep, just under the soil, in the chalk, and of a considerable size. In the lane above Wallhead, in the way to Emshot, they abound in the bank in a darkish sort of marl, and are usually very small and soft: but in Clay's Pond, a little farther on, at the end of the pit, where the soil is dug out for manure, I have occasionally observed them of large dimensions, perhaps fourteen or sixteen inches in diameter. But as these did not consist of firm stone, but were formed of a kind of *terra lapidosa*, or hardened clay, as soon as they were exposed to the rains and frost they mouldered away. These seemed as if they were a very recent production. In the chalk-pit, at the north-west end of the Hanger, large *nautili* are sometimes observed.

In the very thickest strata of our freestone, and at considerable depths, well-diggers often find large scallops or *pectines*, having both shells deeply striated, and ridged and furrowed alternately. They are highly impregnated with, if not wholly composed of, the stone of the quarry.

LETTER IV.

As in a former letter the freestone of this place has been only mentioned incidentally, I shall here become more particular.

This stone is in great request for hearth-stones, and the beds of ovens; and in lining of lime-kilns it turns to good account; for the workmen use sandy loam instead of mortar; the sand of which fluxes,[1] and runs by the intense heat, and so cases over the whole face of the kiln with a strong vitrified coat like glass, that it is well preserved from injuries of weather, and endures thirty or forty years. When chiseled smooth, it makes elegant fronts for houses, equal in colour and grain to the Bath stone; and superior in one respect, that, when seasoned, it does not scale. Decent chimney-pieces are worked from it of much closer and finer grain than Portland; and rooms are floored with it; but it proves rather too soft for this purpose. It is a freestone, cutting in all directions; yet has something of a grain parallel with the horizon, and therefore should not be surbedded, but laid in the same position that it grows in the quarry.[2] On the ground abroad this firestone will not succeed for pavements, because, probably some degrees of saltness prevailing within it, the rain tears the slabs to pieces.[3] Though this stone is too hard to be acted on by

---

[1] There may probably be also in the chalk itself that is burnt for lime a proportion of sand: for few chalks are so pure as to have none.—W.

[2] To *surbed* stone is to set it edgewise, contrary to the posture it had in the quarry, says Dr. Plot, *Oxfordshire*, p. 77. But *surbedding* does not succeed in our dry walls; neither do we use it so in ovens, though he says it is best for Teynton stone.—W.

[3] "Firestone is full of salts, and has no sulphur: must be close-grained, and have no interstices. Nothing supports fire like salts; saltstone perishes exposed to wet and frost."—PLOT'S *Staff.*, p. 152.—W.

vinegar, yet both the white part, and even the blue rag, ferment strongly in mineral acids. Though the white stone will not bear wet, yet in every quarry at intervals there are thin strata of blue rag, which resist rain and frost; and are excellent for pitching of stables, paths, and courts, and for building of dry walls against banks, a valuable species of fencing much in use in this village, and for mending of roads. This rag is rugged and stubborn, and will not hew to a smooth face, but is very durable; yet, as these strata are shallow and lie deep, large quantities cannot be procured but at considerable expense. Among the blue rags turn up some blocks tinged with a stain of yellow or rust colour, which seem to be nearly as lasting as the blue; and every now and then balls of a friable substance, like rust of iron, called rust balls.

In Wolmer Forest I see but one sort of stone, called by the workmen sand or forest-stone. This is generally of the colour of rusty iron, and might probably be worked as iron ore; is very hard and heavy, and of a firm, compact texture, and composed of a small roundish crystalline grit, cemented together by a brown, terrene, ferruginous matter; will not cut without difficulty, nor easily strike fire with steel. Being often found in broad flat pieces, it makes good pavement for paths about houses, never becoming slippery in frost or rain; is excellent for dry walls, and is sometimes used in buildings. In many parts of that waste it lies scattered on the surface of the ground; but is dug on Weaver's Down, a vast hill on the eastern verge of that forest, where the pits are shallow and the stratum thin. This stone is imperishable.

From a notion of rendering their work the more elegant, and giving it a finish, masons chip this stone into small fragments about the size of the head of a large nail, and then stick the pieces into the wet mortar along the joints of their freestone walls; this embellishment carries an odd appearance, and has occasioned strangers sometimes to ask us pleasantly, "whether we fastened our walls together with tenpenny nails"

LETTER V.

Among the singularities of this place the two rocky hollow lanes, the one to Alton, and the other to the forest, deserve our attention. These roads, running through the malm lands, are, by the traffic of ages, and the fretting of water, worn down through the first stratum of our freestone, and partly through the second; so that they look more like water-courses than roads; and are bedded with naked rag for furlongs together. In many places they are reduced sixteen or eighteen feet beneath the level of the fields; and after floods, and in frosts, exhibit very grotesque and wild appearances, from the tangled roots that are twisted among the strata, and from the torrents rushing down their broken sides; and especially when those cascades are frozen into icicles, hanging in all the fanciful shapes of frost-work. These rugged gloomy scenes affright the ladies when they peep down into them from the paths above, and make timid horsemen shudder while they ride along them; but delight the naturalist with their various botany, and particularly with the curious *filices* with which they abound.

The manor of Selborne, was it strictly looked after, with all its kindly aspects, and all its sloping coverts, would swarm with game; even now hares, partridges, and pheasants abound; and in old days woodcocks were as plentiful. There are few quails, because they more affect open fields than enclosures; after harvest some few landrails are seen.

[A man brought me a landrail or daker-hen, a bird so rare in this district, that we seldom see more than one or two in a season, and those only in autumn. This is deemed a bird of passage by all the writers; yet from its formation, seems to be poorly qualified for migration; for its wings are short, and placed so forward, and out of the centre of gravity, that it flies in a very heavy and embarrassed manner, with its legs hanging down; and can hardly be sprung a second time, as it runs very fast, and seems to depend more on the swiftness of its feet than on its flying.

When we came to draw it, we found the entrails so soft and tender in appearance, they might have been dressed like the ropes of a woodcock. The craw or crop was small and lank, containing a mucus; the gizzard thick and strong, and filled with small shell snails, some whole, and many ground to pieces through the attrition which is occasioned by the muscular force and motion of that intestine. We saw no gravels among the food: perhaps the shell snails might perform the functions of gravels or pebbles, and might grind one another. Landrails used to abound formerly, I remember, in the low wet bean-fields of Christian Malford in North Wilts, and in the meadows near Paradise Gardens at Oxford, where I have often heard them cry crex, crex. The bird mentioned above weighed seven and a half ounces, was fat and tender. and in flavour like the

flesh of a woodcock. The liver was very large and delicate.—
Observations on Nature.[1]

The parish of Selborne, by taking in so much of the forest,
is a vast district. Those who tread the bounds are employed
part of three days in the business, and are of opinion that the
outline, in all its curves and indentings, does not comprise less
than thirty miles.

The village stands in a sheltered spot, secured by the Hanger
from the strong westerly winds. The air is soft, but rather
moist from the effluvia of so many trees; yet perfectly healthy
and free from agues.

The quantity of rain that falls on it is very considerable, as
may be supposed in so woody and mountainous a district. As
my experience in measuring the water is but of short date, I
am not qualified to give the mean quantity.[2] I only know that

	Inch.	Hund.
From May 1, 1779, to the end of the year there fell .	28	37 !
Jan. 1, 1780, to Jan. 1, 1781 . . .	27	32
Jan. 1, 1781, to Jan. 1, 1782 . . .	30	71
Jan. 1, 1782, to Jan. 1, 1783 . . .	50	26 !
Jan. 1, 1783, to Jan. 1, 1784 . . .	33	71
Jan. 1, 1784, to Jan. 1, 1785 . . .	38	80
Jan. 1, 1785, to Jan. 1, 1786 . . .	31	55
Jan. 1, 1786, to Jan. 1, 1787 . . .	39	57

The village of Selborne, and large hamlet of Oakhanger,
with the single farms, and many scattered houses along the
verge of the forest, contain upwards of six hundred and seventy
inhabitants.

We abound with poor; many of whom are sober and industrious, and live comfortably in good stone or brick cottages,
which are glazed, and have chambers above stairs; mud buildings we have none. Besides the employment from husbandry,
the men work in hop-gardens, of which we have many; and
fell and bark timber. In the spring and summer the women
weed the corn; and enjoy a second harvest in September by
hop-picking. Formerly, in the dead months they availed
themselves greatly by spinning wool, for making of barragons,

---

[1] It has been thought better to introduce these Observations in the text, where they
fit in with the subject, than to print them separately.—ED.

[2] A very intelligent gentleman assures me (and he speaks from upwards of forty
years' experience), that the mean rain of any place cannot be ascertained till a person
has measured it for a very long period. "If I had only measured the rain," says he,
"for the four first years, from 1740 to 1743, I should have said the mean rain at Lyndon was 16¼ inches for the year; if from 1740 to 1750, 18¼ inches. The mean rain
before 1763 was 20¼ inches, from 1763 and since 25¼ inches, from 1770 to 1780, 26 inches.
If only 1773, 1774, and 1775, had been measured, Lyndon mean rain would have been
called 32 inches."—W.

a genteel corded stuff, much in vogue at that time for summer wear; and chiefly manufactured at Alton, a neighbouring town, by some of the people called Quakers; but from circumstances this trade is at an end.[1] The inhabitants enjoy a good share of health and longevity; and the parish swarms with children.

LETTER VI.

Should I omit to describe with some exactness the forest of Wolmer, of which three-fifths perhaps lie in this parish, my account of Selborne would be very imperfect, as it is a district abounding with many curious productions, both animal and vegetable; and has often afforded me much entertainment both as a sportsman and as a naturalist.

The royal forest of Wolmer is a tract of land of about seven miles in length, by two and a half in breadth, running nearly from north to south, and is abutted on (to begin to the south, and so to proceed eastward) by the parishes of Greatham, Lysse, Rogate, and Trotton, in the county of Sussex; by Bramshot, Hedleigh, and Kingsley. This royalty consists entirely of sand covered with heath and fern; but is somewhat diversified with hills and dales, without having one standing tree in the whole extent. In the bottoms, where the waters stagnate, are many bogs, which formerly abounded with subterraneous trees; though Dr. Plot says positively,[2] that "there never were any fallen trees hidden in the mosses of the southern counties". But he was mistaken: for I myself have seen cottages on the verge of this wild district, whose timbers consisted of a black hard wood, looking like oak, which the owners assured me they procured from the bogs by probing the soil with spits, or some such instruments: but the peat is so much cut out, and the moors have been so well examined, that none has been found of late.[3] Besides the oak, I have also been shown pieces

---

[1] Since the passage above was written, I am happy in being able to say that the spinning employment is a little revived, to the no small comfort of the industrious housewife.—W.

[2] See his *History of Staffordshire.*—W.

[3] Old people have assured me, that on a winter's morning they have discovered these trees, in the bogs, by the hoar frost, which lay longer over the space where they are concealed than in the surrounding morass. Nor does this seem to be a fanciful notion, but consistent with true philosophy. Dr. Hales saith, "That the warmth of the earth, at some depth under ground, has an influence in promoting a thaw, as well as the change of the weather from a freezing to a thawing state, is manifest from this observation, viz. Nov. 29th, 1731, a little snow having fallen in the night, it was, by eleven the next morning, mostly melted away on the surface of the earth, except in

of fossil wood of a paler colour, and softer nature, which the inhabitants called fir: but, upon a nice examination, and trial by fire, I could discover nothing resinous in them; and therefore rather suppose that they were parts of a willow or alder, or some such aquatic tree.

This lonely domain is a very agreeable haunt for many sorts of wild fowls, which not only frequent it in the winter, but breed there in the summer; such as lapwings, snipes, wild-ducks, and, as I have discovered within these few years, teals. Partridges in vast plenty are bred in good seasons on the verge of this forest, into which they love to make excursions; and in particular, in the dry summers of 1740 and 1741, and some years after, they swarmed to such a degree that parties of un-reasonable sportsmen killed twenty and sometimes thirty brace in a day.

But there was a nobler species of game in this forest, now extinct, which I have heard old people say abounded much before shooting flying became so common, and that was the heath-cock, or black-game.[1] When I was a little boy I re-collect one coming now and then to my father's table. The last pack remembered was killed about thirty-five years ago; and within these ten years one solitary grey hen was sprung by some beagles in beating for a hare. The sportsmen cried out "A hen pheasant!" but a gentleman present, who had often seen black-game in the north of England, assured me that it was a grey hen.

Nor does the loss of our black-game prove the only gap in the *Fauna Selborniensis*; for another beautiful link in the chain of beings is wanting: I mean the red deer, which toward the beginning of this century amounted to about five hundred head, and made a stately appearance. There is an old keeper, now alive, named Adams, whose great grandfather (mentioned in a perambulation taken in 1635), grandfather, father, and self, enjoyed the head keepership of Wolmer Forest in suc-cession for more than a hundred years. This person assures

several places in Bushy Park, where there were drains dug and covered with earth, on which the snow continued to lie, whether those drains were full of water or dry; as also where elm-pipes lay under ground: a plain proof this, that those drains inter-cepted the warmth of the earth from ascending from greater depths below them; for the snow lay where the drain had more than four feet depth of earth over it. It con-tinued also to lie on thatch, tiles, and the tops of walls."—See Hale's *Hæmastatics*, p. 360. QUERE: Might not such observations be reduced to domestic use, by pro-moting the discovery of old obliterated drains and wells about houses; and in Roman stations and camps lead to the finding of pavements, baths and graves, and other hidden relics of curious antiquity?

[1] Or grouse.

me, that his father has often told him, that Queen Anne, as she was journeying on the Portsmouth road, did not think the forest of Wolmer beneath her royal regard. For she came out of the great road at Lippock, which is just by, and, reposing herself on a bank smoothed for that purpose, lying about half a mile to the east of Wolmer Pond, and still called Queen's Bank, saw with great complacency and satisfaction the whole herd of red deer brought by the keepers along the vale before her, consisting then of about five hundred head. A sight this, worthy of the attention of the greatest sovereign! But he farther adds that, by means of the Waltham blacks, or to use his own expression, as soon as they began blacking, they were reduced to about fifty head, and so continued decreasing till the time of the late Duke of Cumberland. It is now more than thirty years ago that his highness sent down a huntsman, and six yeoman-prickers, in scarlet jackets laced with gold, attended by the stag-hounds; ordering them to take every deer in this forest alive, and to convey them in carts to Windsor. In the course of the summer they caught every stag, some of which showed extraordinary diversion; but in the following winter, when the hinds were also carried off, such fine chases were exhibited as served the country people for matter of talk and wonder for years afterwards. I saw myself one of the yeoman-prickers single out a stag from the herd, and must confess that it was the most curious feat of activity I ever beheld, superior to anything in Mr. Astley's riding-school. The exertions made by the horse and deer much exceeded all my expectations; though the former greatly excelled the latter in speed. When the devoted deer was separated from his companions, they gave him, by their watches, law, as they called it, for twenty minutes; when, sounding their horns, the stop-dogs were permitted to pursue, and a most gallant scene ensued.

LETTER VII.

Though large herds of deer do much harm to the neighbour-hood, yet the injury to the morals of the people is of more moment than the loss of their crops. The temptation is irresistible; for most men are sportsmen by constitution: and there is such an inherent spirit for hunting in human nature, as scarce any inhibitions can restrain. Hence, towards the beginning of this century, all this country was wild about deer-stealing. Unless he was a hunter, as they affected to call themselves, no young person was allowed to be possessed of manhood or gallantry. The Waltham blacks at length committed such enormities, that government was forced to interfere with that severe and sanguinary act called the "Black Act",[1] which now comprehends more felonies than any law that ever was framed before. And, therefore, a late Bishop of Winchester, when urged to re-stock Waltham Chase,[2] refused, from a motive worthy of a prelate, replying "that it had done mischief enough already".

Our old race of deer-stealers is hardly extinct yet: it was but a little while ago that, over their ale, they used to recount the exploits of their youth; such as watching the pregnant hind to her lair, and, when the calf was dropped, paring its feet with a penknife to the quick, to prevent its escape, till it was large and fat enough to be killed; the shooting at one of their neighbours with a bullet in a turnip-field by moonshine, mistaking him for a deer; and the losing a dog in the following extraordinary manner: some fellows, suspecting that a calf new-fallen was deposited in a certain spot of thick fern, went, with a lurcher, to surprise it; when the parent-hind rushed out of the brake, and, taking a vast spring with all her feet close together, pitched upon the neck of the dog, and broke it short in two.

Another temptation to idleness and sporting was a number of rabbits, which possessed all the hillocks and dry places: but these being inconvenient to the huntsmen, on account of their burrows, when they came to take away the deer they permitted the country people to destroy them all.

Such forests and wastes, when their allurements to irregularities are removed, are of considerable service to neighbourhoods that verge upon them, by furnishing them with peat and turf for their firing; with fuel for the burning their lime; and with ashes for their grasses; and by maintaining their geese and their stock of young cattle at little or no expense.

The manor farm of the parish of Greatham has an admitted claim, I see (by an old record taken from the Tower of London), of turning all live stock on the forest, at proper seasons, *bidentibus exceptis* (sheep excepted).[3] The reason, I presume,

---

[1] Statute 9 Geo. I. cap. 22.

[2] This chase remains unstocked to this day; the bishop was Dr. Hoadly.—W.

[3] For this privilege the owners of that estate used to pay to the king annually seven bushels of oats.—W

why sheep[1] are excluded is because, being such close grazers, they would pick out all the finest grasses, and hinder the deer from thriving.

Though (by statute 4 and 5 Wm. and Mary, c. 23) "to burn on any waste, between Candlemas and Midsummer, any grig, ling, heath and furze, goss or fern, is punishable with whipping and confinement in the house of correction"; yet, in this forest, about March or April, according to the dryness of the season, such vast heath-fires are lighted up, that they often get to a masterless head, and, catching the hedges, have sometimes been communicated to the underwoods, woods, and coppices, where great damage has ensued. The plea for these burnings is, that when the old coat of heath, etc., is consumed, young will sprout up, and afford much tender brouze for cattle; but where there is large old furze, the fire, following the roots, consumes the very ground; so that for hundreds of acres nothing is to be seen but smother and desolation, the whole circuit round looking like the cinders of a volcano; and, the soil being quite exhausted, no traces of vegetation are to be found for years. These conflagrations, as they take place usually with a north-east or east wind, much annoy this village with their smoke, and often alarm the country; and, once in particular, I remember that a gentleman, who lives beyond Andover, coming to my house, when he got on the downs between that town and Winchester, at twenty-five miles distance, was surprised much with smoke and a hot smell of fire; and concluded that Alresford was in flames; but, when he came to that town, he then had apprehensions for the next village, and so on to the end of his journey.

On two of the most conspicuous eminences of this forest stand two arbours or bowers, made of the boughs of oak; the one called Waldon Lodge, the other Brimstone Lodge: these the keepers renew annually on the feast of St. Barnabas, taking the old materials for a perquisite. The farm called Blackmoor, in this parish, is obliged to find the posts and brushwood for the former; while the farms at Greatham, in rotation, furnish for the latter; and are all enjoined to cut and deliver the materials at the spot. This custom I mention, because I look upon it to be of very remote antiquity.

---

[1] In the Holt, where a full stock of fallow-deer has been kept up till lately, no sheep are admitted to this day.—W.

LETTER VIII.

On the verge of the forest, as it is now circumscribed, are three considerable lakes, two in Oakhanger, of which I have nothing particular to say; and one called Bin's, or Bean's Pond, which is worthy the attention of a naturalist or a sportsman. For, being crowded at the upper end with willows, and with *carex cespitosa*,[1] it affords such a safe and pleasing shelter to wild-ducks, teals, snipes, etc., that they breed there. In the winter this covert is also frequented by foxes, and sometimes by pheasants; and the bogs produce many curious plants.[2]

By a perambulation of Wolmer Forest and the Holt, made in 1635, and the eleventh year of Charles I. (which now lies before me), it appears that the limits of the former are much circumscribed. For, to say nothing of the farther side, with which I am not so well acquainted, the bounds on this side, in old times, came into Binswood; and extended to the ditch of Wardleham Park, in which stands the curious mount called King John's Hill, and Lodge Hill; and to the verge of Hartley Mauduit, called Mauduit Hatch; comprehending also Short Heath, Oakhanger, and Oakwoods; a large district, now private property, though once belonging to the royal domain.

It is remarkable that the term purlieu is never once mentioned in this long roll of parchment. It contains, besides the perambulation, a rough estimate of the value of the timbers, which were considerable, growing at that time in the district of the Holt;[3] and enumerates the officers, superior and inferior, of those joint forests, for the time being, and their ostensible fees and perquisites. In those days, as at present, there were hardly any trees in Wolmer Forest.

Within the present limits of the forest are three considerable lakes, Hogmer, Cranmer, and Wolmer; all of which are stocked with carp, tench, eels, and perch; but the fish do not thrive well, because the water is hungry, and the bottoms are a naked sand.

A circumstance respecting these ponds, though by no means

[1] I mean that sort which, rising into tall hassocks, is called by the foresters torrets; a corruption, I suppose, of turrets.—W.

[2] See Letter XLI. to Mr. Barrington.

[3] In the beginning of the summer of 1787, the royal forests of Wolmer and Holt were measured by persons sent down by government.—W.

peculiar to them, I cannot pass over in silence; and that is, that instinct by which in summer all the kine, whether oxen, cows, calves, or heifers, retire constantly to the water during the hotter hours; where, being more exempt from flies, and inhaling the coolness of that element, some belly deep, and some only to midleg, they ruminate and solace themselves from about ten in the morning till four in the afternoon, and then return to their feeding. During this great proportion of the day they drop much dung, in which insects nestle; and so supply food for the fish, which would be poorly subsisted but from this contingency. Thus Nature, who is a great econo-mist, converts the recreation of one animal to the support of another! Thomson, who was a nice observer of natural occurrences, did not let this pleasing circumstance escape him. He says in his "Summer",

> "A various group the herds and flocks compose;
> ————————on the grassy bank
> Some ruminating lie; while others stand
> Half in the flood, and, often bending, sip
> The circling surface."

Wolmer Pond, so called, I suppose, for eminence sake, is a vast lake for this part of the world, containing, in its whole circumference, 2,646 yards, or very near a mile and a half. The length of the north-west and opposite side is about 704 yards, and the breadth of the south-west end about 456 yards. This measurement, which I caused to be made with good exactness, gives an area of about sixty-six acres, exclusive of a large irregular arm at the north-east corner, which we did not take into the reckoning.

On the face of this expanse of waters, and perfectly secure from fowlers, lie all day long, in the winter season, vast flocks of ducks, teals, and widgeons, of various denominations; where they preen and solace and rest themselves, till towards sunset, when they issue forth in little parties (for in their natural state they are all birds of the night) to feed in the brooks and meadows; returning again with the dawn of the morning. Had this lake an arm or two more, and were it planted round with thick covert (for now it is perfectly naked), it might make a valuable decoy.

Yet neither its extent, nor the clearness of its water, nor the resort of various and curious fowls, nor its picturesque groups of cattle, can render this meer so remarkable as the great quantity of coins that were found in its bed about forty years ago. But, as such discoveries more properly belong to the antiquities of this place, I shall suppress all particulars for the present, till I enter professedly on my series of letters respecting the more remote history of this village and district.

LETTER IX.

By way of supplement, I shall trouble you once more on this subject, to inform you that Wolmer, with her sister forest Ayles Holt, alias Alice Holt,[1] as it is called in old records, is held by grant from the crown for a term of years.

The grantees that the author remembers are Brigadier-General Emanuel Scroope Howe, and his lady, Ruperta, who was a daughter of Prince Rupert; a Mr. Mordaunt, of the Peterborough family, who married a dowager Lady Pembroke; Henry Bilson Legge and lady; and now Lord Stawell, their son.

The lady of General Howe lived to an advanced age, long surviving her husband; and, at her death, left behind her many curious pieces of mechanism of her father's constructing, who was a distinguished mechanic and artist, as well as warrior; and among the rest, a very complicated clock, lately in possession of Mr. Elmer, the celebrated game-painter at Farnham, in the county of Surrey.

Though these two forests are only parted by a narrow range of enclosures, yet no two soils can be more different; for the Holt consists of a strong loam, of a miry nature, carrying a good turf, and abounding with oaks that grow to be large timber; while Wolmer is nothing but a hungry, sandy, barren waste.

The former being all in the parish of Binsted, is about two miles in extent from north to south, and near as much from east to west; and contains within it many woodlands and lawns, and the great lodge where the grantees reside, and a smaller lodge called Goose Green; and is abutted on by the parishes of Kingsley, Frinsham, Farnham, and Bentley; all of which have right of common.

One thing is remarkable: that though the Holt has been of old well stocked with fallow-deer, unrestrained by any pales

---

[1] In Rot. Inquisit. de statu forest. in Scaccar. 36 Edw. III., it is called Aisholt. In the same, "Tit. Woolmer and Aisholt Hantisc. Dominus Rex habet unam capellam in haia suâ de Kingesle." "Haia, sepes, sepimentum, parcus; a Gall. haie and haye."—SPELMAN'S *Glossary.*—W.

or fences more than a common hedge, yet they were never seen within the limits of Wolmer; nor were the red deer of Wolmer ever known to haunt the thickets or glades of the Holt.

At present the deer of the Holt are much thinned and reduced by the night hunters, who perpetually harass them in spite of the efforts of numerous keepers, and the severe penalties that have been put in force against them as often as they have been detected, and rendered liable to the lash of the law. Neither fines nor imprisonments can deter them; so impossible is it to extinguish the spirit of sporting which seems to be inherent in human nature.

General Howe turned out some German wild boars and sows in his forests, to the great terror of the neighbourhood, and, at one time, a wild bull or buffalo; but the country rose upon them and destroyed them.

A very large fall of timber, consisting of about one thousand oaks, has been cut this spring (viz., 1784) in the Holt forest: one-fifth of which, it is said, belongs to the grantee, Lord Stawell. He lays claim also to the lop and top; but the poor of the parishes of Binsted and Frinsham, Bentley and Kingsley, assert that it belongs to them, and assembling in a riotous manner, have actually taken it all away. One man, who keeps a team, has carried home for his share forty sacks of wood. Forty-five of these people his lordship has served with actions. These trees, which were very sound and in high perfection, were winter-cut, viz., in February and March, before the bark would run. In old times the Holt was estimated to be eighteen miles, computed measure from water-carriage, viz., from the town of Chertsey, on the Thames; but now it is not half that distance, since the Wey is made navigable up to the town of Godalming in the county of Surrey.

LETTER X.

August 4th, 1767.

It has been my misfortune never to have had any neighbours whose studies have led them towards the pursuit of natural knowledge; so that, for want of a companion to quicken my industry and sharpen my attention, I have made but slender progress in a kind of information to which I have been attached from my childhood.

As to swallows (*Hirundines rusticæ*) being found in a torpid state during the winter in the Isle of Wight, or any part of this country, I never heard any such account worth attending to. But a clergyman of an inquisitive turn assures me that when he was a great boy, some workmen, in pulling down the battlements of a church tower early in the spring, found two or three swifts (*Hirundines apodes*)[1] among the rubbish, which were at first appearance dead, but on being carried towards the fire revived. He told me, that out of his great care to preserve them, he put them in a paper bag, and hung them by the kitchen fire, where they were suffocated.

Another intelligent person has informed me, that while he was a schoolboy at Brighthelmstone, in Sussex, a great fragment of the chalk cliff fell down one stormy winter on the beach, and that many people found swallows among the rubbish; but on my questioning him whether he saw any of those birds himself, to my no small disappointment, he answered me in the negative; but that others assured me they did.

Young broods of swallows began to appear this year on July 11th, and young martins (*Hirundines urbicæ*) were then fledged in their nests. Both species will breed again once. For I see by my fauna of last year, that young broods came forth so late as September 18th. Are not these late hatchings more in favour of hiding than migration? Nay, some young martins remained in their nests last year so late as September 29th; and yet they totally disappeared with us by the 5th October.

How strange it is that the swift, which seems to live exactly the same life with the swallow and house-martin, should leave us before the middle of August invariably, while the latter stay often till the middle of October. And once I saw numbers of house-martins on the 7th November. The martins and red-wing fieldfares were flying in sight together, an uncommon assemblage of summer and winter birds!

[Writing nearly twenty-one years later (*March 23rd*, 1788), White gives us, in his *Observations on Nature*, the following additional notes on the hirundines:—

" A gentleman, who was this week on a visit at Waverley, took the opportunity of examining some of the holes in the sand-banks with which that district abounds. As these are undoubtedly bored by bank martins, and are the places where they avowedly breed, he was in hopes they might have slept

[1] *Cypselus apus.*

there also, and that he might have surprised them just as they
were awaking from their winter slumbers. When he had dug
for some time, he found the holes were horizontal and serpentine, as I had observed before; and that the nests were deposited at the inner end, and had been occupied by broods in
former summers, but no torpid birds were to be found. He
opened and examined about a dozen holes. Another gentleman made the same search many years ago, with as little
success. These holes were in depth about two feet.

"March 21st, 1790. A single bank or sand-martin was seen
hovering and playing round the sand-pit at Short Heath, where
in the summer they abound.

"April 9th, 1793. A sober hind assures us, that this day,
on Wishhanger common between Hedleigh and Frinsham, he
saw several bank martins playing in and out, and hanging
before some nest-holes in a sand-hill, where these birds usually
nestle.

"The incident confirms my suspicions, that this species of
hirundo is to be seen first of any; and gives great reason to
suppose that they do not leave their wild haunts at all, but
are secreted amidst the clefts and caverns of those abrupt
cliffs, where they usually spend their summers.

"The late severe weather considered, it is not very probable
that these birds should have migrated so early from a tropical
region, through all these cutting winds and pinching frosts;
but it is easy to suppose that they may, like bats and flies,
have been awakened by the influence of the sun, amidst their
secret *latebræ* or lurking-places, where they have spent the uncomfortable foodless months in a torpid state, and in the profoundest of slumbers.

"There is a large pond at Wishhanger, which induces these
sand-martins to frequent that district. For I have ever remarked that they haunt near great waters, either rivers or
lakes."

Somewhat later White writes:—"During the severe winds
that often prevail late in the spring, it is not easy to say how
the hirundines subsist; for they withdraw themselves, and are
hardly ever seen, nor do any insects appear for their support.
That they can retire to rest, and sleep away these uncomfortable periods, as bats do, is a matter rather to be suspected than
proved; or do they not rather spend their time in deep and
sheltered vales near waters, where insects are more likely
to be found? Certain it is, that hardly any individuals of

this genus have at such times been seen for several days together.

"September 13th, 1791. The congregating flocks of hirundines on the church and tower are very beautiful and amusing. When they fly off together from the roof, on any alarm, they quite swarm in the air. But they soon settle in heaps, and preening their feathers, and lifting up their wings to admit the sun, seem highly to enjoy the warm situation. Thus they spend the heat of the day, preparing for their emigration, and, as it were, consulting when and where they are to go. The flight about the church seems to consist chiefly of house-martins, about 400 in number; but there are other places of rendezvous about the village frequented at the same time.

"It is remarkable that though most of them sit on the battlements and roof, yet many hang or cling for some time by their claws against the surface of the walls, in a manner not practised by them at any other time of their remaining with us.

"The swallows seem to delight more in holding their assemblies on trees.

"November 3rd, 1789. Two swallows were seen this morning at Newton vicarage-house, hovering and settling on the roofs and out-buildings. None have been observed at Selborne since October 11th. It is very remarkable that after the hirundines have disappeared for some weeks, a few are occasionally seen again; sometimes in the first week in November, and that only for one day. Do they not withdraw and slumber in some hiding-place in the interval? For we cannot suppose they had emigrated to warmer climes and so returned again for one day. Is it not more probable that they are awakened from sleep, and like the bats, are come forth to collect a little food? Bats appear at all seasons through the autumn and spring months, when the thermometer is at 50°, because then phalænæ and moths are stirring. These swallows looked like young ones."]

A little yellow bird (it is either a species of the *Alauda trivialis*, or rather perhaps of the *Motacilla trochilus*) still continues to make a sibilous shivering noise in the tops of tall woods.[1] The *Stoparola* of Ray (for which we have as yet no name in these parts) is called in your zoology the fly-catcher.[2] There is one circumstance characteristic of this bird which

[1] See Letter XVI. to Mr. Pennant.
[2] *Muscicapa grisola.*

seems to have escaped observation, and that is, it takes its stand on the top of some stake or post, from whence it springs forth on its prey, catching a fly in the air, and hardly ever touching the ground, but returning still to the same stand for many times together.

I perceive there are more than one species of the *Motacilla trochilus*: Mr. Derham supposes, in "Ray's Philos. Letters", that he has discovered three.[1] In these there is again an instance of some very common birds that have as yet no English name.

Mr. Stillingfleet makes a question whether the black-cap (*Motacilla atricapilla*) be a bird of passage or not: I think there is no doubt of it: for, in April, in the first fine weather, they come trooping all at once, into these parts, but are never seen in the winter. They are delicate songsters.

Numbers of snipes breed every summer in some moory ground on the verge of this parish. It is very amusing to see the cock bird on wing at that time, and to hear his piping and humming notes.

I have had no opportunity yet of procuring any of those mice which I mentioned to you in town. The person that brought me the last says they are plenty in harvest, at which time I will take care to get more; and will endeavour to put the matter out of doubt, whether it be a nondescript species or not.

I suspect much there may be two species of water-rats. Ray says, and Linnæus after him, that the water-rat is web-footed behind. Now I have discovered a rat on the banks of our little stream that is not web-footed, and yet is an excellent swimmer and diver: it answers exactly to the *Mus amphibius* of Linnæus (see *Syst. Nat.*), which he says swims and dives in ditches, "*natat in fossis et urinatur*". I should be glad to procure one with feet spreading out like a palm, "*plantis palmatis*". Linnæus seems to be in a puzzle about his *Mus amphibius*, and to doubt whether it differs from his *Mus terrestris*; which, if it be, as he allows, the "*Mus agrestis capite grandi brachyuros*",[2] of Ray, is widely different from the water-rat, both in size, make, and manner of life.

As to the *Falco*, which I mentioned in town, I shall take the

---

[1] Modern ornithologists recognize three, the willow-wren, the wood-wren, and the chiff-chaff.

[2] This *Mus agrestis* of Ray is the short-tailed field-mouse or vole, *Arvicola agrestis* of Linnæus · the water-rat or water-vole is *Arv. amphibius*.

liberty to send it down to you in Wales; presuming on your candour that you will excuse me if it should appear as familiar to you as it is strange to me. Though mutilated *"qualem dices . . . antehac fuisse, tales cum sint reliquiæ!"* ("Such as you would say it had formerly been from the remains that are".)

It haunted a marshy piece of ground in quest of wild-ducks and snipes; but, when it was shot, had just knocked down a rook, which it was tearing in pieces. I cannot make it answer to any of our English hawks; neither could I find any like it at the curious exhibition of stuffed birds in Spring Gardens. I found it nailed up at the end of a barn, which is the country-man's museum.

The parish I live in is a very abrupt, uneven country, full of hills and woods, and therefore full of birds.

LETTER XI.

SELBORNE, *September 9th,* 1767.

It will not be without impatience that I will wait for your thoughts with regard to the *Falco*; as to its weight, breadth, etc., I wish I had set them down at the time; but, to the best of my remembrance, it weighed two pounds and eight ounces, and measured, from wing to wing, thirty-eight inches. Its cere and feet were yellow, and the circle of its eyelids a bright yellow. As it had been killed some days, and the eyes were sunk, I could make no good observation on the colour of the pupils and the irides.[1]

The most unusual birds I ever observed in these parts were a pair of hoopoes (*Upupa*), which came several years ago in the summer, and frequented an ornamented piece of ground, which joins to my garden, for some weeks. They used to march about in a stately manner, feeding in the walks many times in the day; and seemed disposed to breed in my outlet; but were frighted and persecuted by idle boys, who would never let them be at rest.

Three grosbeaks (*Loxia coccothraustes*)[2] appeared some years ago in my fields, in the winter; one of which I shot. Since that, now and then, one is occasionally seen in the same dead season.

[1] Irides, plural of iris, the coloured circle which surrounds the pupil of the eye.
[2] *Coccothraustes vulgaris.*

[Mr. B. shot a cock grosbeak which he had observed to haunt his garden for more than a fortnight. I began to accuse this bird of making sad havoc among the buds of the cherries, gooseberries, and wall-fruit of all the neighbouring orchards. Upon opening its crop or craw, no buds were to be seen; but a mass of kernels of the stones of fruits. Mr. B. observed that this bird frequented the spot where plum-trees grow, and that he had seen it with somewhat hard in its mouth, which it broke with difficulty; these were the stones of damsons. The Latin ornithologists call this bird *Coccothraustes*, *i.e.*, berry-breaker, because with its large horny beak it cracks and breaks the shells of stone-fruits for the sake of the seed or kernel. Birds of this sort are rarely seen in England, and only in winter.—*Observations on Nature*.]

A crossbill (*Loxia curvirostra*) was killed last year in this neighbourhood.

Our streams, which are small, and rise only at the end of the village, yield nothing but the bull's head or miller's thumb (*Gobius fluviatilis capitatus*), the trout (*Trutta fluviatilis*), the eel (*Anguilla*), the lampern (*Lampœtra parva et fluviatilis*), and the stickle-back (*Pisciculus aculeatus*).

We are twenty miles from the sea, and almost as many from a great river, and therefore see but little of sea birds. As to wild fowls, we have a few teems of ducks bred in the moors where the snipes breed; and multitudes of widgeons and teals in hard weather frequent our lakes in the forest.

Having some acquaintance with a tame brown owl, I find that it casts up the fur of mice, and the feathers of birds in pellets, after the manner of hawks; when full, like a dog, it hides what it cannot eat.

The young of the barn-owl are not easily raised, as they want a constant supply of fresh mice; whereas the young of the brown owl eat indiscriminately all that is brought; snails, rats, kittens, puppies, magpies, and any kind of carrion or offal.

The house-martins have eggs still, and squab young. The last swift I observed was about the 21st August: it was a straggler.

Red-starts, fly-catchers, white-throats, and *Reguli non cristati*,[1] still appear: but I have seen no blackcaps lately.

I forgot to mention that I once saw, in Christ Church College quadrangle in Oxford, on a very sunny warm morning, a house-

[1] See Letter I. to Daines Barrington.

martin flying about, and settling on the parapet, so late as the 20th November.

At present I know only two species of bats, the common *Vespertilio murinus* and the *Vespertilio auritus*.

I was much entertained last summer with a tame bat, which would take flies out of a person's hand. If you gave it any-thing to eat, it brought its wings round before the mouth, hovering and hiding its head in the manner of birds of prey when they feed. The adroitness it showed in shearing off the wings of flies, which were always rejected, was worthy of ob-servation, and pleased me much. Insects seemed to be most acceptable, though it did not refuse raw flesh when offered; so that the notion that bats go down chimneys and gnaw men's bacon seems no improbable story. While I amused myself with this wonderful quadruped, I saw it several times confute the vulgar opinion, that bats when down upon a flat surface cannot get on the wing again, by rising with great ease from the floor. It ran, I observed, with more dispatch than I was aware of; but in a most ridiculous and grotesque manner.

Bats drink on the wing, like swallows, by sipping the surface, as they play over pools and streams. They love to frequent waters, not only for the sake of drinking, but on account of insects, which are found over them in the greatest plenty. As I was going some years ago, pretty late, in a boat from Rich-mond to Sunbury, on a warm summer's evening, I think I saw myriads of bats between the two places; the air swarmed with them all along the Thames, so that hundreds were in sight at a time.

LETTER XII.

November 4th, 1767.

It gave me no small satisfaction to hear that the *Falco* turned out an uncommon one.[1] I must confess I should have been better pleased to have heard that I had sent you a bird that you had never seen before; but that, I find, would be a difficult task.

I have procured some of the mice mentioned in my former letter,[2] a young one and a female with young, both of which

[1] This hawk proved to be a *Falco peregrinus*, a variety.—**W.**
[2] Letter X.

I have preserved in brandy. From the colour, shape, size, and manner of nesting, I make no doubt but that the species is nondescript. They are much smaller, and more slender, than the *Mus domesticus medius* of Ray; and have more of the squirrel or dormouse colour; their belly is white, a straight line along their sides divides the shades of their back and belly. They never enter into houses; are carried into ricks and barns with the sheaves; abound in harvest; and build their nests amidst the straws of the corn above the ground, and sometimes in thistles. They breed as many as eight at a litter, in a little round nest composed of the blades of grass or wheat.

One of these nests I procured this autumn, most artificially platted, and composed of the blades of wheat, perfectly round, and about the size of a cricket-ball; with the aperture so ingeniously closed, that there was no discovering to what part it belonged. It was so compact and well filled, that it would roll across the table without being discomposed, though it contained eight little mice that were naked and blind. As this nest was perfectly full, how could the dam come at her litter respectively so as to administer a teat to each? Perhaps she opens different places for that purpose, adjusting them again when the business is over; but she could not possibly be contained herself in the ball with her young, which moreover would be daily increasing in bulk. This wonderful cradle, an elegant instance of the efforts of instinct, was found in a wheat-field suspended in the head of a thistle.

A gentleman, curious in birds, wrote me word that his servant had shot one last January, in that severe weather, which he believed would puzzle me. I called to see it this summer, not knowing what to expect, but the moment I took it in hand, I pronounced it the male *Garrulus bohemicus* or German silk-tail, from the five peculiar crimson tags or points which it carries at the ends of five of the short remiges.[1] It cannot, I suppose, with any propriety, he called an English bird; and yet I see, by Ray's Philosophical Letters, that great flocks of them, feeding on haws, appeared in this kingdom in the winter of 1685.

The mention of haws puts me in mind that there is a total failure of that wild fruit, so conducive to the support of many of the winged nation. For the same severe weather, late in the spring, which cut off all the produce of the more tender

---

[1] *Remiges*—the large quills of the wings of birds.

and curious trees, destroyed also that of the more hardy and common.

Some birds, haunting with the missel-thrushes, and feeding on the berries of the yew tree, which answered to the description of the *Merula torquata*, or ring-ouzel, were lately seen in this neighbourhood. I employed some people to procure me a specimen, but without success.[1]

Query: Might not canary birds be naturalised to this climate, provided their eggs were put, in the spring, into the nests of some of their congeners, as goldfinches, greenfinches, &c.? Before winter perhaps they might be hardened, and able to shift for themselves.

About ten years ago I used to spend some weeks yearly at Sunbury, which is one of those pleasant villages lying on the Thames, near Hampton Court. In the autumn, I could not help being much amused with those myriads of the swallow kind which assemble in those parts. But what struck me most was, that, from the time they began to congregate, forsaking the chimneys and houses, they roosted every night in the osier-beds of the aits of that river. Now this resorting towards that element, at that season of the year, seems to give some countenance to the northern opinion (strange as it is) of their retiring under water. A Swedish naturalist is so much persuaded of that fact, that he talks in his "Calendar of Flora", as familiarly of the swallow's going under water in the beginning of September, as he would of his poultry going to roost a little before sunset.

An observing gentleman in London writes me word that he saw a house-martin, on the twenty-third of last October, flying in and out of its nest in the Borough. And I myself, on the twenty-ninth of last October (as I was travelling through Oxford), saw four or five swallows hovering round and settling on the roof of the county hospital.

Now is it likely that these poor little birds (which perhaps had not been hatched but a few weeks) should, at that late season of the year, and from so midland a county, attempt a voyage to Goree or Senegal, almost as far as the equator?[2]

I acquiesce entirely in your opinion—that, though most of the swallow kind may migrate, yet that some do stay behind and hide with us during the winter.

As to the short-winged soft-billed birds, which come trooping

---

[1] See Letters XIII. and XX.
[2] See *Adanson's Voyage to Senegal.*—W.

in such numbers in the spring, I am at a loss even what to suspect about them. I watched them narrowly this year, and saw them abound till about Michaelmas, when they appeared no longer. Subsist they cannot openly among us, and yet elude the eyes of the inquisitive: and, as to their hiding, no man pretends to have found any of them in a torpid state in the winter. But with regard to their migration, what difficulties attend that supposition—that such feeble bad fliers (who the summer long never flit but from hedge to hedge) should be able to traverse vast seas and continents in order to enjoy milder seasons amidst the regions of Africa!

LETTER XIII.

SELBORNE, *Jan.* 22*nd*, 1768.

As in one of your former letters you expressed the more satisfaction from my correspondence on account of my living in the most southerly county; so now I may return the compliment, and expect to have my curiosity gratified by your living much more to the north.

For many years past I have observed that towards Christmas vast flocks of chaffinches have appeared in the fields; many more, I used to think, than could be hatched in any one neighbourhood. But, when I came to observe them more narrowly, I was amazed to find that they seemed to me to be almost all hens. I communicated my suspicions to some intelligent neighbours, who, after taking pains about the matter, declared that they also thought them mostly females—at least fifty to one. This extraordinary occurrence brought to my mind the remark of Linnæus, that "before winter all their hen chaffinches migrate through Holland into Italy". Now I want to know, from some curious person in the north, whether there are any large flocks of these finches with them in the winter, and of which sex they mostly consist? For from such intelligence, one might be able to judge whether our female flocks migrate from the other end of the island, or whether they come over to us from the continent.

We have, in the winter, vast flocks of the common linnets; more, I think, than can be bred in any one district. These, I observe, when the spring advances, assemble on some tree in the sunshine, and join all in a gentle sort of chirping, as if they were about to break up their winter quarters and betake themselves to their proper summer homes. It is well known, at least, that the swallows and the fieldfares do congregate with a gentle twittering before they make their respective departure.

You may depend on it that the bunting, *Emberiza miliaria*, does not leave this county in the winter. In January, 1767, I saw several dozen of them, in the midst of a severe frost, among the bushes on the downs near Andover: in our woodland inclosed district it is a rare bird.

Wagtails, both white and yellow, are with us all the winter. Quails crowd to our southern coast, and are often killed in numbers by people that go on purpose.

[While the cows are feeding in the moist low pastures, broods of wagtails, white and gray, run round them, close up to their noses, and under their very bellies, availing themselves of the flies that settle on their legs, and probably finding worms and *larvæ* that are roused by the trampling of their feet. Nature is such an economist, that the most incongrous animals can avail themselves of each other. Interest makes strange friendships.—*Observations on Nature.*]

Mr. Stillingfleet, in his Tracts, says that "if the wheatear (*œnanthe*)[1] does not quit England, it certainly shifts places; for about harvest they are not to be found, where there was before great plenty of them". This well accounts for the vast quantities that are caught about that time on the south downs near Lewes, where they are esteemed a delicacy. There have been shepherds, I have been credibly informed, that have made many pounds in a season by catching them in traps. And though such multitudes are taken, I never saw (and I am well acquainted with those parts) above two or three at a time, for they are never gregarious. They may perhaps migrate in general; and, for that purpose, draw towards the coast of Sussex in autumn: but that they do not all withdraw I am sure; because I see a few stragglers in many counties, at all times of the year, especially about warrens and stone quarries.

I have no acquaintance, at present, among the gentlemen of the navy; but have written to a friend, who was a sea-chaplain in the late war, desiring him to look into his minutes, with respect to birds that settled on their rigging during their voyage up or down the Channel. What Hasselquist says on that subject is remarkable; there were little short-winged birds frequently coming on board his ship all the way from our

[1] *Saxicola œnanthe* (Linn.).

Channel quite up to the Levant, especially before squally weather.

What you suggest with regard to Spain is highly probable. The winters of Andalusia are so mild that, in all likelihood, the soft-billed birds that leave us at that season may find insects sufficient to support them there.

Some young man, possessed of fortune, health, and leisure, should make an autumnal voyage into that kingdom; and should spend a year there, investigating the natural history of that vast country. Mr. Willughby[1] passed through that kingdom on such an errand; but he seems to have skirted along in a superficial manner and an ill-humour, being much disgusted at the rude dissolute manners of the people.

I have no friend left now at Sunbury to apply to about the swallows roosting on the aits of the Thames: nor can I hear any more about those birds which I suspected were *Merulæ torquatæ*.

As to the small mice, I have farther to remark, that though they hang their nests for breeding up amidst the straws of the standing corn, above the ground; yet I find that, in the winter, they burrow deep in the earth, and make warm beds of grass: but their grand rendezvous seems to be in corn-ricks, into which they are carried at harvest. A neighbour housed an oat-rick lately, under the thatch of which were assembled nearly a hundred, most of which were taken, and some I saw. I measured them, and found that, from nose to tail, they were just two inches and a quarter, and their tails just two inches long. Two of them, in a scale, weighed down just one copper halfpenny, which is about the third of an ounce avoirdupois: so that I suppose they are the smallest quadrupeds in this island. A full-grown *Mus medius domesticus* weighs, I find, one ounce lumping weight, which is more than six times as much as the mouse above; and measures from nose to rump four inches and a quarter, and the same in its tail. We have had a very severe frost and deep snow this month. My thermometer was one day fourteen degrees and a half below the freezing-point, within doors. The tender evergreens were injured pretty much. It was very providential that the air was still, and the ground well covered with snow, else vegetation in general must have suffered prodigiously. There is reason to believe that some days were more severe than any since the year 1739–40.

[1] See *Ray's Travels*, p. 466.—W.

LETTER XIV.

SELBORNE, *March 12th*, 1768.

If some curious gentleman would procure the head of a fallow-deer, and have it dissected, he would find it furnished with two spiracula, or breathing places, besides the nostrils; probably analogous to the *puncta lachrymalia*[1] in the human head. When deer are thirsty they plunge their noses, like some horses, very deep under water, while in the act of drinking, and continue them in that situation for a considerable time: but, to obviate any inconveniency, they can open two vents, one at the inner corner of each eye, having a communication with the nose. Here seems to be an extraordinary provision of nature worthy our attention; and which has not, that I know of, been noticed by any naturalist. For it looks as if these creatures would not be suffocated, though both their mouths and nostrils were stopped. This curious formation of the head may be of singular service to beasts of chase, by affording them free respiration: and no doubt these additional nostrils are thrown open when they are hard run.[2] Mr. Ray observed that at Malta, the owners slit up the nostrils of such asses as were hard worked: for they, being naturally strait or small, did not admit air sufficient to serve them when they travelled, or laboured, in that hot climate. And we know that grooms, and gentlemen of the turf, think large nostrils necessary, and a perfection, in hunters and running horses.

Oppian, the Greek poet, by the following line, seems to have had some notion that stags have four spiracula:

"Τετραδυμοι ρίνες, πιουρες ὦνοιηδι διαυλοι."
"Quadrifidæ nares, quadruplices ad respirationem canales."

OPP. CYN. Lib. ii. l. 181.

("Nostrils with four divisions, fourfold passages for breathing.")

Writers, copying from one another, make Aristotle say that

---

[1] The lachrymal ducts—small tubes which convey the tears from the lachrymal gland to the eye.

[2] In answer to this account Mr. Pennant sent me the following curious and pertinent reply:—"I was much surprised to find in the antelope something analogous to what you mention as so remarkable in deer. This animal also has a long slit beneath each eye, which can be opened and shut at pleasure. On holding an orange to one, the creature made as much use of these orifices as of his nostrils, applying them to the fruit, and seeming to smell it through them."—W.

It seems to be the general opinion of naturalists that the slit in question subserves some other sense unknown to us.

goats breathe at their ears; whereas he asserts just the con-trary:—"Αλκμαιων γαρ ουκ αληθη λεγει, φαμενος αναπνειν τας αιγας κατα τα ωτα." "Alcmæon does not advance what is true, when he avers that goats breathe through their ears."—*History of Animals*, book i., chap. xi.

LETTER XV.

SELBORNE, *March* 30th, 1768.

Some intelligent country people have a notion that we have in these parts, a species of the *genus mustelinum*, besides the weasel, stoat, ferret, and polecat; a little reddish beast, not much bigger than a field-mouse, but much longer, which they call a *cane*. This piece of intelligence can be little depended on; but farther inquiry may be made.

A gentleman in this neighbourhood had two milk-white rooks in one nest. A booby of a carter, finding them before they were able to fly, threw them down and destroyed them, to the regret of the owner, who would have been glad to have pre-served such a curiosity in his rookery. I saw the birds myself nailed against the end of a barn, and was surprised to find that their bills, legs, feet, and claws were milk-white.

[Rooks are continually fighting and pulling each other's nests to pieces; these proceedings are inconsistent with living in such close community. And yet if a pair offer to build on a single tree, the nest is plundered and demolished at once. Some rooks roost on their nest-trees. The twigs which the rooks drop in building supply the poor with brushwood to light their fires. Some unhappy pairs are not permitted to finish any nest till the rest have completed their building. As soon as they get a few sticks together, a party comes and demolishes the whole. As soon as rooks have finished their nests, and before they lay, the cocks begin to feed the hens, who receive their bounty with a fondling tremulous voice and fluttering wings, and all the little blandishments that are expressed by the young while in a helpless state. This gallant deportment of the males is continued through the whole season of incubation.[1]]

A shepherd saw, as he thought, some white larks on a down

---

[1] After the first brood of rooks is sufficiently fledged, they all leave their nest-trees in the daytime, and resort to some distant place in search of food, but return regu-larly every evening, in vast flights, to their nest-trees, where, after flying round several times with much noise and clamour till they are all assembled together, they take up their abode for the night.

above my house this winter: were not these the *Emberiza nivalis*, the snow-flake of the *British Zoology*? No doubt they were.

A few years ago I saw a cock bullfinch in a cage, which had been caught in the fields after it was come to its full colours. In about a year it began to look dingy; and, blackening every succeeding year, it became coal-black at the end of four. Its chief food was hempseed. Such influence has food on the colour of animals! The pied and mottled colours of domesticated animals are supposed to be owing to high, various, and unusual food.

I had remarked for years, that the root of the cuckoo-pint (*arum*) was frequently scratched out of the dry banks of hedges, and eaten in severe snowy weather. After observing, with some exactness, myself, and getting others to do the same, we found it was the thrush kind that searched it out. The root of the *arum* is remarkably warm and pungent.

Our flocks of female chaffinches have not yet forsaken us. The blackbirds and thrushes are very much thinned down by that fierce weather in January.

In the middle of February I discovered, in my tall hedges, a little bird that raised my curiosity: it was of that yellow-green colour that belongs to the *salicaria* kind,[1] and, I think, was soft-billed. It was no *parus*; and was too long and too big for the golden-crowned wren, appearing most like the largest willow-wren. It hung sometimes with its back downwards, but never continuing one moment in the same place. I shot at it, but it was so desultory that I missed my aim.

I wonder that the stone-curlew, *Charadrius œdicnemus*, should be mentioned by the writers as a rare bird: it abounds in all the champaign parts of Hampshire and Sussex, and breeds, I think, all the summer, having young ones, I know, very late in the autumn. Already they begin clamouring in the evening. They cannot, I think, with any propriety, be called, as they are by Mr. Ray, "*circa aquas versantes*"[2]; for with us, by day at least, they haunt only the most dry, open, upland fields and sheep-walks, far removed from water: what they may do in the night I cannot say. Worms are their usual food, but they also eat toads and frogs.

---

[1] Supposed to be the chiff-chaff, of which White subsequently writes:—"The smallest uncrested willow-wren, or chiff-chaff, is the next early summer bird which we have remarked; it utters two sharp piercing notes, so loud in hollow woods as to occasion an echo, and is usually first heard about the 20th March.

[2] "Dwellers by ponds or water-courses."

I can show you some good specimens of my new mice. Linnæus perhaps would call the species *Mus minimus.*

LETTER XVI.

SELBORNE, *April* 18*th*, 1768.

The history of the stone-curlew, *Charadrius œdicnemus*, is as follows. It lays its eggs, usually two, never more than three, on the bare ground, without any nest, in the field; so that the countryman, in stirring his fallows, often destroys them. The young run immediately from the egg like partridges, etc., and are withdrawn to some flinty field by the dam, where they skulk among the stones, which are their best security; for their feathers are so exactly of the colour of our grey spotted flints, that the most exact observer, unless he catches the eye of the young bird, may be eluded. The eggs are short and round; of a dirty white, spotted with dark bloody blotches. Though I might not be able, just when I pleased, to procure you a bird, yet I could show you them almost any day; and any evening you may hear them round the village, for they make a clamour which may be heard a mile. *Œdicnemus* is a most apt and expressive name for them, since their legs seem swollen like those of a gouty man. After harvest I have shot them before the pointers in turnip-fields.

[On the 27th February, 1788, stone-curlews were heard to pipe: and on March 1st, after it was dark, some were passing over the village, as might be perceived by their quick short note, which they use in their nocturnal excursions by way of watchword, that they may not stray and lose their companions.

Thus, we see, that retire whithersoever they may in the winter, they return again early in the spring, and are, as it now appears, the first summer birds that come back. Perhaps the mildness of the season may have quickened the migration of the curlews this year.

They spend the day in high elevated fields and sheep-walks; but seem to descend in the night to streams and meadows, perhaps for water, which their upland haunts do not afford them.—*Observations on Nature.*]

I make no doubt but there are three species of the willow-wrens; two I know perfectly, but have not been able yet to procure the third. No two birds can differ more in their notes, and that constantly, than those two that I am acquainted with;

for the one has a joyous, easy, laughing note, the other a harsh loud chirp. The former is every way larger, and three-quarters of an inch longer, and weighs two drams and a half, while the latter weighs but two; so the songster is one-fifth heavier than the chirper. The chirper (being the first summer-bird of passage that is heard, the wryneck sometimes excepted) begins his two notes in the middle of March, and continues them through the spring and summer till the end of August, as appears by my journals. The legs of the larger of these two are flesh-coloured; of the less, black.

The grasshopper-lark began his sibilous note in my fields last Saturday. Nothing can be more amusing than the whisper of this little bird, which seems to be close by though at a hundred yards distance; and when close at your ear, is scarce any louder than when a great way off. Had I not been a little acquainted with insects, and known that the grasshopper kind is not yet hatched, I should have hardly believed but that it had been a *locusta* whispering in the bushes. The country people laugh when you tell them that it is the note of a bird. It is a most artful creature, skulking in the thickest part of a bush; and will sing at a yard distance, provided it be concealed. I was obliged to get a person to go on the other side of the hedge where it haunted, and then it would run, creeping like a mouse, before us for a hundred yards together, through the bottom of the thorns; yet it would not come into fair sight; but in a morning early, and when undisturbed, it sings on the top of a twig, gaping and shivering with its wings. Mr. Ray himself had no knowledge of this bird, but received his account from Mr. Johnson, who apparently confounds it with the *Reguli non cristati*, from which it is very distinct.

The fly-catcher (*Stoparola*, Ray) has not yet appeared; it usually breeds in my vine. The redstart begins to sing: its note is short and imperfect, but is continued till about the middle of June. The willow-wrens (the smaller sort) are horrid pests in a garden, destroying the peas, cherries, currants, etc.; and are so tame that a gun will not scare them.

My countrymen talk much of a bird that makes a clatter with its bill against a dead bough, or some old pales, calling it a jar-bird. I procured one to be shot in the very fact; it proved to be the *Sitta Europæa* (the nuthatch). Mr. Ray says that the less spotted woodpecker does the same. This noise may be heard a furlong or more off.

Now is the only time to ascertain the short-winged summer birds; for, when the leaf is out, there is no making any remarks on such a restless tribe; and when once the young begin to appear it is all confusion: there is no distinction of genus, species, or sex.[1]

In breeding-time snipes play over the moors, piping and humming; they always hum as they are descending. Is not their hum ventriloquous like that of the turkey? Some suspect it is made by their wings.

This morning I saw the golden-crowned wren, whose crown glitters like burnished gold. It often hangs like a titmouse, with its back downwards.

LETTER XVII.

SELBORNE, *June* 18*th*, 1768.

On Wednesday last arrived your agreeable letter of June 10th. It gives me great satisfaction to find that you pursue these studies still with such vigour, and are in such forwardness with regard to reptiles and fishes.

The reptiles, few as they are, I am not acquainted with, so well as I could wish, with regard to their natural history. There is a degree of dubiousness and obscurity attending the propagation of this class of animals, something analogous to that of the *cryptogamia* in the sexual system of plants: and the case is the same with regard to some of the fishes; as the eel, etc.

[1] A list of the summer birds of passage discovered in this neighbourhood, ranged somewhat in the order in which they appear:—

			LINNÆI NOMINA.
Smallest willow-wren,	..	..	*Motacilla trochilus.*
Wryneck, ..	..	..	*Junx torquilla.*
House-swallow, ..	..	..	*Hirundo rustica.*
Martin, ..	..	..	*Hirundo urbica.*
Sand-martin, ..	..	..	*Hirundo riparia.*
Cuckoo, ..	..	..	*Cuculus canorus.*
Nightingale, ..	..	..	*Motacilla luscinia.*
Blackcap, ..	..	..	*Motacilla atricapilla.*
Whitethroat, ..	..	..	*Motacilla sylvia.*
Middle willow-wren, ..	..	..	*Motacilla trochilus.*
Swift, .	..	..	*Hirundo apus.*
Stone-curlew? ..	..	..	*Charadrius œdicnemus?*
Turtle-dove? ..	..	..	*Turtur aldrovandi?*
Grasshopper-lark, ..	..	..	*Alauda trivialis.*
Land-rail, ..	..	..	*Rallus crex.*
Largest willow-wren, ..	..	..	*Motacilla trochilus.*
Redstart, ..	..	..	*Motacilla phœnicura.*
Goat-sucker, or fern-owl,	..	..	*Caprimulgus europæus.*
Fly-catcher, ..	..	..	*Muscicapa grisola.*

The method in which toads bring forth seems to be very much in the dark. Some authors say that they are viviparous: and yet Ray classes them among his oviparous animals; and is silent with regard to the manner of their bringing forth. Perhaps they may be ἔσω μὲν ᾠοτόκοι, ἔξω δε ζωοτόκοι ("interiorly oviparous, externally viviparous"), as is known to be the case with the viper.[1]

That of frogs (or at least the appearance of it) is notorious to everybody: and yet I never saw, or read of toads being observed in the same situation. It is strange that the matter with regard to the venom of toads has not been yet settled. That they are not noxious to some animals is plain: for ducks, buzzards, owls, stone-curlews, and snakes, eat them, to my knowledge, with impunity. And I well remember the time, but was not eye-witness to the fact (though numbers of persons were) when a quack at this village ate a toad to make the country-people stare; afterwards he drank oil.

I have been informed also, from undoubted authority, that some ladies (ladies you will say of peculiar taste) took a fancy to a toad, which they nourished summer after summer, for many years, till he grew to a monstrous size, with the maggots which turn to flesh-flies. The reptile used to come forth every evening from a hole under the garden-steps; and was taken up, after supper, on the table to be fed. But at last a tame raven, kenning him as he put forth his head, gave him such a severe stroke with his horny beak as put out one eye. After this accident the creature languished for some time and died.

I need not remind a gentleman of your extensive reading of the excellent account there is from Mr. Derham, in Ray's *Wisdom of God in the Creation*, concerning the migration of frogs from their breeding ponds. In this account he at once subverts that foolish opinion of their dropping from the clouds in rain; showing that it is from the grateful coolness and moisture of those showers that they are tempted to set out on their travels, which they defer till those fall. Frogs are as yet in their tadpole state; but, in a few weeks, our lanes, paths, fields, will swarm for a few days with myriads of those emigrants, no larger than my little finger nail. Swammerdam gives a most accurate account of the method and situation in which the male impregnates the spawn of the female. How wonderful is the economy of Providence with regard to the limbs of so vile a reptile! While it is an aquatic

[1] There is no doubt that both toads and frogs lay eggs.

D

it has a fish-like tail, and no legs; as soon as the legs sprout, the tail drops off as useless, and the animal betakes itself to the land.[1]

Merret, I trust, is widely mistaken when he advances that the *Rana arborea* (or tree-frog) is an English reptile; it abounds in Germany and Switzerland.

It is to be remembered that the *Salamandra aquatica* of Ray (the water-newt or eft) will frequently bite at the angler's bait, and is often caught on his hook. I used to take it for granted that the *Salamandra aquatica* was hatched, lived, and died, in the water. But John Ellis, Esq., F.R.S. (the coralline Ellis), asserts, in a letter to the Royal Society, dated June 5th, 1766, in his account of the *mud inguana*, an amphibious biped from South Carolina, that the water-eft, or newt, is only the larva of the land-eft, as tadpoles are of frogs. Lest I should be suspected to misunderstand his meaning, I shall give it in his own words. Speaking of the *opercula* or coverings to the gills of the *mud inguana*, he proceeds to say that, "The form of these pennated coverings approaches very near to what I have some time ago observed in the larva or aquatic state of our English *lacerta*, known by the name of eft, or newt; which serve them for coverings to their gills, and for fins to swim with while in this state; and which they lose, as well as the fins of their tails, when they change their state and become land animals, as I have observed, by keeping them alive for some time myself".

Linnæus, in his *Systema Naturæ*, hints more than once at what Mr. Ellis advances.

Providence has been so indulgent to us as to allow of but one venomous reptile of the serpent kind in these kingdoms, and that is the viper. As you propose the good of mankind to be an object of your publications, you will not omit to mention common salad-oil as a sovereign remedy against the bite of the viper. As to the blindworm (*Anguis fragilis*, so-called because it snaps in sunder with a small blow), I have found, on examination, that it is perfectly innocuous. A neighbouring yeoman (to whom I am indebted for some good hints) killed and opened a female viper about the 27th May: he found her filled with a chain of eleven eggs, about the size of those of a blackbird; but none of them were advanced so far towards a state of maturity as to contain any rudiments

---

[1] White was mistaken here: the tail of the tadpole does not drop off, but is trans-formed.

of young. Though they are oviparous, yet they are viviparous also, hatching their young within their bellies, and then bringing them forth. Whereas snakes lay chains of eggs every summer in my melon beds, in spite of all that my people can do to prevent them; which eggs do not hatch till the spring following, as I have often experienced. Several intelligent folks assure me that they have seen the viper open her mouth and admit her helpless young down her throat on sudden surprises, just as the female opossum does her brood into the pouch under her belly, upon the like emergencies; and yet the London viper-catchers insist on it, to Mr. Barrington, that no such thing ever happens. The serpent kind eat, I believe, but once in a year; or rather, but only just at one season of the year. Country people talk much of a water-snake, but, I am pretty sure, without any reason; for the common snake (*Coluber natrix*) delights much to sport in the water, perhaps with a view to procure frogs and other food.

I cannot well guess how you are to make out your twelve species of reptiles, unless it be by the various species, or rather varieties, of our *lacerti*, of which Ray enumerates five. I have not had opportunity of ascertaining these, but remember well to have seen, formerly, several beautiful green *lacerti* on the sunny sandbanks near Farnham, in Surrey;[1] and Ray admits there are such in Ireland.

[In his *Observations* White has the following notes on a snake's slough: "About the middle of this month (September) we found in a field near a hedge the slough of a large snake, which seemed to have been newly cast. From circumstances it appeared as if turned wrong side outward, and as drawn off backward, like a stocking or woman's glove. Not only the whole skin, but scales from the very eyes are peeled off, and appear in the head of the slough like a pair of spectacles. The reptile, at the time of changing his coat, had entangled himself intricately in the grass and weeds, so that the friction of the stalks and blades might promote this curious shifting of his exuviæ.

————"Lubrica serpens
Exuit in spinis vestem."—LUCRET.

("The slippery snake rids itself of its coat with a thorn.")

"It would be a most entertaining sight could a person be an eye-witness to such a feat, and see the snake in the act of

[1] See Letter XXII.

changing his garment. As the convexity of the scales of the eyes in the slough is now inward, that circumstance alone is a proof that the skin has been turned; not to mention that now the present inside is much darker than the outer. If you look through the scales of the snake's eyes from the concave side, viz., as the reptile used them, they lessen objects much. Thus it appears from what has been said, that snakes crawl out of the mouth of their own sloughs, and quit the tail part last, just as eels are skinned by a cook maid. While the scales of the eyes are growing loose, and a new skin is forming, the creature in appearance must be blind, and feel itself in an awkward uneasy situation."]

LETTER XVIII.

SELBORNE, *July 27th*, 1768.

I received your obliging and communicative letter of June 28th while I was on a visit at a gentleman's house, where I had neither books to turn to, nor leisure to sit down, to return you an answer to many queries, which I wanted to resolve in the best manner that I am able.

A person, by my order, has searched our brooks, but could find no such fish as the *Gasterosteus pungitius*; he found the *Gasterosteus aculeatus* in plenty. This morning, in a basket, I packed a little earthen pot full of wet moss, and in it some sticklebacks, male and female, the females big with spawn: some lamperns; some bull's heads; but I could procure no minnows. This basket will be in Fleet Street by eight this evening; so I hope Mazel will have them fresh and fair to-morrow morning. I gave some directions, in a letter, to what particulars the engraver should be attentive.

Finding, while I was on a visit, that I was within a reasonable distance of Ambresbury, I sent a servant over to that town, and procured several living specimens of loaches, which he brought, safe and brisk, in a glass decanter. They were taken in the gullies that were cut for watering the meadows. From these fishes (which measured from two to four inches in length) I took the following description: "The loach, in its general aspect, has a pellucid appearance; its back is mottled with irregular collections of small black dots, not reaching much below the *linea lateralis*, as are the back and tail fins; a black line runs from each eye down to the nose; its belly is of a silvery white; the upper jaw projects beyond the lower, and is surrounded with six feelers, three on each side; its pectoral fins are large, its ventral much smaller; the fin behind its anus small; its dorsal-fin large, containing eight spines; its tail, where it joins to the tail-fin, remarkably broad, without any taperness, so as to be characteristic of this genus; the tail-fin is broad, and square at the end. From the breadth and muscular strength of the tail it appears to be an active, nimble fish."

In my visit I was not very far from Hungerford, and did not forget to make some inquiries concerning the wonderful method of curing cancers by means of toads. Several intelligent persons, both gentry and clergy, do, I find, give a great deal of credit to what is asserted in the papers, and I myself dined with a clergyman who seemed to be persuaded that what is related is matter of fact; but, when I came to attend to his account, I thought I discerned circumstances which did not a little invalidate the woman's story of the manner in which she came by her skill. She says of herself " that, labouring under a virulent cancer, she went to some church where there was a vast crowd; on going into a pew she was accosted by a strange clergyman, who, after expressing compassion for her situation, told her that if she would make such an application of living toads as is mentioned she would be well ". Now is it likely that this unknown gentleman should express so much tenderness for this single sufferer, and not feel any for the many thousands that daily languish under this terrible disorder? Would he not have made use of this invaluable nostrum for his own emolument; or at least, by some means of publication or other, have found a method of making it public for the good of mankind? In short, this woman (as it appears to me) having set up for a cancer-doctress, finds it expedient to amuse the country with this dark and mysterious relation.

The water-eft has not, that I can discern, the least appearance of any gills; for want of which it is continually rising to the surface of the water to take in fresh air. I opened a big-bellied one indeed, and found it full of spawn. Not that this circumstance at all invalidates the assertion that they are *larvæ*; for the *larvæ* of insects are full of eggs, which they exclude the instant they enter their last state. The water-eft is continually climbing over the brims of the vessel, within which we keep it in water, and wandering away; and people every summer see numbers crawling out of the pools where they are hatched up the dry banks. There are varieties of them, differing in colour; and some have fins up their tail and back, and some have not

---

LETTER XIX.

SELBORNE, *August 17th*, 1768.

I have now, past dispute, made out three distinct species of the willow-wrens (*Motacillæ trochili*) which constantly and invariably use distinct notes. But at the same time I am obliged to confess that I know nothing of your willow-lark. In my letter of April 18th, I had told you peremptorily that I knew your willow-lark, but had not seen it then; but when I came to procure it, it proved in all respects a very *Motacilla trochilus*, only that it is a size larger than the two other, and the yellow-green of the whole upper part of the body is more vivid, and the belly of a clearer white.[1] I have specimens of the three sorts now lying before me, and can discern that there are three gradations of sizes, and that the least has black legs, and the the other two flesh-coloured ones. The yellowest bird is considerably the largest, and has its quill-feathers and secondary feathers tipped with white, which the others have not. This last haunts only the tops of trees in high beechen woods, and makes a sibilous grasshopper-like noise, now and then, at short intervals, shivering a little with its wings when it sings; and is, I make no doubt now, the *Regulus non cristatus* of Ray, which he says " *cantat voce stridulâ locustæ*" ("sings with the stridulous voice of a grasshopper"). Yet this great ornithologist never suspected that there were three species.

LETTER XX.

SELBORNE, *October 8th*, 1768.

It is, I find, in zoology as it is in botany; all nature is so full that that district produces the greatest variety which is the most examined. Several birds, which are said to belong to the north only, are it seems often in the south. I have discovered this summer three species of birds with us, which writers mention as only to be seen in the northern counties. The first that was brought me (on the 14th May), was the sandpiper,

[1] Doubtless the wood-wren (*Ph. sibilatrix*).

Tringa hypoleucus: it was a cockbird, and haunted the banks of
some ponds near the village; and, as it had a companion,
doubtless intended to have bred near that water. Besides, the
owner has told me since, that on recollection, he has seen some
of the same birds round his ponds in former summers.

The next bird that I procured (on the 21st May) was a male
red-backed butcher bird, *Lanius collurio*. My neighbour, who
shot it, says that it might easily have escaped his notice, had
not the outcries and chattering of the whitethroats and other
small birds drawn his attention to the bush where it was; its
craw was filled with the legs and wings of beetles.

The next rare birds (which were procured for me last week)
were some ring-ousels, *Turdi torquati.*

This week twelve months a gentleman from London, being
with us, was amusing himself with a gun, and found, he told
us, on an old yew hedge where there were berries, some birds
like blackbirds, with rings of white round their necks: a neighbouring farmer also at the same time observed the same; but,
as no specimens were procured, little notice was taken. I
mentioned this circumstance to you in my letter of November
4th, 1767 (you, however, paid but small regard to what I said,
as I had not seen these birds myself); but last week the afore-
said farmer, seeing a large flock, twenty or thirty, of these
birds, shot two cocks and two hens; and says, on recollection,
that he remembers to have observed these birds again last
spring, about Lady-day, as it were on their return to the north.
Now perhaps these ousels are not the ousels of the north of
England, but belong to the more northern parts of Europe; and
may retire before the excessive rigour of the frosts in those
parts, and return to breed in the spring, when the cold abates.
If this be the case, here is discovered a new bird of winter
passage, concerning whose migrations the writers are silent;
but if these birds should prove the ousels of the north of
England, then here is a migration disclosed within our own
kingdom never before remarked. It does not yet appear
whether they retire beyond the bounds of our island to the
south; but it is most probable that they usually do, or else one
cannot suppose that they would have continued so long unnoticed in the southern countries. The ousel is larger than a
blackbird, and feeds on haws; but last autumn (when there
were no haws) it fed on yew-berries: in the spring it feeds on
ivy-berries, which ripen only at that season, in March and
April.

I must not omit to tell you (as you have been so lately on the study of reptiles) that my people, every now and then of late, draw up with a bucket of water from my well, which is sixty-three feet deep, a large black warty lizard with a fin-tail and yellow belly. How they first came down at that depth, and how they were ever to have got out thence without help, is more than I am able to say.

My thanks are due to you for your trouble and care in the examination of a buck's head. As far as your discoveries reach at present, they seem much to corroborate my suspicions; and I hope Mr. —— may find reason to give his decision in my favour; and then, I think, we may advance this extraordinary provision of nature as a new instance of the wisdom of God in the creation.

As yet I have not quite done with my history of the *œdicnemus*, or stone-curlew; for I shall desire a gentleman in Sussex (near whose house these birds congregate in vast flocks in the autumn) to observe nicely when they leave him (if they do leave him), and when they return again in the spring: I was with this gentleman lately, and saw several single birds.

LETTER XXI.

SELBORNE, *Nov. 28th*, 1768.

With regard to the *œdicnemus*, or stone-curlew, I intend to write very soon to my friend near Chichester, in whose neighbourhood these birds seem most to abound; and shall urge him to take particular notice when they begin to congregate, and afterwards to watch them most narrowly whether they do not withdraw themselves during the dead of the winter. When I have obtained information with respect to this circumstance, I shall have finished my history of the stone-curlew, which I hope will prove to your satisfaction, as it will be, I trust, very near the truth. This gentleman, as he occupies a large farm of his own, and is abroad early and late, will be a very proper spy upon the motions of these birds; and besides, as I have prevailed on him to buy the Naturalist's Journal (with which he is much delighted), I shall expect that he will be very exact in his dates. It is very extraordinary, as you observe, that a bird so common with us should never straggle to you.

And here will be the properest place to mention, while J

think of it, an anecdote which the above-mentioned gentleman told me when I was last at his house; which was that, in a warren joining to his outlet, many daws (*Corvi monedulæ*) build every year in the rabbit-burrows under-ground. The way he and his brothers used to take their nests, while they were boys, was by listening at the mouths of the holes; and, if they heard the young ones cry, they twisted the nest out with a forked stick. Some water-fowls (viz., the puffins) breed, I know, in that manner; but I should never have suspected the daws of building in holes on the flat ground.

Another very unlikely spot is made use of by daws as a place to breed in, and that is Stonehenge. These birds deposit their nests in the interstices between the upright and the impost stones of that amazing work of antiquity: which circumstance alone speaks the prodigious height of the upright stones, that they should be tall enough to secure those nests from the annoyance of shepherd-boys, who are always idling round that place.

One of my neighbours last Saturday, November 26th, saw a martin in a sheltered bottom: the sun shone warm, and the bird was hawking briskly after flies. I am now perfectly satisfied that they do not all leave this island in the winter.

You judge very right, I think, in speaking with reserve and caution concerning the cures done by toads: for, let people advance what they will on such subjects, yet there is such a propensity in mankind towards deceiving and being deceived, that one cannot safely relate anything from common report, especially in print, without expressing some degree of doubt and suspicion.

Your approbation, with regard to my new discovery of the migration of the ring-ousel, gives me satisfaction; and I find you concur with me in suspecting that they are foreign birds which visit us. You will be sure, I hope, not to omit to make inquiry whether your ring-ousels leave your rocks in the autumn. What puzzles me most, is the very short stay they make with us; for in about three weeks they are all gone. I shall be very curious to remark whether they will call on us at their return in the spring, as they did last year.

I want to be better informed with regard to ichthyology. If fortune had settled me near the seaside, or near some great river, my natural propensity would soon have urged me to have made myself acquainted with their productions; but as I have lived mostly in inland parts, and in an upland district, my knowledge of fishes extends little farther than to those common sorts which our brooks and lakes produce.

LETTER XXII.

SELBORNE, *Jan.* 2*nd*, 1769.

As to the pecularity of jackdaws building with us under the ground in rabbit burrows, you have, in part, hit upon the reason; for, in reality, there are hardly any towers or steeples in all this county. And perhaps, Norfolk excepted, Hampshire and Sussex are as meanly furnished with churches as almost any counties in the kingdom. We have many livings of two or three hundred pounds a year, whose houses of worship make little better appearance than dovecots. When I first saw Northamptonshire, Cambridgeshire, and Huntingdonshire, and the fens of Lincolnshire, I was amazed at the number of spires which presented themselves in every point of view. As an admirer of prospects, I have reason to lament this want in my own county; for such objects are very necessary ingredients in an elegant landscape.

What you mention with respect to reclaimed toads raises my curiosity. An ancient author, though no naturalist, has well remarked that "every kind of beasts, and of birds, and of serpents, and things in the sea, is tamed, and hath been tamed, of mankind".[1]

It is a satisfaction to me to find that a green lizard has actually been procured for you in Devonshire; because it corroborates my discovery, which I made many years ago, of the same sort, on a sunny sandbank near Farnham, in Surrey. I am well acquainted with the South Hams of Devonshire; and can suppose that district, from its southerly situation, to be a proper habitation for such animals in their best colours.

Since the ring-ousels of your vast mountains do certainly not forsake them against winter, our suspicions that those which visit this neighbourhood about Michaelmas are not English birds, but driven from the more northern parts of Europe by the frosts, are still more reasonable; and it will be worth your pains to endeavour to trace from whence they come, and to inquire why they make so very short a stay.

In your account of your error with regard to the two species of herons, you incidentally gave me great entertain

[1] James iii. 7.

ment in your description of the heronry at Cressi Hall; which
is a curiosity I never could manage to see. Fourscore nests
of such a bird on one tree is a rarity which I would ride half
as many miles to have a sight of. Pray be sure to tell me in
your next whose seat Cressi Hall is, and near what town it
lies. I have often thought that those vast extents of fens
have never been sufficiently explored. If half-a-dozen gentlemen, furnished with a good strength of water-spaniels, were
to beat them over for a week, they would certainly find more
species.

There is no bird, I believe, whose manners I have studied
more than that of the *caprimulgus* (the goat-sucker), as it is a
wonderful and curious creature; but I have always found
that though sometimes it may chatter as it flies, as I know it
does, yet in general it utters its jarring note sitting on a
bough; and I have for many a half-hour watched it as it sat
with its under mandible quivering, and particularly this
summer. It perches usually on a bare twig, with its head
lower than its tail, in an attitude well expressed by your
draughtsman in the folio *British Zoology*. This bird is most
punctual in beginning its song exactly at the close of day;
so exactly that I have known it strike up more than once
or twice just at the report of the Portsmouth evening gun,
which we can hear when the weather is still. It appears
to me past all doubt that its notes are formed by organic
impulse, by the powers of the parts of its windpipe, formed
for sound, just as cats purr. You will credit me, I hope,
when I assure you that, as my neighbours were assembled in
an hermitage on the side of a steep hill where we drink tea,
one of these churn-owls came and settled on the cross of that
little straw edifice and began to chatter, and continued his
note for many minutes; and we were all struck with wonder
to find that the organs of that little animal, when put in
motion, gave a sensible vibration to the whole building! This
bird also sometimes makes a small squeak, repeated four or
five times; and I have observed that to happen when the
cock has been pursuing the hen in a toying way through the
boughs of a tree.

It would not be at all strange if your bat, which you have
procured, should prove a new one, since five species have
been found in a neighbouring kingdom. The great sort
that I mentioned is certainly a nondescript; I saw but one
this summer, and that I had no opportunity of taking.

Your account of the Indian grass was entertaining. I am no angler myself; but inquiring of those that are, what they supposed that part of their tackle to be made of?—they replied, "Of the intestines of a silkworm".

Though I must not pretend to great skill in entomology, yet I cannot say that I am ignorant of that kind of knowledge; I may now and then perhaps be able to furnish you with a little information.

The vast rains ceased with us much about the same time as with you, and since we have had delicate weather. Mr. Barker, who has measured the rain for more than thirty years, says, in a late letter, that more has fallen this year than in any he ever attended to; though from July 1763 to January 1764, more fell than in any seven months of this year.

LETTER XXIII.

SELBORNE, *Feb. 28th*, 1769.

It is not improbable that the Guernsey lizard and our green lizards may be specifically the same; all that I know is that, when some years ago many Guernsey lizards were turned loose in Pembroke College garden, in the University of Oxford, they lived a great while, and seemed to enjoy themselves very well, but never bred. Whether this circumstance will prove anything either way I shall not pretend to say.

I return you thanks for your account of Cressi Hall; but recollect, not without regret, that in June 1746 I was visiting for a week together at Spalding, without ever being told that such a curiosity was just at hand. Pray send me word in your next what sort of tree it is that contains such a quantity of herons' nests; and whether the heronry consists of a whole grove of wood, or only of a few trees.

It gave me satisfaction to find we accorded so well about the *caprimulgus*; all I contended for was to prove that it often chatters sitting as well as flying; and therefore the noise was voluntary, and from organic impulse, and not from the resistance of the air against the hollow of its mouth and throat.

If ever I saw anything like actual migration, it was last Michaelmas Day. I was travelling, and out early in the morning; at first there was a vast fog; but, by the time that I was got seven or eight miles from home towards the coast, the sun broke out into a delicate warm day. We were then on a large heath or common, and I could discern, as the mist began to break away, great numbers of swallows (*Hirundines rusticæ*) clustering on the stunted shrubs and bushes, as if they had roosted there all night. As soon as the air became clear and pleasant they were all on the wing at once; and, by a placid and easy flight, proceeded on southward towards the sea; after this I did not see any more flocks, only now and then a straggler.

I cannot agree with those persons that assert that the swallow kind disappear some and some gradually, as they come, for the bulk of them seem to withdraw at once; only some stragglers stay behind a long while, and do never, there is the greatest reason to believe, leave this island. Swallows seem to lay themselves up, and to come forth in a warm day, as bats do continually of a warm evening, after they have disappeared for weeks. For a very respectable gentleman assured me that, as he was walking with some friends under Merton wall on a remarkably hot noon, either in the last week in December or the first week in January, he espied three or four swallows huddled together on the moulding of one of the windows of that college. I have frequently remarked that swallows are seen later at Oxford than elsewhere: is it owing to the vast massy buildings of that place, to the many waters round it, or to what else?

When I used to rise in the morning last autumn, and see the swallows and martins clustering on the chimneys and thatch of the neighbouring cottages, I could not help being touched with a secret delight, mixed with some degree of mortification; with delight, to observe with how much ardour and punctuality those poor little birds obeyed the strong impulse towards migration or hiding, imprinted on their minds by their great Creator; and with some degree of mortification, when I reflected that, after all our pains and inquiries, we are yet not quite certain to what regions they do migrate; and are still farther embarrassed to find that some do not actually migrate at all.[1]

These reflections made so strong an impression on my imagination, that they became productive of a composition that may perhaps amuse you for a quarter of an hour when next I have the honour of writing to you.

[1] See the note on the migration of swallows in the Introduction.

LETTER XXIV.

SELBORNE, *May 29th*, 1769.

The *Scarabæus fullo* I know very well, having seen it in collections; but have never been able to discover one wild in its natural state. Mr. Banks told me he thought it might be found on the sea-coast.

On the 13th April I went to the sheep-down, where the ring-ousels have been observed to make their appearance at spring and fall, in their way perhaps to the north or south; and was much pleased to see these birds about the usual spot. We shot a cock and a hen; they were plump and in high condition. The hen had but very small rudiments of eggs within her, which proves they are late breeders; whereas those species of the thrush kind that remain with us the whole year have fledged young before that time. In their crops was nothing very distinguishable, but somewhat that seemed like blades of vegetables nearly digested. In autumn they feed on haws and yew-berries, and in the spring on ivy-berries. I dressed one of these birds, and found it juicy and well flavoured. It is remarkable that they make but a few days' stay in their spring visit, but rest near a fortnight at Michaelmas. These birds, from the observations of three springs and two autumns, are most punctual in their return; and exhibit a new migration unnoticed by the writers, who supposed they never were to be seen in any southern countries.

One of my neighbours lately brought me a new *Salicaria,* which at first I suspected might have proved your willow-lark,[1] but on a nicer examination, it answered much better to the description of that species which you shot at Revesby, in Lincolnshire. My bird I describe thus: "It is a size less than the grasshopper-lark; the head, back, and coverts of the wings, of a dusky brown, without those dark spots of the grasshopper-lark; over each eye is a milk-white stroke; the chin and throat are white, and the under parts of a yellowish white; the rump is tawny, and the feathers of the tail sharp pointed; the bill is dusky and sharp, and the legs are dusky; the hinder claw long and crooked".[2] The person that shot it says that it sung so like a reed-sparrow that he took it for one; and that it

---

[1] For this *Salicaria,* see Letter, August 30, 1769.—W.

[2] *Salicaria phragmitis.*

sings all night: but this account merits farther inquiry. For my part, I suspect it is a second sort of *Locustella*, hinted at by Dr. Derham in Ray's Letters. He also procured me a grass-hopper-lark.

The question that you put with regard to those genera of animals that are peculiar to America, viz., how they came there, and whence? is too puzzling for me to answer; and yet so obvious as often to have struck me with wonder. If one looks into the writers on that subject little satisfaction is to be found. Ingenious men will readily advance plausible arguments to support whatever theory they shall choose to maintain; but then the misfortune is, every one's hypothesis is each as good as another's, since they are all founded on conjecture. The late writers of this sort, in whom may be seen all the arguments of those that have gone before, as I remember, stock America from the western coast of Africa and the south of Europe; and then break down the Isthmus that bridged over the Atlantic. But this is making use of a violent piece of machinery; it is a difficulty worthy of the interposition of a god! "*Incredulus odi*"—"I am disgustedly incredulous".

To THOMAS PENNANT, Esquire.

THE NATURALIST'S SUMMER-EVENING WALK.

——— equidem credo, quia sit divinitus illis
Ingenium. Virg. *Georg.*

When day declining sheds a milder gleam,
What time the may-fly[1] haunts the pool or stream;
When the still owl skims round the grassy mead,
What time the timorous hare limps forth to feed;
Then be the time to steal adown the vale,
And listen to the vagrant[2] cuckoo's tale;
To hear the clamorous curlew call his mate,
Or the soft quail his tender pain relate;
To see the swallow sweep the dark'ning plain
Belated, to support her infant train;

[1] The angler's may-fly, the *Ephemera vulgata* LINN., comes forth from its aurelia state, and emerges out of the water about six in the evening, and dies about eleven at night, determining the date of its fly state in about five or six hours. They usually begin to appear about the 4th June, and continue in succession for near a fortnight. See Swammerdam, Derham, Scopoli, &c.—W.

[2] Vagrant cuckoo; so called because, being tied down by no incubation or attendance about the nutrition of its young, it wanders without control.—W.

To mark the swift in rapid giddy ring
Dash round the steeple, unsubdued of wing;
Amusive birds!—say where your hid retreat
When the frost rages and the tempests beat;
Whence your return by such nice instinct led,
When spring, soft season, lifts her bloomy head?
Such baffled searches mock man's prying pride,
The GOD of NATURE is your secret guide!

    While deep'ning shades obscure the face of day,
To yonder bench leaf-shelter'd let us stray,
'Till blended objects fail the swimming sight,
And all the fading landscape sinks in night;
To hear the drowsy dorr come brushing by
With buzzing wing, or the shrill cricket[1] cry;
To see the feeding bat glance through the wood;
To catch the distant falling of the flood;
While o'er the cliff th' awaken'd churn-owl hung
Through the still gloom protracts his chattering song;
While high in air, and poised upon his wings,
Unseen, the soft enamour'd[2] woodlark sings:
These, NATURE'S works, the curious mind employ,
Inspire a soothing melancholy joy:
As fancy warms, a pleasing kind of pain
Steals o'er the cheek, and thrills the creeping vein!

    Each rural sight, each sound, each smell combine;
The tinkling sheep-bell or the breath of kine;
The new-mown hay that scents the swelling breeze,
Or cottage chimney smoking through the trees.

    The chilling night-dews fall:—away, retire!
For see, the glow-worm lights her amorous fire![3]
Thus, ere night's veil had half obscured the sky,
Th' impatient damsel hung her lamp on high·
True to the signal, by love's meteor led,
Leander hasten'd to his Hero's bed.

---

[1] *Gryllus campestris.*

[2] In hot summer nights wood-larks soar to a prodigious height, and hang singing in the air.—W.

[3] The light of the female glow-worm (as she often crawls up the stalk of a grass to make herself more conspicuous) is a signal to the male, which is a slender dusky *Scarabæus.*—W. This was, and indeed is still, the generally received notion, but the fact is that both sexes of the glow-worm are phosphorescent.

LETTER XXV.

SELBORNE, *Aug.* 30*th*, 1769.

It gives me satisfaction to find that my account of the ousel migration pleases you. You put a very shrewd question when you ask me how I know that their autumnal migration is southward? Was not candour and openness the very life of natural history, I should pass over this query just as a sly commentator does over a crabbed passage in a classic; but common ingenuousness obliges me to confess, not without some degree of shame, that I only reasoned in that case from analogy. For as all other autumnal birds migrate from the northward to us, to partake of our milder winters, and return to the northward again when the rigorous cold abates, so I concluded that the ring-ousels did the same, as well as their congeners the fieldfares; and especially as ring-ousels are known to haunt cold mountainous countries: but I have good reason to suspect since that they may come to us from the westward; because I hear from very good authority, that they breed on Dartmoor; and that they forsake that wild district about the time that our visitors appear, and do not return till late in the spring.

I have taken a great deal of pains about your *salicaria* and mine, with a white stroke over its eye and a tawny rump. I have surveyed it alive and dead, and have procured several specimens, and am perfectly persuaded myself (and trust you will soon become convinced of the same) that it is no more nor less than *Passer arundinaceus minor* of Ray. This bird, by some means or other, seems to be entirely omitted in the *British Zoology*; and one reason probably was because it is so strangely classed in Ray, who ranges it among his *Pici affines*. It ought no doubt to have gone among his *aviculæ caudâ unicolore*,[1] and among your slender-billed small birds of the same division. Linnæus might with great propriety have put it into his genus of *motacilla*; and *Motacilla salicaria* of his *Fauna Suecica* seems to come the nearest to it. It is no uncommon bird, haunting the sides of ponds and rivers where there is covert, and the reeds and sedges of moors. The country people in some places call it the sedge-bird.[5] It sings

[1] Small birds with tail of one colour.
[2] The sedge-warbler (*Salicaria phragmitis*).

incessantly night and day during the breeding-time, imitating the note of a sparrow, a swallow, a skylark; and has a strange hurrying manner in its song. My specimens correspond most minutely to the description of your fen *salicaria* shot near Revesby. Mr. Ray has given an excellent characteristic of it when he says: "*Rostrum et pedes in hâc aviculâ multò majores sunt quâm pro corporis ratione*". "The beak and the feet of this little bird are much too large in proportion to its body."

I have got you the egg of an *œdicnemus*, or stone-curlew, which was picked up in a fallow on the naked ground; there were two, but the finder inadvertently crushed one with his foot before he saw them.

When I wrote to you last year on reptiles, I wish I had not forgot to mention the faculty that snakes have of stinking in self-defence, *se defendendo*. I knew a gentleman who kept a tame snake, which was in its person as sweet as any animal while in good humour and unalarmed; but as soon as a stranger, or a dog or cat, came in, it fell to hissing, and filled the room with such nauseous effluvia as rendered it hardly supportable. Thus the skunck, or stonck, of Ray's *Synop. Quadr.* is an innocuous and sweet animal; but, when pressed hard by dogs and men, it can eject such a most pestilent and fetid smell and excrement, that nothing can be more horrible.

A gentleman sent me lately a fine specimen of the *Lanius minor cinerascens cum maculâ in scapulis albâ, Raii*; which is a bird that, at the time of your publishing your two first volumes of *British Zoology*, I find you had not seen. You have described it well from Edwards's drawing.

LETTER XXVI.

SELBORNE, *December 8th*, 1769.

I was much gratified by your communicative letter on your return from Scotland, where you spent some considerable time, and gave yourself good room to examine the natural curiosities of that extensive kingdom, both those of the islands, as well as those of the highlands. The usual bane of such expeditions is hurry, because men seldom allot themselves half the time they should do; but, fixing on a day for their return, post from place to place, rather as if they were on a journey that required dispatch, than as philosophers investigating the works of nature. You must have made, no doubt, many discoveries, and laid up a good fund of materials for a future edition of the *British Zoology*; and will have no reason to repent that you have bestowed so much pains on a part of Great Britain that perhaps was never so well examined before.

It has always been matter of wonder to me that fieldfares, which are so congenerous to thrushes and blackbirds, should never choose to breed in England; but that they should not think even the highlands cold and northerly, and sequestered enough, is a circumstance still more strange and wonderful. The ring-ousel, you find, stays in Scotland the whole year round; so that we have reason to conclude that those migrators that visit us for a short space every autumn do not come from thence.

And here, I think, will be the proper place to mention that those birds were most punctual again in their migration this autumn, appearing, as before, about the 30th September; but their flocks were larger than common, and their stay protracted somewhat beyond the usual time. If they came to spend the whole winter with us, as some of their congeners do, and then left us, as they do, in spring, I should not be so much struck with the occurrence, since it would be similar to that of the other winter birds of passage; but when I see them for a fortnight at Michaelmas, and again for about a week in the middle of April, I am seized with wonder, and long to be informed whence these travellers come, and whither they go, since they seem to use our hills merely as an inn or baiting place.

Your account of the greater brambling, or snow-fleck, is very amusing; and strange it is that such a short-winged bird should delight in such perilous voyages over the northern ocean! Some country people in the winter time have every now and then told me that they have seen two or three white larks on our downs; but, on considering the matter, I begin to suspect that these are some stragglers of the birds we are talking of, which sometimes perhaps may rove so far to the southward.

It pleases me to find that white hares are so frequent on the Scottish mountains, and especially as you inform me that it is a distinct species; for the quadrupeds of Britain are so few, that every new species is a great acquisition.

The eagle-owl, could it be proved to belong to us, is so majestic a bird, that it would grace our *fauna* much. I never was informed before where wild-geese are known to breed.

You admit, I find, that I have proved your fen *salicaria* to be the lesser reed-sparrow of Ray; and I think you may be secure that I am right, for I took very particular pains to clear up that matter, and had some fair specimens; but, as they were not well preserved, they are decayed already. You will, no doubt, insert it in its proper place in your next edition. Your additional plates will much improve your work.

De Buffon, I know, has described the water shrew-mouse: but still I am pleased to find you have discovered it in Lincolnshire, for the reason I have given in the article of the white hare.

As a neighbour was lately ploughing a dry, chalky field, far removed from any water, he turned out a water-rat, that was curiously laid up in a hybernaculum artificially formed of grass and leaves. At one end of the burrow lay above a gallon of potatoes regularly stowed, on which it was to have supported itself for the winter. But the difficulty with me is how this *amphibius mus* came to fix its winter station at such a distance from the water. Was it determined in its choice of that place by the mere accident of finding the potatoes which were planted there; or is it the constant practice of the aquatic rat to forsake the neighbourhood of the water in the colder months?

Though I delight very little in analogous reasoning, knowing how fallacious it is with respect to natural history; yet, in the following instance, I cannot help being inclined to think it may conduce towards the explanation of a difficulty that I have mentioned before, with respect to the invariable early retreat of the *Hirundo apus*, or swift, so many weeks before its congeners; and that not only with us, but also in Andalusia, where they also begin to retire about the beginning of August.

The great large bat[1] (which by-the-by is at present a nondescript in England, and what I have never been able yet to procure) retires or migrates very early in the summer; it also ranges very high for its food, feeding in a different region of the air; and that is the reason I never could procure one. Now this is exactly the case with the swifts; for they take

[1] The little bat appears almost every month in the year, but I have never seen the large one till the end of April, nor after July. They are most common in June, but never very plentiful.—W.

their food in a more exalted region than the other species, and are very seldom seen hawking for flies near the ground, or over the surface of the water. From hence I would conclude that these *Hirundines* and the larger bats are supported by some sorts of high-flying gnats, scarabs, or *phalænæ*, that are of short continuance; and that the short stay of these strangers is regulated by the defect of their food.

By my journal it appears that curlews clamoured on to October 31st; since which I have not seen nor heard any. Swallows were observed on to November 3rd.

LETTER XXVII.

SELBORNE, *Feb. 22nd*, 1770.

Hedgehogs abound in my gardens and fields. The manner in which they eat the roots of the plantain in my grass-walks is very curious; with their upper mandible, which is much longer than their lower, they bore under the plant, and so eat the root off upwards, leaving the leaves untouched. In this respect they are serviceable, as they destroy a very troublesome weed; but they deface the walks in some measure by digging little round holes. It appears, by the dung that they drop upon the turf, that beetles are no inconsiderable part of their food. In June last I procured a litter of four or five young hedgehogs, which appeared to be about five or six days old: they, I find, like puppies, are born blind, and could not see when they came to my hands. No doubt their spines are soft and flexible at the time of their birth, or else the poor dam would have but a bad time of it in the critical moment of parturition, but it is plain they soon harden; for these little pigs had such stiff prickles on their backs and sides as would easily have fetched blood, had they not been handled with caution. Their spines are quite white at this age; and they have little hanging ears, which I do not remember to be discernible in the old ones. They can, in part, at this age draw their skin down over their faces; but are not able to contract themselves into a ball, as they do, for the sake of defence, when full grown. The reason, I suppose, is, because the curious muscle that enables the creature to roll itself up in a ball was not then arrived at its full tone and firmness. Hedgehogs make a deep and warm hybernaculum[1]

1 *Hybernaculum*—Winter-nest.

with leaves and moss, in which they conceal themselves for the winter: but I never could find that they stored in any winter provision, as some quadrupeds certainly do.

I have discovered an anecdote with respect to the fieldfare (*Turdus pilaris*), which I think is particular enough; this bird, though it sits on trees in the daytime, and procures the greatest part of its food from whitethorn hedges; yea, moreover, builds on very high trees, as may be seen by the *Fauna Suecica*; yet always appears with us to roost on the ground. They are seen to come in flocks just before it is dark, and to settle and nestle among the heath on our forest. And besides, the larkers in dragging their nets by night, frequently catch them in the wheat stubbles; while the bat-fowlers, who take many redwings in the hedges, never entangle any of this species. Why these birds, in the matter of roosting, should differ from all their congeners, and from themselves also with respect to their proceedings by day, is a fact for which I am by no means able to account.

I have somewhat to inform you of concerning the moose-deer; but in general foreign animals fall seldom in my way; my little intelligence is confined to the narrow sphere of my own observations at home.

LETTER XXVIII.

SELBORNE, *March*, 1770.

On Michaelmas-day 1768 I managed to get a sight of the female moose belonging to the Duke of Richmond, at Goodwood; but was greatly disappointed, when I arrived at the spot, to find that it died, after having appeared in a languishing way for some time on the morning before. However, understanding that it was not stripped, I proceeded to examine this rare quadruped; I found it in an old greenhouse, slung under the belly and chin by ropes, and in a standing posture; but, though it had been dead for so short a time, it was in so putrid a state that the stench was hardly supportable. The grand distinction between this deer, and any other species that I have ever met with, consisted in the strange length of its legs; on which it was tilted up much in the manner of the birds of the *grallæ* order. I measured it, as they do a horse, and found that, from the ground to the withers it was just five feet four inches; which height answers exactly to sixteen hands, a growth that few horses arrive at: but then, with this length of legs, its neck was remarkable short, no more than twelve inches; so that, by straddling with one foot forward and the other backward, it grazed on the plain ground, with the greatest difficulty, between its legs; the ears were vast and lopping, and as long as the neck; the head was about twenty inches long, and ass-like; and had such a redundancy of upper lip as I never saw before, with huge nostrils. This lip, travellers say, is esteemed a dainty dish in North America. It is very reasonable to suppose that this creature supports itself chiefly by browsing off trees, and by wading after water plants; towards which way of livelihood the length of its legs and great lip must contribute much. I have read somewhere that it delights in eating the *nymphœa*, or water-lily. From the fore-feet to the belly behind the shoulder it measured three feet and eight inches: the length of the legs before and behind consisted a great deal in the *tibia*, which was strangely long; but, in my haste to get out of the stench, I forgot to measure that joint exactly. Its scut seemed to be about an inch long; the colour was a grizzly black; the mane about four inches long; the fore-hoofs were upright and shapely, the hind flat and splayed. The spring before it was only two years old, so that most probably it was not then come to its growth. What a vast tall beast must a full-grown stag be! I have been told some arrive at ten feet and a half! This poor creature had at first a female companion of the same species, which died the spring before. In the same garden was a young stag, or red deer, between whom and this moose it was hoped that there might have been a breed; but their inequality of height must have always been a bar to such a hope. I should have been glad to have examined the teeth, tongue, lips, hoofs, etc., minutely; but the putrefaction precluded all farther curiosity. This animal, the keeper told me, seemed to enjoy itself best in the extreme frost of the former winter. In the house they showed me the horn of a male moose, which had no front antlers, but only a broad palm with some snags on the edge. The noble owner of the dead moose proposed to make a skeleton of her bones.

Please to let me hear if my female moose corresponds with that you saw; and whether you think still that the American moose and European elk are the same creature.

LETTER XXIX.

SELBORNE, *May* 12*th*, 1770.

Last month we had such a series of cold turbulent weather, such a constant succession of frost, and snow, and hail, and tempest, that the regular migration or appearance of the summer birds was much interrupted. Some did not show themselves (at least were not heard) till weeks after their usual time; as the blackcap and whitethroat; and some have not been heard yet, as the grasshopper-lark and largest willow-wren. As to the fly-catcher, I have not seen it; it is indeed one of the latest, but should appear about this time: and yet amidst all this meteorous strife and war of the elements, two swallows discovered themselves as long ago as April 11th, in frost and snow; but they withdrew quickly, and were not visible again for many days. House-martins, which are always more backward than swallows, were not observed till May came in.

Among the monogamous birds several are to be found, after pairing-time, single, and of each sex; but whether this state of celibacy is matter of choice or necessity, is not so easy discoverable. When the house-sparrows deprive my martins of their nests, as soon as I cause one to be shot, the other, be it cock or hen, presently procures a mate, and so for several times following.

I have known a dove-house infested by a pair of white owls, which made great havoc among the young pigeons: one of the owls was shot as soon as possible; but the survivor readily found a mate, and the mischief went on. After some time the new pair were both destroyed, and the annoyance ceased.

Another instance I remember of a sportsman, whose zeal for the increase of his game being greater than his humanity, after pairing-time he always shot the cock-bird of every couple of partridges upon his grounds; supposing that the rivalry of many males interrupted the breed: he used to say that, though he had widowed the same hen several times, yet he found she was still provided with a fresh paramour, that did not take her away from her usual haunt.

Again: I knew a lover of setting, an old sportsman, who has often told me that soon after harvest he has frequently taken small coveys of partridges, consisting of cock-birds alone; these he pleasantly used to call old bachelors.

There is a propensity belonging to common house-cats that is very remarkable; I mean their violent fondness for fish, which appears to be their most favourite food: and yet nature in this instance seems to have planted in them an appetite that, unassisted, they know not how to gratify: for of all quadrupeds cats are the least disposed towards water; and will not, when they can avoid it, deign to wet a foot, much less to plunge into that element.

Quadrupeds that prey on fish are amphibious: such is the otter, which by nature is so well formed for diving, that it makes great havoc among the inhabitants of the waters. Not supposing that we had any of those beasts in our shallow brooks, I was much pleased to see a male otter, brought to me, weighing twenty-one pounds, that had been shot on the bank of our stream below the Priory, where the rivulet divides the parish of Selborne from Harteley Wood.

LETTER XXX.

SELBORNE, *Aug. 1st*, 1770.

The French, I think, in general are strangely prolix in their natural history. What Linnæus says with respect to insects holds good in every other branch: "*Verbositas præsentis sæculi, calamitas artis*". "The verbosity of the present generation is the calamity of art."

Pray how do you approve of Scopoli's new work? As I admire his *Entomologia*, I long to see it.

I forgot to mention in my last letter (and had not room to insert in the former) that the male moose, in rutting time, swims from island to island, in the lakes and rivers of North America, in pursuit of the females. My friend, the chaplain, saw one killed in the water as it was on that errand in the river St. Lawrence: it was a monstrous beast, he told me; but he did not take the dimensions.

When I was last in town our friend Mr. Barrington most obligingly carried me to see many curious sights. As you were then writing to him about horns, he carried me to see many strange and wonderful specimens. There is, I remember, at Lord Pembroke's at Wilton, a horn room furnished with more than thirty different pairs; but I have not seen that house lately.

Mr. Barrington showed me many astonishing collections of

stuffed and living birds from all quarters of the world. After I had studied over the latter for a time, I remarked that every species almost that came from distant regions, such as South America, the coast of Guinea, etc., were thick-billed birds of the *loxia* and *fringilla* genera; and no *motacillæ* or *muscicapæ* were to be met with. When I came to consider, the reason was obvious enough; for the hard-billed birds subsist on seeds which are easily carried on board; while the soft-billed birds, which are supported by worms and insects, or, what is a *succedaneum* for them, fresh raw meat, can meet with neither in long and tedious voyages. It is from this defect of food that our collections (curious as they are) are defective, and we are deprived of some of the most delicate and lively genera.

LETTER XXXI.

SELBORNE, *Sept. 14th*, 1770.

You saw, I find, the ring-ousels again among their native crags; and are further assured that they continue resident in those cold regions the whole year. From whence then do our ring-ousels migrate so regularly every September, and make their appearance again, as if in their return, every April? They are more early this year than common, for some were seen at the usual hill on the fourth of this month.

An observing Devonshire gentleman tells me that they frequent some parts of Dartmoor, and breed there; but leave those haunts about the end of September, or beginning of October, and return again about the end of March.

Another intelligent person assures me that they breed in great abundance all over the peak of Derby, and are called there tor-ousels; withdraw in October and November, and return in spring. This information seems to throw some light on my new migration.

Scopoli's new work[1] (which I have just procured) has its merit in ascertaining many of the birds of the Tirol and Carniola. Monographers, come from whence they may, have, I think, fair pretence to challenge some regard and approbation from the lovers of natural history; for, as no man can alone investigate the works of nature, these partial writers may, each in their department, be more accurate in their discoveries, and freer from errors, than more general writers; and so by

[1] *Annus Primus Historico-Naturalis.*—W.

degrees may pave the way to an universal correct natural history. Not that Scopoli is so circumstantial and attentive to the life and conversation of his birds as I could wish: he advances some false facts; as when he says of the *Hirundo urbica* that *"pullos extra nidum non nutrit"*: "it does not feed its young after they leave the nest". This assertion I know to be wrong from repeated observation this summer; for house-martins do feed their young flying, though it must be acknowledged not so commonly as the house-swallow; and the feat is done in so quick a manner as not to be perceptible to indifferent observers. He also advances some (I was going to say) improbable facts; as when he says of the woodcock that *"pullos rostro portat fugiens ab hoste"*: "it carries its young in its beak as it flies from its enemies". But candour forbids me to say absolutely that any fact is false because I have never been witness to such a fact. I have only to remark that the long unwieldy bill of the woodcock is perhaps the worst adapted of any among the winged creation for such a feat of natural affection.

LETTER XXXII.

SELBORNE, *October 29th*, 1770.

After an ineffectual search in Linnæus, Brisson, &c., I begin to suspect that I discern my brother's *Hirundo hyberna* in Scopoli's new discovered *Hirundo rupestris*. His description of " *Supra murina, subtus albida; rectrices maculâ ovali albâ in latere interno; pedes nudi, nigri; rostrum nigrum; remiges obscuriores quam plumæ dorsales; rectrices remigibus concolores; caudâ emarginatâ, nec forcipatâ,*" [1] agrees very well with the bird in question; but when he comes to advance that it is "of the size of the house-martin", "*statura hirundinis urbicæ*", and that "*definitio hirundinis ripariæ Linnæi huic quoque conveniit*" ("the description of the bank-martin of Linnæus fits this bird also "), he in some measure invalidates all he has said; at least he shows at once that he compares them to these species merely from memory; for I have compared the birds themselves, and find they differ widely in every circumstance of shape, size, and colour. How-

[1] " Above it is of a mouse-colour, below whitish; the guiding feathers have an oval white spot on the inner side; the feet are bare and black, the beak black, the wing feathers duskier than those of the back, the guiding feathers of the same colour as the wings; the tail well-defined, but undivided."

ever, as you will have a specimen, I shall be glad to hear what your judgment is in the matter.

Whether my brother is forestalled in his nondescript or not, he will have the credit of first discovering that they spend their winters under the warm and sheltery shores of Gibraltar and Barbary.

Scopoli's characters of his ordines and genera are clear, just, and expressive, and much in the spirit of Linnæus. These few remarks are the result of my first perusal of Scopoli's *Annus Primus*.

The bane of our science is the comparing one animal to the other by memory: for want of caution in this particular Scopoli falls into errors: he is not so full with regard to the manners of his indigenous birds as might be wished, as you justly observe: his Latin is easy, elegant, and expressive, and very superior to Kramer's.[7]

I am pleased to see that my description of the moose corresponds so well with yours.

LETTER XXXIII.

SELBORNE, *Nov. 26th*, 1770.

I was much pleased to see, among the collection of birds from Gibraltar, some of those short-winged English summer birds of passage, concerning whose departure we have made so much inquiry. Now if these birds are found in Andalusia to migrate to and from Barbary, it may easily be supposed that those that come to us may migrate back to the continent, and spend their winters in some of the warmer parts of Europe. This is certain, that many soft-billed birds that come to Gibraltar appear there only in spring and autumn, seeming to advance in pairs towards the northward, for the sake of breeding during the summer months; and retiring in parties and broods towards the south at the decline of the year; so that the rock of Gibraltar is the great rendezvous, and place of observation, from whence they take their departure each way towards Europe or Africa. It is therefore no mean discovery, I think, to find that our small short-winged summer birds of passage are to be seen spring and autumn on the very skirts of Europe; it is a presumptive proof of their emigrations.

Scopoli seems to me to have found the *Hirundo melba*, the

1 See his *Elenchus vegetabilium et animalium per Austriam inferiorem, &c.*—W.

great Gibraltar swift, in Tirol, without knowing it. For what is his *Hirundo alpina* but the afore-mentioned bird in other words? Says he, "*Omnia prioris*" (meaning the swift); "*sed pectus album; paulo major priore*"; "it has all the qualities of the former except that its breast is white, and it is a little larger in size". I do not suppose this to be a new species. It is true also of the *melba*, that "it builds among the lofty Alpine rocks": "*nidificat in excelsis Alpium rupibus*". *Vide Annum Primum.*

My Sussex friend, a man of observation and good sense, but no naturalist, to whom I applied on account of the stone-curlew (*œdicnemus*), sends me the following account: "In looking over my *Naturalist's Journal* for the month of April, I find the stone-curlews are first mentioned on the seventeenth and eighteenth, which date seems to me rather late. They live with us all the spring and summer, and at the beginning of autumn prepare to take leave by getting together in flocks. They seem to me a bird of passage that may travel into some dry hilly country south of us, probably Spain, because of the abundance of sheep-walks in that country; for they spend their summers with us in such districts. This conjecture I hazard, as I have never met with any one that has seen them in England in the winter. I believe they are not fond of going near the water, but feed on earth-worms, that are common on sheep-walks and downs. They breed on fallows and lay-fields abounding with grey mossy flints, which much resemble their young in colour; among which they skulk and conceal themselves. They make no nest, but lay their eggs on the bare ground, producing in common but two at a time. There is reason to think their young run soon after they are hatched; and that the old ones do not feed them, but only lead them about at the time of feeding, which, for the most part, is in the night". Thus far, my friend.

In the manners of this bird you see there is something very analogous to the bustard, whom it also somewhat resembles in aspect and make, and in the structure of its feet.

For a long time I have desired my relation to look out for these birds in Andalusia; and now he writes me word that, for the first time, he saw one dead in the market on the 3rd of September.

When the *œdicnemus* flies it stretches out its legs straight behind, like a heron.

LETTER XXXIV.

SELBORNE, *March* 30*th*, 1771.

There is an insect with us, especially on chalky districts, which is very troublesome and teasing all the latter end of the summer, getting into people's skins, especially those of women and children, and raising tumours which itch intolerably. This animal (which we call a harvest bug) is very minute, scarce discernible to the naked eye; of a bright scarlet colour, and of the genus of *Acarus*. They are to be met with in gardens on kidney-beans, or any legumens, but prevail only in the hot months of summer. Warreners, as some have assured me, are much infested by them on chalky downs; where these insects swarm sometimes to so infinite a degree as to discolour their nets, and to give them a reddish cast, while the men are so bitten as to be thrown into fevers.

There is a small long shining fly in these parts very troublesome to the housewife, by getting into the chimneys, and laying its eggs in the bacon while it is drying; these eggs produce maggots called jumpers, which, harbouring in the gammons and best parts of the hogs, eat down to the bone, and make great waste. This fly I suspect to be a variety of the *Musca putris* of Linnæus; it is to be seen in the summer in farm-kitchens on the bacon-racks and about the mantel-pieces, and on the ceilings.

The insect that infests turnips and many crops in the garden (destroying often whole fields while in their seedling leaves) is an animal that wants to be better known. The country people here call it the turnip-fly and black-dolphin; but I know it to be one of the *coleoptera*; the "*Chrysomela oleracea, saltatoria, femoribus posticis crassissimis*".[1] In very hot summers they abound to an amazing degree, and, as you walk in a field or in a garden, make a pattering like rain, by jumping on the leaves of the turnips or cabbages.

There is an *oestrus*, known in these parts to every plough-boy; which, because it is omitted by Linnæus, is also passed over by late writers; and that is the *curvicauda* of old Moufet, mentioned by Derham in his *Physico-Theology*, p. 250; an insect worthy of remark for depositing its eggs as it flies in so dextrous a manner on the single hairs of the legs and flanks of

---

[1] "The jumping *Chrysomela* with the posterior part of the thigh very thick."

grass-horses. But then Derham is mistaken when he advances that this *oestrus* is the parent of that wonderful star-tailed maggot which he mentions afterwards; for more modern entomologists have discovered that singular production to be derived from the egg of the *Musca chamœleon*.

A full history of noxious insects hurtful in the field, garden and house, suggesting all the known and likely means of destroying them, would be allowed by the public to be a most useful and important work. What knowledge there is of this sort lies scattered, and wants to be collected; great improvements would soon follow of course. A knowledge of the properties, economy, propagation, and in short of the life and conversation of these animals, is a necessary step to lead us to some method of preventing their depredations.

As far as I am a judge, nothing would recommend entomology more than some neat plates that should well express the generic distinctions of insects according to Linnæus; for I am well assured that many people would study insects, could they set out with a more adequate notion of those distinctions than can be conveyed at first by words alone.

LETTER XXXV.

SELBORNE, 1771.

Happening to make a visit to my neighbour's peacocks, I could not help observing that the trains of those magnificent birds appear by no means to be their tails; those long feathers growing not from their *uropygium*, but all up their backs. A range of short brown stiff feathers, about six inches long, fixed in the *uropygium*, is the real tail, and serves as the fulcrum to prop the train, which is long and top-heavy, when set on end. When the train is up, nothing appears of the bird before but its head and neck; but this would not be the case were those long feathers fixed only in the rump, as may be seen by the turkey-cock when in a strutting attitude. By a strong muscular vibration these birds can make the shafts of their long feathers clatter like the swords of a sword dancer; they then trample very quick with their feet, and run backwards towards the females.

I should tell you that I have got an uncommon *Calculus œgogropila*, taken out of the stomach of a fat ox; it is perfectly round, and about the size of a large Seville orange; such are, I think, usually flat.

LETTER XXXVI.

Sept., 1771.

The summer through I have seen but two of that large species of bat which I call *Vespertilio altivolans*, from its manner of feeding high in the air: I procured one of them, and found it to be a male; and made no doubt, as they accompanied together, that the other was a female; but, happening in an evening or two to procure the other likewise, I was somewhat disappointed, when it appeared to be also of the same sex. This circumstance, and the great scarcity of this sort, at least in these parts, occasions some suspicions in my mind whether it is really a species, or whether it may not be the male part of the more known species, one of which may supply many females; as is known to be the case in sheep and some other quadrupeds. But this doubt can only be cleared by a farther examination, and some attention to the sex, of more specimens.

In the extent of their wings they measured fourteen inches and a half; and four inches and a half from the nose to the tip of the tail; their heads were large, their nostrils bilobated, their shoulders broad and muscular; and their whole bodies fleshy and plump. Nothing could be more sleek and soft than their fur, which was of a bright chestnut colour; their maws were full of food, but so macerated that the quality could not be distinguished; their livers, kidneys, and hearts were large, and their bowels covered with fat. They weighed each, when entire, full one ounce and one drachm. Within the ear there was somewhat of a peculiar structure that I did not understand perfectly, but refer it to the observation of the curious anatomist. These creatures sent forth a very rancid and offensive smell.

LETTER XXXVII.

SELBORNE, 1771.

On the 12th of July I had a fair opportunity of contemplating the motions of the *Caprimulgus*, or fern-owl, as it was playing round a large oak that swarmed with *Scarabæi solstitiales*, or fern-chafers. The powers of its wing were wonderful, exceeding, if possible, the various evolutions and quick turns of the swallow genus. But the circumstance that pleased me most was, that I saw it distinctly, more than once, put out its short leg while on the wing, and, by a bend of the head, deliver somewhat into its mouth. If it takes any part of its prey with its foot, as I have now the greatest reason to suppose it does these chafers, I no longer wonder at the use of its middle toe, which is curiously furnished with a serrated claw.

[The following interesting particulars respecting the fern-owl, from White's *Observations on Nature*, will fittingly find a place here:—

The country people have a notion that the fern-owl, or churn-owl, or eve-jarr, which they also call a puckeridge, is very injurious to weanling calves, by inflicting as it strikes at them, the fatal distemper known to cow-leeches by the name of puckeridge. Thus does this harmless ill-fated bird fall under a double imputation which it by no means deserves—in Italy, of sucking the teats of goats, whence it is called *Caprimulgus*; and with us, of communicating a deadly disorder to cattle. But the truth of the matter is, the malady above-mentioned is occasioned by the *Œstrus bovis*, a dipterous insect, which lays its eggs along the chines of kine, where the maggots, when hatched, eat their way through the hide of the beast into the flesh, and grow to a very large size. I have just talked with a man who says he has more than once stripped calves who have died of the puckeridge; that the ail or complaint lay along the chine, where the flesh was much swelled, and filled with purulent matter. Once I myself saw a large rough maggot of this sort squeezed out of the back of a cow.

These maggots in Essex are called wornils.

The least observation and attention would convince men, that these birds neither injure the goatherd nor the grazier, but are perfectly harmless, and subsist alone, being night birds, on night insects, such as *scarabœi* and *phalœnœ*; and through the month of July mostly on the *Scarabœus solstitialis*, which in many districts abounds at that season. Those that we have opened, have always had their craws stuffed with large night moths and their eggs, and pieces of chafers; nor does it any-wise appear how they can, weak and unarmed as they seem, inflict any harm upon kine, unless they possess the powers of animal magnetism and can affect them by fluttering over them.

A fern-owl, this evening (August 27th) showed off in a very unusual and entertaining manner, by hawking round and round the circumference of my great spreading oak for twenty times following, keeping mostly close to the grass, but occa-

F

sionally glancing up amidst the boughs of the tree. This amusing bird was then in pursuit of a brood of some particular *phalœna* belonging to the oak, of which there are several sorts; and exhibited on the occasion a command of wing superior, I think, to that of the swallow itself.

When a person approaches the haunt of fern-owls in an evening, they continue flying round the head of the obtruder; and by striking their wings together above their backs, in the manner that the pigeons called smiters are known to do, make a smart snap; perhaps at that time they are jealous for their young, and their noise and gesture are intended by way of menace.

Fern-owls have an attachment to oaks, no doubt on account of food; for the next evening we saw one again several times among the boughs of the same tree; but it did not skim round its stem over the grass, as on the evening before. In May these birds find the *Scarabœus melolontha* on the oak, and the *Scarabœus solstitialis* at midsummer. These peculiar birds can only be watched and observed for two hours in the twenty-four; and then in dubious twilight an hour after sunset and an hour before sunrise.

On this day (July 14th, 1789), a woman brought me two eggs of a fern-owl or evening jarr, which she found on the verge of the Hanger, to the left of the hermitage under a beechen shrub. This person, who lives just at the foot of the Hanger, seems well acquainted with these nocturnal swallows, and says she has often found their eggs near that place, and that they lay only two at a time on the bare ground. The eggs were oblong, dusky, and streaked somewhat in the manner of the plumage of the parent bird, and were equal in size at each end. The dam was sitting on the eggs when found, which contained the rudiments of young, and would have been hatched perhaps in a week. From hence we may see the time of their breeding, which corresponds pretty well with that of the swift, as does also the period of their arrival. Each species is usually seen about the beginning of May. Each breeds but once in a summer; each lays only two eggs.

July 4th, 1790. The woman who brought me two fern-owl's eggs last year on July 14th, on this day produced me two more, one of which had been laid this morning, as appears plainly, because there was only one in the nest the evening before. They were found, as last July, on the verge of the down above the hermitage under a beechen shrub, on the naked ground. Last year those eggs were full of young, just ready to be hatched.

These circumstances point out the exact time when these curious nocturnal migratory birds lay their eggs and hatch their young. Fern-owls, like snipes, stone-curlews, and some other birds, make no nest. Birds that build on the ground do not make much of nests.]

Swallows and martins, the bulk of them I mean, have forsaken us sooner this year than usual; for on September 22nd they rendezvoused in a neighbour's walnut-tree, where it seemed probable they had taken up their lodging for the night. At the dawn of the day, which was foggy, they arose all together in infinite numbers, occasioning such a rushing from the strokes of their wings against the hazy air, as might be heard to a considerable distance: since that no flock has appeared, only a few stragglers.

Some swifts stayed late, till the 22nd of August—a rare instance! for they usually withdraw within the first week.[1]

On September 24th three or four ring-ousels appeared in my fields for the first time this season; how punctual are these visitors in their autumnal and spring migrations!

LETTER XXXVIII.

SELBORNE, *March 15th*, 1773.

By my journal for last autumn it appears that the house-martins bred very late, and stayed very late in these parts; for, on the 1st of October, I saw young martins in their nest nearly fledged; and again on the 21st of October, we had at the next house a nest full of young martins just ready to fly; and the old ones were hawking for insects with great alertness. The next morning the brood forsook their nest, and were flying round the village. From this day I never saw one of the swallow kind till November 3rd; when twenty, or perhaps thirty, house-martins were playing all day long by the side of the hanging wood, and over my field. Did these small weak birds, some of which were nestling twelve days ago, shift their quarters at this late season of the year to the other side of the northern tropic? Or rather, is it not more probable that the next church, ruin, chalk-cliff, steep covert, or perhaps sand-bank, lake or pool (as a more northern naturalist would say), may

[1] See Letter LII. to Mr. Barrington.

become their hybernaculum, and afford them a ready and obvious retreat?

We now begin to expect our vernal migration of ring-ousels every week. Persons worthy of credit assure me that ring-ousels were seen at Christmas 1770 in the forest of Bere, on the southern verge of this county. Hence we may conclude that their migrations are only internal, and not extended to the continent southward, if they do at first come at all from the northern parts of this island only, and not from the north of Europe. Come from whence they will, it is plain, from the fearless disregard that they show for men or guns, that they have been little accustomed to places of much resort. Navigators mention that in the Isle of Ascension, and other such desolate districts, birds are so little acquainted with the human form that they settle on men's shoulders; and have no more dread of a sailor than they would have of a goat that was grazing. A young man at Lewes, in Sussex, assured me that about seven years ago ring-ousels abounded so about that town in the autumn that he killed sixteen himself in one afternoon; he added further, that some had appeared since in every autumn; but he could not find that any had been observed before the season in which he shot so many. I myself have found these birds in little parties in the autumn cantoned all along the Sussex downs, wherever there were shrubs and bushes, from Chichester to Lewes; particularly in the autumn of 1770.

LETTER XXXIX.

SELBORNE, *Nov. 9th,* 1773

As you desire me to send you such observations as may occur, I take the liberty of making the following remarks, that you may, according as you think me right or wrong, admit or reject what I here advance, in your intended new edition of the *British Zoology.*

The osprey was shot about a year ago at Frinsham Pond, a great lake, at about six miles from hence, while it was sitting on the handle of a plough and devouring a fish: it used to precipitate itself into the water, and so take its prey by surprise.

A great ash-coloured butcher-bird was shot last winter in Tisted Park, and a red-backed butcher-bird at Selborne: they are *raræ aves* in this county.

Crows go in pairs all the year round.

Cornish choughs abound, and breed on Beechy Head, and on all the cliffs of the Sussex coast.

The common wild pigeon, or stock-dove, is a bird of passage in the south of England, seldom appearing till towards the end of November; is usually the latest winter-bird of passage. Before our beechen woods were so much destroyed we had myriads of them, reaching in strings for a mile together as they went out in a morning to feed. They leave us early in spring: where do they breed?

The people of Hampshire and Sussex call the missel-bird the storm-cock, because it sings early in the spring in blowing showery weather; its song often commences with the year: with us it builds much in orchards.

A gentleman assures me he has taken the nests of ring-ousels on Dartmoor: they build in banks on the sides of streams.

Titlarks not only sing sweetly as they sit on trees, but also as they play and toy about on the wing; and particularly while they are descending, and sometimes they stand on the ground.

Adanson's testimony seems to me to be very poor evidence that European swallows migrate during our winter to Senegal: he does not talk at all like an ornithologist; and probably saw only the swallows of that country, which I know build within Governor O'Hara's hall against the roof. Had he known European swallows, would he not have mentioned the species?

The house-swallow washes by dropping into the water as it flies: this species appears commonly about a week before the house-martin, and about ten or twelve days before the swift.

In 1772 there were young house-martins in their nest till October 23rd.

The swift appears about ten or twelve days later than the house-swallow: viz., about the 24th or 26th of April.

Whin-chats and stone-chatters stay with us the whole year.

Some wheatears continue with us the winter through.

Wagtails, all sorts, remain with us all the winter.

Bullfinches, when fed on hempseed, often become wholly black.

We have vast flocks of female chaffinches all the winter, with hardly any males among them.

When you say[1] that in breeding-time the cock-snipes make a bleating noise, and I a drumming (perhaps I should rather

[1] *British Zoology*, vol. ii. p. 358.

have said a humming), I suspect we mean the same thing. However, while they are playing about on the wing they certainly make a loud piping with their mouths: but whether that bleating or humming is ventriloquous, or proceeds from the motion of their wings, I cannot say; but this I know, that when this noise happens the bird is always descending, and his wings are violently agitated.

Soon after the lapwings have done breeding they congregate, and, leaving the moors and marshes, betake themselves to downs and sheep-walks.

Two years ago last spring the little auk was found alive and unhurt, but fluttering and unable to rise, in a lane a few miles from Alresford, where there is a great lake: it was kept awhile, but died.

I saw young teals taken alive in the ponds of Wolmer Forest in the beginning of July last, along with flappers, or young wild-ducks.

Speaking of the swift (vol. iv. p. 15, *Brit. Zoology*), that page says "its drink the dew"; whereas it should be "it drinks on the wing"; for all the swallow kind sip their water as they sweep over the face of pools or rivers: like Virgil's bees, they drink flying—"*flumina summa libant*". In this method of drinking perhaps this genus may be peculiar.

Of the sedge-bird be pleased to say it sings most part of the night; its notes are hurrying, but not unpleasing, and imitative of several birds; as the sparrow, swallow, skylark. When it happens to be silent in the night, by throwing a stone or clod into the bushes where it sits you immediately set it a-singing; or in other words, though it slumbers sometimes, yet as soon as it is awakened it reassumes its song.

LETTER XL.

SELBORNE, *Sept. 2nd*, 1774.

Before your letter arrived, and of my own accord, I had been remarking and comparing the tails of the male and female swallow, and this ere any young broods appeared; so that there was no danger of confounding the dams with their *pulli*: and besides, as they were then always in pairs, and busied in the employ of nidification, there could be no room for mistaking the sexes, nor the individuals of different chimneys the one for the other. From all my observations, it constantly appeared that each sex has the long feathers in its tail that give it that forked shape; with this difference, that they are longer in the tail of the male than in that of the female.

Nightingales, when their young first come abroad, and are helpless, make a plantive and jarring noise; and also a snapping or cracking, pursuing people along the hedges as they walk: these last sounds seem intended for menace and defiance.

The grasshopper-lark chirps all night in the height of summer.

Swans turn white the second year, and breed the third.

Weasels prey on moles, as appears by their being sometimes caught in mole-traps.

Sparrow-hawks sometimes breed in old crows' nests, and the kestril in churches and ruins.

There are supposed to be two sorts of eels in the island of Ely. The threads sometimes discovered in eels are perhaps their young: the generation of eels is very dark and mysterious.

Hen-harriers breed on the ground, and seem never to settle on trees.

[Of this handsome bird White has the following notes in his *Observations on Nature*:—" A neighbouring gentleman sprung a pheasant in a wheat stubble, and shot at it; when, notwithstanding the report of the gun, it was immediately pursued by the blue hawk, known by the name of the hen-harrier, but escaped into some covert. He then sprung a second, and a third, in the same field, that got away in the same manner; the hawk hovering round him all the while that he was beating the field, conscious no doubt of the game that lurked in the stubble. Hence we may conclude that this bird of prey was rendered very daring and bold by hunger, and that hawks cannot always seize their game when they please. We may farther observe, that they cannot pounce their quarry on the ground where it might be able to make a stout resistance, since so large a fowl as a pheasant could not but be visible to the piercing eye of a hawk, when hovering over the field. Hence that propensity of cowering and squatting till they are almost trod on, which no doubt was intended as a mode of security; though long rendered destructive to the whole race of gallinæ by the invention of nets and guns."]

When redstarts shake their tails they move them horizontally, as dogs do when they fawn: the tail of a wagtail, when in motion, bobs up and down like that of a jaded horse.

Hedge-sparrows have a remarkable flirt with their wings in breeding-time; as soon as frosty mornings come they make a very piping plaintive noise.

Many birds which become silent about midsummer reassume their notes again in September; as the thrush, blackbird, woodlark, willow-wren, etc.; hence August is by much the most mute month, the spring, summer, and autumn through. Are birds induced to sing again because the temperament of autumn resembles that of spring?

Linnæus ranges plants geographically; palms inhabit the tropics, grasses the temperate zones, and mosses and lichens the polar circles; no doubt animals may be classed in the same manner with propriety.

House-sparrows build under eaves in the spring; as the weather becomes hotter they get out for coolness, and nest in plum-trees and apple-trees. These birds have been known sometimes to build in rooks' nests, and sometimes in the forks of boughs under rooks' nests.

As my neighbour was housing a rick he observed that his dogs devoured all the little red mice that they could catch, but rejected the common mice; and that his cats ate the common mice, refusing the red.

Redbreasts sing all through the spring, summer, and autumn. The reason that they are called autumn songsters is, because in the two first seasons their voices are drowned and lost in the general chorus; in the latter their song becomes distinguishable. Many songsters of the autumn seem to be the young cock redbreasts of that year: notwithstanding the prejudices in their favour, they do much mischief in gardens to the summer-fruits.[1]

The titmouse, which early in February begins to make two quaint notes, like the whetting of a saw, is the marsh titmouse: the great titmouse sings with three cheerful joyous notes, and begins about the same time.

Wrens sing all the winter through, frost excepted.

House-martins came remarkably late this year both in Hampshire and Devonshire: is this circumstance for or against either hiding or migration?

Most birds drink sipping at intervals; but pigeons take a long-continued draught, like quadrupeds.

Notwithstanding what I have said in a former letter, no

---

[1] They eat also the berries of the ivy, the honey-suckle, and *Euonymus europæus,* or spindle-tree.—W.

gray crows were ever known to breed on Dartmoor; it was my mistake.

The appearance and flying of the *Scarabœus solstitialis*, or fern-chafer, commence with the month of July, and cease about the end of it. These scarabs are the constant food of *Caprimulgi*, or fern owls, through that period. They abound on the chalky downs and in some sandy districts, but not in the clays.

In the garden of the Black Bear inn in the town of Reading, is a stream or canal running under the stables and out into the fields on the other side of the road: in this water are many carps, which lie rolling about in sight, being fed by travellers, who amuse themselves by tossing them bread; but as soon as the weather grows at all severe, these fishes are no longer seen, because they retire under the stables, where they remain till the return of spring. Do they lie in a torpid state? If they do not, how are they supported?

The note of the white-throat, which is continually repeated, and often attended with odd gesticulations on the wing, is harsh and displeasing. These birds seem of a pugnacious disposition; for they sing with an erected crest and attitudes of rivalry and defiance; are shy and wild in breeding-time, avoiding neighbourhoods, and haunting lonely lanes and commons; nay, even the very tops of the Sussex Downs, where there are bushes and covert; but in July and August they bring their broods into gardens and orchards, and make great havoc among the summer-fruits.

The black-cap has in common a full, sweet, deep, loud, and wild pipe; yet that strain is of short continuance, and his motions are desultory; but when that bird sits calmly and engages in song in earnest, he pours forth very sweet, but inward melody, and expresses great variety of soft and gentle modulations, superior perhaps to those of any of our warblers, the nightingale excepted.

Black-caps mostly haunt orchards and gardens; while they warble their throats are wonderfully distended.

The song of the redstart is superior, though somewhat like that of the white-throat; some birds have a few more notes than others. Sitting very placidly on the top of a tall tree in a village, the cock sings from morning to night: he affects neighbourhoods, and avoids solitude, and loves to build in orchards and about houses; with us he perches on the vane of a tall maypole.

The fly-catcher is of all our summer birds the most mute and the most familiar; it also appears the last of any. It builds in a vine, or a sweetbriar, against the wall of a house, or in the hole of a wall, or on the end of a beam or plate, and often close to the post of a door where people are going in and out all day long. This bird does not make the least pretension to song, but uses a little inward wailing note when it thinks its young in danger from cats or other annoyances; it breeds but once, and retires early.

Selborne parish alone can and has exhibited at times more than half the birds that are ever seen in all Sweden; the former has produced more than one hundred and twenty species, the latter only two hundred and twenty-one. Let me add also that it has shown near half the species that were ever known in Great Britain.[1]

On a retrospect, I observe that my long letter carries with it a quaint and magisterial air, and is very sententious; but when I recollect that you requested stricture and anecdote, I hope you will pardon the didactic manner for the sake of the information it may happen to contain.

LETTER XLI.

It is matter of curious inquiry to trace out how those species of soft-billed birds that continue with us the winter through, subsist during the dead months. The imbecility of birds seems not to be the only reason why they shun the rigour of our winters; for the robust wryneck (so much resembling the hardy race of woodpeckers) migrates, while the feeble little golden-crowned wren, that shadow of a bird, braves our severest frosts without availing himself of houses or villages, to which most of our winter birds crowd in distressful seasons, while this keeps aloof in fields and woods; but perhaps this may be the reason why they may often perish, and why they are almost as rare as any bird we know.

I have no reason to doubt but that the soft-billed birds, which winter with us, subsist chiefly on insects in their aurelia state. All the species of wagtails in severe weather haunt shallow streams near their spring-heads, where they never

---

[1] Sweden 221, Great Britain 252 species.—W.

freeze; and, by wading, pick out the aurelias of the genus of *Phryganeœ*, &c.[1]

Hedge-sparrows frequent sinks and gutters in hard weather, where they pick up crumbs and other sweepings; and in mild weather they procure worms, which are stirring every month in the year, as any one may see that will only be at the trouble of taking a candle to a grass-plot on any mild winter's night. Redbreasts and wrens in the winter haunt outhouses, stables, and barns, where they find spiders and flies that have laid themselves up during the cold season. But the grand support of the soft-billed birds in winter is that infinite profusion of aurelia of the *Ordo lepidoptera*, which is fastened to the twigs of trees and their trunks; to the pales and walls of gardens and buildings; and is found in every cranny and cleft of rock or rubbish, and even in the ground itself.

Every species of titmouse winters with us; they have what I call a kind of intermediate bill between the hard and the soft, between the Linnæan genera of *Fringilla* and *Motacilla*. One species alone spends its whole time in the woods and fields, never retreating for succour in the severest seasons to houses and neighbourhoods; and that is the delicate long-tailed titmouse, which is almost as minute as the golden-crowned wren; but the blue titmouse or nun (*Parus cœruleus*), the cole-mouse (*Parus ater*), the great black-headed titmouse (*Fringillago*),[2] and the marsh titmouse (*Parus palustris*), all resort at times to buildings, and in hard weather particularly. The great titmouse, driven by stress of weather, much frequents houses; and, in deep snows, I have seen this bird, while it hung with its back downwards (to my no small delight and admiration), draw straws lengthwise from out the eaves of thatched houses, in order to pull out the flies that were concealed between them, and that in such numbers that they quite defaced the thatch, and gave it a ragged appearance.

The blue titmouse, or nun, is a great frequenter of houses, and a general devourer. Besides insects, it is very fond of flesh; for it frequently picks bones on dunghills: it is a vast admirer of suet, and haunts butchers' shops. When a boy, I have known twenty in a morning caught with snap mouse-traps, baited with tallow or suet. It will also pick holes in apples left on the ground, and be well entertained with the seeds on the head of a sunflower. The blue, marsh, and great

---

[1] See Derham's *Physico-Theology*, p. 235.—W.

[2] *Parus major* (Linn.).

titmice will, in very severe weather, carry away barley and oat-straws from the sides of ricks.

How the wheatear and whinchat support themselves in winter cannot be so easily ascertained, since they spend their time on wild heaths and warrens; the former especially, where there are stone quarries: most probably it is that their maintenance arises from the aureliæ of the *Ordo Lepidoptera*, which furnish them with a plentiful table in the wilderness.

LETTER XLII.

SELBORNE, *March 9th*, 1775.

Some future faunist, a man of fortune, will, I hope, extend his visits to the kingdom of Ireland; a new field and a country little known to the naturalist.   He will not, it is to be wished, undertake that tour unaccompanied by a botanist, because the mountains have scarcely been sufficiently examined; and the southerly counties of so mild an island may possibly afford some plants little to be expected within the British dominions. A person of a thinking turn of mind will draw many just remarks from the modern improvements of that country, both in arts and agriculture, where premiums obtained long before they were heard of with us.   The manners of the wild natives, their superstitions, their prejudices, their sordid way of life, will extort from him many useful reflections.   He should also take with him an able draughtsman|; for he must by no means pass over the noble castles and seats, the extensive and picturesque lakes and waterfalls, and the lofty stupendous mountains so little known, and so engaging to the imagination when described and exhibited in a lively manner; such a work would be well received.

As I have seen no modern map of Scotland, I cannot pretend to say how accurate or particular any such may be; but this I know, that the best old maps of that kingdom are very defective.

The great obvious defect that I have remarked in all maps of Scotland that have fallen in my way is a want of a coloured line, or stroke, that shall exactly define the just limits of that district called the Highlands.   Moreover, all the great avenues to that mountainous and romantic country want to be well distinguished.   The military roads formed by General Wade are so great and Roman-like an undertaking that they well merit attention. My old map, Moll's Map, takes notice of Fort William, but could not mention the other forts that have been erected long since; therefore a good representation of the chain of forts should not be omitted. *Coryarrich*

The celebrated zigzag up the Coryarich must not be passed over. Moll takes notice of Hamilton and Drumlanrig, and such capital houses; but a new survey, no doubt, should represent every seat and castle remarkable for any great event, or celebrated for its paintings, &c. Lord Breadalbane's seat and beautiful policy are too curious and extraordinary to be omitted.

The seat of the Earl of Eglintoun, near Glasgow, is worthy of notice. The pine plantations of that nobleman are very grand and extensive indeed.

LETTER XLIII.

A pair of honey-buzzards, *Buteo apivorus*, sive *vespivorus Raii*,[1] built them a large shallow nest, composed of twigs and lined with dead beechen leaves, upon a tall slender beech near the middle of Selborne Hanger, in the summer of 1780. In the middle of the month of June a bold boy climbed this tree, though standing on so steep and dizzy a situation, and brought down an egg, the only one in the nest, which had been sat on for some time, and contained the embryo of a young bird. The egg was smaller, and not so round as those of the common buzzard; was dotted at each end with small red spots, and surrounded in the middle with a broad bloody zone.

The hen-bird was shot, and answered exactly to Mr. Ray's description of that species; had a black cere, short thick legs, and a long tail. When on the wing this species may be easily distinguished from the common buzzard by its hawk-like appearance, small head, wings not so blunt, and longer tail. This specimen contained in its craw some limbs of frogs and many grey snails without shells. The irides of the eyes of this bird were of a beautiful bright yellow colour.

About the 10th July in the same summer a pair of sparrow-hawks bred in an old crow's nest on a low beech in the same hanger; and as their brood, which was numerous, began to grow up, became so daring and ravenous, that they were a terror to all the dames in the village that had chickens or ducklings under their care. A boy climbed the tree, and found

[1] The bee-eating buzzard, or the wasp-eating buzzard of Ray.

N.B. only egg stolen, hen shot, end of species. Thanks to Mr. White.

the young so fledged that they all escaped from him; but discovered that a good house had been kept: the larder was well-stored with provisions; for he brought down a young blackbird, jay, and house-martin, all clean picked, and some half devoured. The old birds had been observed to make sad havoc for some days among the new-flown swallows and martins, which, being but lately out of their nests, had not acquired those powers and command of wing that enable them, when more mature, to set such enemies at defiance.

*I have seen swifts
bullying hawks.*

LETTER XLIV.

SELBORNE, *Nov. 30th,* 1780.

Every incident that occasions a renewal of our correspondence will ever be pleasing and agreeable to me.

As to the wild wood-pigeon, the *Œnas*, or *Vinago*, of Ray,[1] I am much of your mind; and see no reason for making it the origin of the common house-dove; but suppose those that have advanced that opinion may have been misled by another appellation, often given to the *Œnas*, which is that of stock-dove.

Unless the stock-dove in the winter varies greatly in manners from itself in summer, no species seems more unlikely to be domesticated, and to make a house-dove. We very rarely see the latter settle on trees at all, nor does it ever haunt the woods; but the former as long as it stays with us—from November perhaps to February—lives the same wild life with the ring-dove (*Palumbus torquatus*);[2] frequents coppices and groves, supports itself chiefly by mast, and delights to roost in the tallest beeches. Could it be known in what manner stock-doves build, the doubt would be settled with me at once, provided they construct their nests on trees, like the ring-dove, as I much suspect they do.

You received, you say, last spring a stock-dove from Sussex; and are informed that they sometimes breed in that county. But why did not your correspondent determine the place of its nidification, whether on rocks, cliffs, or trees? If he was not an adroit ornithologist I should doubt the fact, because people with us perpetually confound the stock-dove with the ring-dove.

For my own part, I readily concur with you in supposing

[1] *Columba œnas* (Linn.).

[2] *Columba palumbus* (Linn.).

that house-doves are derived from the small blue rock-pigeon, for many reasons. In the first place the wild stock-dove is manifestly larger than the common house-dove, against the usual rule of domestication, which generally enlarges the breed. Again, those two remarkable black spots on the remiges of each wing of the stock-dove, which are so characteristic of the species, would not, one should think, be totally lost by its being reclaimed; but would often break out among its descendants. But what is worth a hundred arguments is the instance you give in Sir Roger Mostyn's house-doves in Cærnarvonshire; which, though tempted by plenty of food and gentle treatment, can never be prevailed on to inhabit their cote for any time; but, as soon as they begin to breed, betake themselves to the fastnesses of Ormshead, and deposit their young in safety amidst the inaccessible caverns, and precipices of that stupendous promontory. "Though you drive out Nature with a pitchfork, she will ever return."

"Naturam expellas furcâ . . . tamen usque recurret."

I have consulted a sportsman, now in his seventy-eighth year, who tells me that fifty or sixty years back, when the beechen woods were much more extensive than at present, the number of wood-pigeons was astonishing; that he has often killed near twenty in a day: and that with a long wild-fowl piece he has shot seven or eight at a time on the wing as they came wheeling over his head: he moreover adds, which I was not aware of, that often there were among them little parties of small blue doves, which he calls rockiers. The food of these numberless emigrants was beech-mast and some acorns; and particularly barley, which they collected in the stubbles. But of late years, since the vast increase of turnips, that vegetable has furnished a great part of their support in hard weather; and the holes they pick in these roots greatly damage the crop. From this food their flesh has contracted a rancidness which occasions them to be rejected by nicer judges of eating, who thought them before a delicate dish. They were shot not only as they were feeding in the fields, and especially in snowy weather, but also at the close of the evening, by men who lay in ambush among the woods and groves to kill them as they came in to roost.[1] These are the principal circumstances relating to this wonderful internal migration, which with us takes place towards the end of November, and ceases early in

[1] "Some old sportsmen say that the main part of these flocks used to withdraw as soon as the heavy Christmas frosts were over."—W.

the spring. Last winter we had in Selborne high wood about a hundred of these doves; but in former times the flocks were so vast, not only with us but all the district round, that on mornings and evenings they traversed the air, like rooks, in strings, reaching for a mile together. When they thus rendezvoused here by thousands, if they happened to be suddenly roused from their roost-trees on an evening,

> "Their rising all at once was like the sound
> Of thunder heard remote".

It will by no means be foreign to the present purpose to add, that I had a relation in this neighbourhood who made it a practice, for a time, whenever he could procure the eggs of a ring-dove, to place them under a pair of doves that were sitting in his own pigeon-house; hoping thereby, if he could bring about a coalition, to enlarge his breed, and teach his own doves to beat out into the woods, and to support themselves by mast; the plan was plausible, but something always interrupted the success; for though the birds were usually hatched, and sometimes grew to half their size, yet none ever arrived at maturity. I myself have seen these foundlings in their nest displaying a strange ferocity of nature, so as scarcely to bear to be looked at, and snapping with their bills by way of menace. In short, they always died, perhaps for want of proper sustenance: but the owner thought that by their fierce and wild demeanour they frighted their foster-mothers, and so were starved.

Virgil, as a familiar occurrence, by way of simile, describes a dove haunting the cavern of a rock in such engaging numbers, that I cannot refrain from quoting the passage: and John Dryden has rendered it so happily in our language, that without farther excuse I shall add his translation also.

> " Qualis speluncâ subitò commota Columba,
>   Cui domus, et dulces latebroso in pumice nidi,
>   Fertur in arva volans, plausumque exterrita pennis,
>   Dat tecto ingentem—mox aere lapsa quieto,
>   Radit iter liquidum, celeres neque commovet alas."
>   VIRGIL. Æn. v. 213–217.

> " As when a dove her rocky hold forsakes,
>   Rous'd, in a fright her sounding wings she shakes;
>   The cavern rings with clattering:—out she flies,
>   And leaves her callow care, and cleaves the skies ·
>   At first she flutters:—but at length she springs
>   To smoother flight, and shoots upon her wings."

LETTERS TO THE
HON. DAINES BARRINGTON.

LETTER I.

SELBORNE, *June 30th*, 1769.

While I was in town last month I partly engaged that I would sometimes do myself the honour to write to you on the subject of natural history; and I am the more ready to fulfil my promise, because I see you are a gentleman of great candour, and one that will make allowances; especially where the writer professes to be an outdoor naturalist, one that takes his observations from the subject itself, and not from the writings of others.

The following is a list of the summer birds of passage which I have discovered in this neighbourhood, ranged somewhat in the order in which they appear:

	RAII NOMINA.	USUALLY APPEARS ABOUT
1. Wryneck,[1]	*Junx, sive torquilla.*	The middle of March: harsh note.
2. Smallest willow-wren,	*Regulus non cristatus.*	March 23rd: chirps till September.
3. Swallow,	*Hirundo domestica.*	April 13th.
4. Martin,	*Hirundo rustica.*	Ditto.
5. Sand-martin,	*Hirundo riparia.*	Ditto.
6. Black-cap,	*Atricapilla.*	Ditto: a sweet wild note.
7. Nightingale,	*Luscinia.*	Beginning of April.
8. Cuckoo,	*Cuculus.*	Middle of April.
9. Middle willow-wren,	*Regulus non cristatus.*	Ditto: a sweet plaintive note.
10. White-throat,	*Ficedula affinis.*	Ditto: mean note; sings on till September.
11. Redstart,	*Ruticilla.*	Ditto: more agreeable song.
12. Stone-curlew,	*Œdicnemus.*	End of March: loud nocturnal whistle.
13. Turtle-dove,	*Turtur.*	
14. Grasshopper-lark,	*Alauda minima locustæ voce.*	Middle April: a small sibilous note, till the end of July.
15. Swift,	*Hirundo apus.*	About April 27th.
16. Lessreed-sparrow,	*Passer arundinaceus minor.*	A sweet polyglot, but hurrying; it has the notes of many birds.
17. Land-rail,	*Ortygometra.*	A loud harsh note, crex, crex.

[1] These birds appear on the grass plots and walks; they walk a little as well as hop, and thrust their bills into the turf, in quest, I conclude, of ants, which are their food. While they hold their bills in the grass, they draw out their prey with their tongues, which are so long as to be coiled round their heads.—W.

G

	RAII NOMINA.	USUALLY APPEARS ABOUT
18. Largest willow-wren,	Regulus non cristatus.	"Cantat voce stridulâ locustæ";[1] end of April, on the tops of high beeches.
19. Goat-sucker, or fern-owl,	Caprimulgus.	Beginning of May: chatters by night with a singular noise.
20. Fly-catcher,	Stoparola.	May 12th: a very mute bird; this is the latest summer bird of passage.

This assemblage of curious and amusing birds belongs to
ten several genera of the Linnæan system; and are all of the
Ordo of *Passeres*, save the *Junx* and *Cuculus*, which are *Picæ*,
and the *Charadrius* (*Œdicnemus*) and *Rallus* (*Ortygometra*),
which are *Grallæ*.

These birds, as they stand numerically, belong to the
following Linnæan genera:

1,	*Junx.*	13,	*Columba.*
2, 6, 7, 9, 10, 11, 16, 18,	*Motacilla.*	17,	*Rallus.*
3, 4, 5, 15,	*Hirundo.*	19,	*Caprimulgus.*
8,	*Cuculus.*	14,	*Alauda.*
12,	*Charadrius.*	20,	*Muscicapa.*

Most soft-billed birds live on insects, and not on grain and
seeds; and therefore at the end of summer they retire: but
the following soft-billed birds, though insect-eaters, stay with
us the year round:

Redbreast,	*Rubecula.*	These frequent houses; and haunt out-buildings in the winter: eat spiders.
Wren,	*Passer troglodytes.*	
Hedge-sparrow,	*Curruca.*	Haunt sinks for crumbs and other sweepings.
White-wagtail,	*Motacilla alba.*	These frequent shallow rivulets near the spring heads, where they never freeze: eat the aureliæ of *Phryganea.* The smallest birds that walk.
Yellow-wagtail,	*Motacilla flava.*	
Grey-wagtail,	*Motacilla cinerea.*	
Wheatear,	*Œnanthe.*	Some of these are to be seen with us the winter through.
Whinchat,	*Œnanthe secunda.*	
Stone-chatter,	*Œnanthe tertia.*	
Golden-crowned wren,	*Regulus cristatus.*	This is the smallest British bird: haunts the tops of tall trees; stays the winter through.

A list of the winter birds of passage round this neighbourhood, ranged somewhat in the order in which they
appear:

[1] "Sings with the stridulous voice of a grasshopper."

RAII NOMINA.

1. Ring-ousel,	*Merula torquata.*	This is a new migration, which I have lately discovered about Michaelmas week, and again about the 14th March.
2. Redwing,	*Turdus iliacus.*	About old Michaelmas.
3. Fieldfare,	*Turdus pilaris.*	Though a percher by day, roosts on the ground.
4. Royston-crow,	*Cornix cinerea.*	Most frequent on downs.
5. Woodcock,	*Scolopax.*	Appears about old Michaelmas.
6. Snipe,	*Gallinago minor.*	Some snipes constantly breed with us.
7. Jack-snipe,	*Gallinago minima*	
8. Wood-pigeon,	*Œnas.*	Seldom appears till late; not in such plenty as formerly.
9. Wild-swan,	*Cygnus ferus.*	On some large waters.
10. Wild-goose,	*Anser ferus.*	
11. Wild-duck,	*Anas torquata minor.*	
12. Pochard,	*Anas fera fusca.*	
13. Widgeon,	*Penelope.*	
14. Teal, breeds with us in Wolmer Forest,	*Querquedula.*	On our lakes and streams.
15. Grosbeak	*Coccothraustes.*	These are only wanderers that appear occasionally, and are not observant of any regular migration.
16. Crossbill,	*Loxia.*	
17. Silktail,	*Garrulus bohemicus.*	

The birds, as they stand numerically, belong to the following Linnæan genera:

1, 2, 3,	*Turdus.*	9, 10, 11, 12, 13, 14,	*Anas.*
4,	*Corvus.*	15, 16,	*Loxia.*
5, 6, 7,	*Scolopax.*	17,	*Ampelis.*
8,	*Columba.*		

Birds that sing in the night are but few.[1]

Nightingale,	*Luscinia.*	"In shadiest covert hid." MILTON.
Woodlark,	*Alauda arborea.*	Suspended in mid-air.
Less reed-sparrow,	*Passer arundinaceus minor.*	Among reeds and willows

I should now proceed to such birds as continue to sing after midsummer, but, as they are rather numerous, they would exceed the bounds of this paper: besides, as this is now the season for remarking on that subject, I am willing to repeat my observations on some birds concerning the continuation of whose song I seem at present to have some doubt.

---

[1] This list does not exhaust the number of those that sing in the night; it might also include the cuckoo, the skylark, the reed-warbler, and others.

LETTER II.

SELBORNE, *Nov. 2nd*, 1769.

When I did myself the honour to write to you about the end of last June on the subject of natural history, I sent you a list of the summer birds of passage which I have observed in this neighbourhood; and also a list of the winter birds of passage: I mentioned besides those soft-billed birds that stay with us the winter through in the south of England, and those that are remarkable for singing in the night.

According to my proposal, I shall now proceed to such birds (singing birds strictly so called) as continue in full song till after midsummer; and shall range them somewhat in the order in which they first begin to open as the spring advances.

RAII NOMINA.

1. Woodlark,	*Alauda arborea.*	In January, and continues to sing through all the summer and autumn.
2. Song-thrush,	*Turdus simpliciter dictus.*	In February and on to August; reassume their song in autumn.
3. Wren,	*Passer troglodytes.*	All the year, hard frost excepted.
4. Redbreast,	*Rubecula.*	Ditto.
5. Hedge-sparrow,	*Curruca.*	Early in February to July 10th.
6. Yellow-hammer,	*Emberiza flava.*	Early in February, and on through July to August 21st.
7. Skylark,	*Alauda vulgaris.*	In February and on to October.
8. Swallow,	*Hirundo domestica.*	From April to September.
9. Black-cap,	*Atricapilla.*	Beginning of April to July 13th.
10. Titlark,	*Alauda pratorum.*	From middle of April to July 16th.
11. Blackbird,	*Merula vulgaris.*	Sometimes in February and March, and so on to July 23rd; reassumes in autumn.
12. White-throat,	*Ficedulæ affinis.*	In April, and on to July 23rd.
13. Goldfinch,	*Carduelis.*	April, and through to September 16th.
14. Greenfinch,	*Chloris.*	On to July and August 2nd.
15. Less reed-sparrow,	*Passer arundinaceus minor.*	May, on to beginning of July.
16. Common linnet,	*Linaria vulgaris.*	Breeds and whistles on till August; reassumes its note when they begin to congregate in October, and again early before the flocks separate.

Birds that cease to be in full song, and are usually silent at or before midsummer:

RAII NOMINA.

17. Middle willow-wren,	*Regulus non cristatus.*	Middle of June; begins in April.
18. Redstart,	*Ruticilla.*	Ditto: begins in May.
19. Chaffinch,	*Fringilla.*	{ Beginning of June; sings first in February.
20. Nightingale,	*Luscinia.*	{ Middle of June; sings first in April.

Birds that sing for a short time, and very early in the spring:

21. Missel-bird,	*Turdus viscivorus.*	{ January 2nd, 1770; in February. Is called in Hampshire and Sussex the storm-cock, because its song is supposed to forbode windy wet weather; it is the largest singing bird we have.
22. Great titmouse, or ox-eye, }	*Fringillago.*	{ In February, March, April: reassumes for a short time in September.

Birds that have somewhat of a note or song, and yet are hardly to be called singing birds:

23. Golden - crowned wren, }	*Regulus cristatus.*	{ Its note as minute as its person; frequents the tops of high oaks and firs; the smallest British bird.
24. Marsh-titmouse,	*Parus palustris.*	{ Haunts great woods: two harsh sharp notes.
25. Small willow-wren,	*Regulus non cristatus.*	{ Sings in March, and on to September.
26. Largest ditto,	*Ditto.*	{ *Cantat voce stridulâ locustæ;* from end of April to August.
27. Grasshopper-lark,	{ *Alauda minima voce locustæ.*	{ Chirps all night, from the middle of April to the end of July.
28. Martin,	*Hirundo agrestis.*	{ All the breeding-time: from May to September.
29. Bullfinch,	*Pyrrhula.*	
30. Bunting,	*Emberiza alba.*	{ From the end of January to July.

All singing birds, and those that have any pretensions to song, not only in Britain, but perhaps the world through, come under the Linnæan *Ordo* of *Passeres*.

The above-mentioned birds, as they stand numerically, belong to the following Linnæan genera:

1, 7, 10, 27,	*Alauda.*		8, 28,	*Hirundo.*
2, 11, 21,	*Turdus.*		13, 16, 19,	*Fringilla.*
3, 4, 5, 9, 12, 15, 17,	} *Motacilla.*		22, 24,	*Parus.*
18, 20, 23, 25, 26,			14, 29,	*Loxia.*
6, 30,	*Emberiza*			

Birds that sing as they fly are but few:

	RAII NOMINA.	
Skylark,	*Alauda vulgaris.*	Rising, suspended, and falling.
Titlark,	*Alauda pratorum.*	In its descent; also sitting on trees, and walking on the ground.
Woodlark,	*Alauda arborea.*	Suspended; in hot summer nights all night long.
Blackbird,	*Merula.*	Sometimes from bush to bush.
White-throat,	*Ficedulæ affinis.*	Uses when singing on the wing odd jerks and gesticulations.
Swallow,	*Hirundo domestica.*	In soft sunny weather.
Wren,	*Passer troglodytes.*	Sometimes from bush to bush.

Birds that breed most early in these parts:

Raven,	*Corvus.*	Hatches in February and March.
Song-thrush,	*Turdus.*	In March.
Blackbird,	*Merula.*	In March.
Rook,	*Cornix frugilega.*	Builds the beginning of March.
Woodlark,	*Alauda arborea.*	Hatches in April.
Ring-dove,	*Palumbus torquatus.*	Lays the beginning of April.

All birds that continue in full song till after midsummer appear to me to breed more than once.

Most kinds of birds seem to me to be wild and shy somewhat in proportion to their bulk; I mean in this island, where they are much pursued and annoyed; but in Ascension Island, and many other desolate places, mariners have found fowls so unacquainted with a human figure, that they would stand still to be taken; as is the case with boobies, etc. As an example of what is advanced, I remark that the golden-crested wren (the smallest British bird) will stand unconcerned till you come within three or four yards of it, while the bustard (*Otis*), the largest British land fowl, does not care to admit a person within so many furlongs.

LETTER III.

SELBORNE, *Jan. 15th,* 1770.

It was no small matter of satisfaction to me to find that you were not displeased with my little *methodus* of birds. If there was any merit in the sketch, it must be owing to its punctuality. For many months I carried a list in my pocket of the birds that were to be remarked, and, as I rode or walked about my business, I noted each day the continuance or omission of each bird's song; so that I am as sure of the certainty of my facts as a man can be of any transaction whatever.

I shall now proceed to answer the several queries which you put in your two obliging letters, in the best manner that I am able. Perhaps Eastwick, and its environs, where you heard so very few birds, is not a woodland country, and therefore not stocked with such songsters. If you will cast your eye on my last letter, you will find that many species continued to warble after the beginning of July.

The titlark and yellow-hammer breed late, the latter very late; and therefore it is no wonder that they protract their song: for I lay it down as a maxim in ornithology, that as long as there is any incubation going on there is music. As to the redbreast and wren, it is well known to the most incurious observer that they whistle the year round, hard frost excepted; especially the latter.

It was not in my power to procure you a black-cap, or a less reed-sparrow, or sedge-bird, alive. As the first is undoubtedly, and the last, as far as I can yet see, a summer bird of passage, they would require more nice and curious management in a cage than I should be able to give them: they are both distinguished songsters. The note of the former has such a wild sweetness that it always brings to my mind those lines in a song in "As You Like It":

"And tune his merry note
Unto the *wild* bird's throat."—SHAKESPEARE.

The latter has a surprising variety of notes resembling the song of several other birds; but then it has also a hurrying manner, not at all to its advantage: it is notwithstanding a delicate polyglot.

It is new to me that titlarks in cages sing in the night; perhaps only caged birds do so. I once knew a tame redbreast in a cage that always sang as long as candles were in the room; but in their wild state no one supposes they sing in the night.

I should be almost ready to doubt the fact, that there are to be seen much fewer birds in July than in any former month, notwithstanding so many young are hatched daily. Sure I am that it is far otherwise with respect to the swallow tribe, which increases prodigiously as the summer advances: and I saw at the time mentioned, many hundreds of young wagtails on the banks of the Cherwell, which almost covered the meadows.

If the matter appears as you say in the other species, may it not be owing to the dams being engaged in incubation, while the young are concealed by the leaves?

Many times have I had the curiosity to open the stomachs of woodcocks and snipes; but nothing ever occurred that helped to explain to me what their subsistence might be: all that I could ever find was a soft mucus, among which lay many pellucid small gravels.

LETTER IV.

SELBORNE, *Feb.* 19*th*, 1770.

Your observation that "the cuckoo does not deposit its egg indiscriminately in the nest of the first bird that comes in its way, but probably looks out a nurse in some degree congenerous, with whom to intrust its young", is probably new to me; and struck me so forcibly, that I naturally fell into a train of thought that led me to consider whether the fact was so, and what reason there was for it. When I came to recollect and inquire, I could not find that any cuckoo had ever been seen in these parts, except in the nest of the wagtail, the hedge-sparrow, the titlark, the white-throat, and the redbreast, all soft-billed insectivorous birds. The excellent Mr. Willughby mentions the nest of the ring-dove (*Palumbus*), and of the chaffinch (*Fringilla*), birds that subsist on acorns and grains, and such hard food: but then he does not mention them as of his own knowledge, but says afterwards that he saw himself a wagtail feeding a cuckoo. It appears hardly possible that a soft-billed bird should subsist on the same food with the hard-billed: for the former have thin membranaceous stomachs suited to their soft food; while the latter, the granivorous tribe, have strong muscular gizzards, which, like mills, grind, by the help of small gravels and pebbles, what is swallowed. This proceeding of the cuckoo, of dropping its eggs as it were by chance, is such a monstrous outrage on maternal affection, one of the first great dictates of nature; and such a violence on instinct; that, had it only been related of a bird in the Brazils, or Peru, it would never have merited our belief. But yet, should it farther appear that this simple bird, when divested of that natural στοργή (parental love) that seems to raise the kind in general above themselves, and inspire them with extraordinary degrees of cunning and address, may be still endued with a more enlarged faculty of discerning what species are suitable and congenerous nursing-mothers for its disregarded eggs and young, and may deposit them only under their care, this would be adding wonder to wonder, and instancing, in a fresh manner, that the methods of Providence are not subjected to any mode or rule, but astonish us in new lights, and in various and changeable appearances.

What was said by a very ancient and sublime writer concerning the defect of natural affection in the ostrich, may be well applied to the bird we are talking of:

"She is hardened against her young ones, as though they were not hers:

"Because God hath deprived her of wisdom, neither hath He imparted to her understanding."[1]

Query.—Does each female cuckoo lay but one egg in a season, or does she drop several in different nests according as opportunity offers?[2]

[Regarding the food of the ring-dove above referred to, White has the following particulars in his *Observations on Nature*:—

One of my neighbours shot a ring-dove on an evening as it was returning from feed, and going to roost. When his wife had picked and drawn it, she found its craw stuffed with the most nice and tender tops of turnips. These she washed and boiled, and so sat down to a choice and delicate plate of greens, culled and provided in this extraordinary manner.

Hence we may see that graminivorous birds, when grain fails, can subsist on the leaves of vegetables. There is reason to suppose that they would not long be healthy without; for turkeys, though corn fed, delight in a variety of plants, such as cabbage, lettuce, endive, &c., and poultry pick much grass; while geese live for months together on commons by grazing alone.

> "Nought is useless made;——
> ——On the barren heath
> The shepherd tends his flock that daily crop
> Their verdant dinner from the mossy turf
> Sufficient: after them the cackling goose,
> Close-grazer, finds wherewith to ease her want."
>   PHILIPS'S *Cyder*.]

[1] Job xxxix. 16, 17.
[2] There is no doubt that the cuckoo does lay more than one egg in a season.

one has been followed up & found to lay 21. !

LETTER V.

SELBORNE, *April 12th*, 1770.

I heard many birds of several species sing last year after midsummer; enough to prove that the summer solstice is not the period that puts a stop to the music of the woods. The yellow-hammer no doubt persists with more steadiness than any other; but the woodlark, the wren, the redbreast, the swallow, the white-throat, the goldfinch, the common linnet, are all un-doubted instances of the truth of what I advanced.

If this severe season does not interrupt the regularity of the summer migrations, the black-cap will be here in two or three days. I wish it was in my power to procure you one of those songsters; but I am no birdcatcher; and so little used to birds in a cage, that I fear if I had one it would soon die for want of skill in feeding.

Was your reed-sparrow, which you kept in a cage, the thick-billed reed-sparrow of the *Zoology*, p. 320; or was it the less reed-sparrow of Ray, the sedge-bird of Mr. Pennant's last publication (his *Zoology*), p. 16?

As to the matter of long-billed birds growing fatter in mode-rate frosts, I have no doubt within myself what should be the reason. The thriving at those times appears to me to arise altogether from the gentle check which the cold throws upon insensible perspiration. The case is just the same with black-birds, etc.; and farmers, and warreners observe, the first, that their hogs fat more kindly at such times, and the latter that their rabbits are never in such good case as in a gentle frost. But when frosts are severe, and of long continuance, the case is soon altered; for then a want of food soon overbalances the repletion occasioned by a checked perspiration. I have ob-served, moreover, that some human constitutions are more in-clined to plumpness in winter than in summer.

When birds come to suffer by severe frost, I find that the first that fail and die are the redwings, fieldfares, and then the song-thrushes.

You wonder, with good reason, that the hedge-sparrows, etc., can be induced at all to sit on the egg of the cuckoo with-out being scandalized at the vast disproportionate size of the supposititious egg; but the brute creation, I suppose, have very little idea of size, colour, or number. For the common hen, I know, when the fury of incubation is on her, will sit on

* Surely this fatness is only apparent not real, is caused by the puffing out of the feathers so that the bird encases itself in an overcoat of warm air.

a single shapeless stone instead of a nest full of eggs that have been withdrawn: and, moreover, a hen-turkey, in the same circumstances, would sit on in the empty nest till she perished with hunger.

I think the matter might easily be determined whether a cuckoo lays one or two eggs, or more, in a season, by opening a female during the laying-time. If more than one was come down out of the ovary and advanced to a good size, doubtless then she would that spring lay more than one.

I will endeavour to get a hen, and to examine.

Your supposition that there may be some natural obstruc tion in singing birds while they are mute, and that when this is removed the song recommences, is new and bold: I wish you could discover some good grounds for this suspicion.

I was glad you were pleased with my specimen of the *Caprimulgus*, or fern-owl; you were, I find, acquainted with the bird before.

When we meet I shall be glad to have some conversation with you concerning the proposal you make of my drawing up an account of the animals in this neighbourhood. Your partiality towards my small abilities persuades you, I fear, that I am able to do more than is in my power: for it is no small undertaking for a man unsupported and alone to begin a natural history from his own autopsia![1] Though there is endless room for observation in the field of nature, which is boundless, yet investigation (where a man endeavours to be sure of his facts) can make but slow progress; and all that one could collect in many years would go into a very narrow compass.

Some extracts from your ingenious "Investigations of the Difference between the Present Temperature of the Air in Italy", etc., have fallen in my way, and gave me great satisfaction: they have removed the objections that always arose in my mind whenever I came to the passages which you quote. Surely the judicious Virgil, when writing a didactic poem for the region of Italy, could never think of describing freezing rivers, unless such severity of weather pretty frequently occurred!

Two swallows have appeared amidst snows and frost.

---

[1] *Autopsia*—ocular observation.

LETTER VI.

SELBORNE, *May* 21*st*, 1770.

The severity and turbulence of last month so interrupted the regular process of summer migration, that some of the birds do but just begin to show themselves, and others are apparently thinner than usual; as the white-throat, the black-cap, the redstart, the fly-catcher. I well remember that after the very severe spring in the year 1739–40, summer birds of passage were very scarce. They come hither probably with a south-east wind, or when it blows between those points; but in that unfavourable year the winds blowed the whole spring and summer through from the opposite quarters. And yet amidst all these disadvantages two swallows, as I mentioned in my last, appeared this year as early as the 11th April amidst frost and snow; but they withdrew again for a time.

I am not pleased to find that some people seem so little satisfied with Scopoli's new publication;[1] there is room to expect great things from the hands of that man, who is a good naturalist: and one would think that a history of the birds of so distant and southern a region as Carniola would be new and interesting. I could wish to see the work, and hope to get it sent down. Dr. Scopoli is physician to the wretches that work in the quicksilver mines of that district.

When you talked of keeping a reed-sparrow, and giving it seeds, I could not help wondering; because the reed-sparrow which I mentioned to you (*Passer arundinaceus minor Raii*) is a soft-billed bird; and most probably migrates hence before winter; whereas the bird you kept (*Passer torquatus Raii*) abides all the year, and is a thick-billed bird. I question whether the latter be much of a songster; but in this matter I want to be better informed. The former has a variety of hurrying notes, and sings all night. Some part of the song of the former, I suspect, is attributed to the latter. We have plenty of the soft-billed sort; which Mr. Pennant had entirely left out of his *British Zoology*, till I reminded him of his omission. See *British Zoology* last published, p. 16.

I have somewhat to advance on the different manners in which different birds fly and walk; but as this is a subject that I have not enough considered, and is of such a nature as

1 This work he calls his *Annus Primus Historico-Naturalis.*—W.

not to be contained in a small space, I shall say nothing further about it at present.

No doubt the reason why the sex of birds in their first plumage is so difficult to be distinguished is, as you say, "because they are not to pair and discharge their parental functions till the ensuing spring". As colours seem to be the chief external sexual distinction in many birds, these colours do not take place till sexual attachments begin to obtain. And the case is the same in quadrupeds; among whom, in their younger days, the sexes differ but little: but, as they advance to maturity, horns and shaggy manes, beards and brawny necks, etc., etc., strongly discriminate the male from the female. We may instance still farther in our own species, where a beard and stronger features are usually characteristic of the male sex: but this sexual diversity does not take place in earlier life; for a beautiful youth shall be so like a beautiful girl that the difference shall not be discernable;

> "Quem si puellarum insereres choro,
> Mirè sagaces falleret hospites
> Discrimen obscurum, solutis
> Crinibus, ambiguoque vultu."—HOR. (*Odes.*)

("A youth who, if introduced among a lot of girls, would, by the difficulty of distinguishing him from the rest, greatly puzzle even clever strangers, thanks to his loose hair and ambiguous face.")

of Hon. John Russell

LETTER VII.

RINGMER, *near* LEWES, *Oct. 8th,* 1770.

I am glad to hear that Kuckahn is to furnish you with the birds of Jamaica; a sight of the *Hirundines* of that hot and distant island would be a great entertainment to me.

The *Anni* of Scopoli are now in my possession; and I have read the *Annus Primus* with satisfaction; for though some parts of this work are exceptional, and he may advance some mistaken observations, yet the ornithology of so distant a country as Carniola is very curious. Men that undertake only one district are much more likely to advance natural knowledge than those that grasp at more than they can possibly be acquainted with: every kingdom, every province, should have its own monographer.

The reason perhaps why he mentions nothing of Ray's Ornithology may be the extreme poverty and distance of his country, into which the works of our great naturalist may have never yet found their way. You have doubts, I know, whether this Ornithology is genuine, and really the work of Scopoli; as to myself, I think I discover strong tokens of authenticity; the style corresponds with that of his Entomology; and his characters of his Ordines and Genera are many of them new, expressive, and masterly. He has ventured to alter some of the Linnæan genera with sufficient show of reason.

It might perhaps be mere accident that you saw so many swifts and no swallows at Staines; because, in my long observation of those birds, I never could discover the least degree of rivalry or hostility between the species.

Ray remarks that birds of the *Gallinæ* order, as cocks and hens, partridges, and pheasants, etc., are *pulveratrices*, such as dust themselves, using that method of cleansing their feathers, and ridding themselves of their vermin. As far as I can observe, many birds that dust themselves never wash; and I once thought that those birds that wash themselves would never dust; but here I find myself mistaken; for common house-sparrows are great *pulveratrices*, being frequently seen grovelling and wallowing in dusty roads; and yet they are great washers. Does not the skylark dust?

Query.—Might not Mahomet and his followers take one method of purification from these *pulveratrices*? because I find from travellers of credit, that if a strict Mussulman is journeying in a sandy desert where no water is to be found, at stated hours he strips off his clothes, and most scrupulously rubs his body over with sand or dust.

A countryman told me he had found a young fern-owl in the nest of a small bird on the ground; and that it was fed by the little bird. I went to see this extraordinary phenomenon, and found that it was a young cuckoo hatched in the nest of a titlark; it was become vastly too big for its nest, appearing "in sitting there, to have its large wings stretched out beyond the nest":

> . . . . . in tenui re
> Majores pennas nido extendisse . .

and was very fierce and pugnacious, pursuing my finger, as I teased it, for many feet from the nest, and sparring and buffeting with its wings like a game-cock. The dupe of a dam appeared at a distance, hovering about with meat in its mouth, and expressing the greatest solicitude.

In July I saw several cuckoos skimming over a large pond;

and found, after some observation, that they were feeding on the *Libellulæ*, or dragon-flies; some of which they caught as they settled on the weeds, and some as they were on the wing. Notwithstanding what Linnæus says, I cannot be induced to believe that they are birds of prey.

This district affords some birds that are hardly ever heard of at Selborne. In the first place considerable flocks of cross-beaks (*Loxiæ curvirostræ*) have appeared this summer in the pine-groves belonging to this house; the water-ousel is said to haunt the mouth of the Lewes river, near Newhaven; and the Cornish chough builds, I know, all along the chalky cliffs of the Sussex shore.[1]

I was greatly pleased to see little parties of ring-ousels (my newly discovered migrators) scattered, at intervals, all along the Sussex downs, from Chichester to Lewes. Let them come from whence they will, it looks very suspicious that they are cantoned along the coast in order to pass the channel when severe weather advances. They visit us again in April, as it should seem, in their return; and are not to be found in the dead of winter. It is remarkable that they are very tame, and seem to have no manner of apprehensions of danger from a person with a gun. There are bustards on the wide downs near Brighthelmstone. No doubt you are acquainted with the Sussex downs; the prospects and rides round Lewes are most lovely!

As I rode along near the coast I kept a very sharp look-out in the lanes and woods, hoping I might, at this time of the year, have discovered some of the summer short-winged birds of passage crowding towards the coast in order for their departure: but it was very extraordinary that I never saw a redstart, white-throat, black-cap, uncrested wren, fly-catcher, etc. And I remember to have made the same remark in former years, as I usually come to this place annually about this time. The birds most common along the coast at present are the stone-chatters, whinchats, buntings, linnets, some few wheat-ears, titlarks, etc. Swallows and house-martins abound yet, induced to prolong their stay by this soft, still, dry season.

A land tortoise, which has been kept for thirty years in a little walled court belonging to the house where I now am visiting, retires under ground about the middle of November, and comes forth again about the middle of April. When it first appears in the spring it discovers very little inclination

[1] This is no longer the case.

towards food; but in the height of summer grows voracious; and then as the summer declines its appetite declines; so that for the last six weeks in autumn it hardly eats at all. Milky plants, such as lettuces, dandelions, sow-thistles, are its favourite dish. In a neighbouring village one was kept till by tradition it was supposed to be a hundred years old. An instance of vast longevity in such a poor reptile!

LETTER VIII.

SELBORNE, *Dec.* 20*th*, 1770.

The birds that I took for aberdavines were reed-sparrows (*Passeres torquati*).

There are doubtless many home internal migrations within this kingdom that want to be better understood: witness those vast flocks of hen-chaffinches that appear with us in the winter without hardly any cocks among them. Now, was there a due proportion of each sex, it should seem very improbable that any one district should produce such numbers of these little birds; and much more when only one-half of the species appears; therefore we may conclude that the *Fringillæ cœlebs*, for some good purposes, have a peculiar migration of their own in which the sexes part. Nor should it seem so wonderful that the intercourse of sexes in this species of bird should be interrupted in winter; since in many animals, and particularly in bucks and does, the sexes herd separately, except at certain seasons. For this matter of the chaffinches see *Fauna Suecica*, p. 58, and *Systema Naturæ*, p. 318. I see every winter vast flights of hen-chaffinches, but none of cocks.

Your method of accounting for the periodical motions of the British singing birds, or birds of flight, is a very probable one; since the matter of food is a great regulator of the actions and proceedings of the brute creation; there is but one that can be set in competition with it, and that is love. But I cannot quite acquiesce with you in one circumstance when you advance that, "when they have thus feasted, they again separate into small parties of five or six, and get the best fare they can within a certain district, having no inducement to go in quest of fresh-turned earth". Now, if you mean that the business of congregating is quite at an end from the conclusion of wheat sowing to the season of barley and oats, it is not the case with us; for larks and chaffinches, and particularly linnets, flock and congregate as much in the very dead of winter as when the husbandman is busy with his ploughs and harrows.

Surely there can be no doubt but that woodcocks and field-fares leave us in the spring, in order to cross the seas, and to retire to some districts more suitable to the purpose of breeding. That the former pair before they retire, and that the hens are forward with egg, I myself, when I was a sportsman, have often experienced. It cannot indeed be denied but that now and then we hear of a woodcock's nest, or young birds, discovered in some part or other of this island; but then they are all always mentioned as rarities, and somewhat out of the common course of things: but as to redwings and fieldfares, no sportsman or naturalist has ever yet, that I could hear, pretended to have found the nest or young of those species in any part of these kingdoms. And I the more admire at this instance as extraordinary, since, to all appearance, the same food in summer as well as in winter might support them here which maintains their congeners, the blackbirds and thrushes, did they choose to stay the summer through. From hence it appears that it is not food alone which determines some species of birds with regard to their stay or departure. Fieldfares or redwings disappear sooner or later according as the warm weather comes on earlier or later. For I well remember, after that dreadful winter 1739-40, that cold north-east winds continued to blow on through April and May, and that these kind of birds (what few remained of them) did not depart as usual, but were seen lingering about till the beginning of June.

The best authority that we can have for the nidification of the birds above-mentioned in any district, is the testimony of faunists that have written professedly the natural history of particular countries. Now as to the fieldfare, Linnæus, in his *Fauna Suecica,* says of it, that "it builds mostly in trees": "*maximis in arboribus nidificat*"; and of the redwing he says, in the same place, that "it builds in the midst of bushes or hedges, and lays six eggs of a bluish-green colour, with varie-gated black spots": "*nidificat in mediis arbusculis, sive sepibus: ova sex cœruleo-viridia maculis nigris variis*". Hence we may be assured that fieldfares and redwings breed in Sweden. Scopoli says, in his *Annus Primus,* of the woodcock, that "it arrives with us, paired, about the vernal equinox": "*nupta ad nos venit circà æquinoctium vernale*"; meaning in Tyrol, of which he is a native. And afterwards he adds that "it builds its nest in the Alpine marshes, and lays from three to five eggs": "*nidificat in paludibus alpinis: ova ponit 3–5*". It does not appear from Kramer that woodcocks breed at all in Austria; but he says, "*Avis hæc septentrionalium provinciarum æstivo tempore incola est; ubi plerumque nidificat. Appropinquante hyeme australiores provincias petit; hinc circà plenilunium mensis Octobris plerumque Austrian transmigrat. Tunc rursùs circà plenilunium potissimum mensis Martii per Austrian matrimonio juncta ad septentrionales provincias redit*".[1] For the whole passage (which I have abridged) see *Elenchus*, etc., p. 351. This seems to be a full proof of the migration of woodcocks; though little is proved concerning the place of breeding.[2]

There fell in the county of Rutland, in three weeks of this present very wet weather, seven inches and a half of rain, which is more than has fallen in any three weeks for these thirty years past in that part of the world. A mean quantity in that county for one year is twenty inches and a half.

LETTER IX.

FYFIELD, *near* ANDOVER, *Feb. 12th*, 1771.

You are, I know, no great friend to migration; and the well-attested accounts from various parts of the kingdom seem to justify you in your suspicions, that at least many of the swallow kind do not leave us in the winter, but lay themselves up like insects and bats in a torpid state, and slumber away the more uncomfortable months till the return of the sun and fine weather awakens them.

But then we must not, I think, deny migration in general; because migration certainly does subsist in some places, as my brother in Andalusia has fully informed me. Of the motions of these birds he has ocular demonstration, for many weeks together, both spring and fall; during which periods myriads of the swallow kind traverse the straits from north to south, and from south to north, according to the season. And these vast migrations consist not only of *Hirundines* but of bee-birds, hoopoes, *Oropendolas*, or golden thrushes, etc., etc., and also of

---

[1] "This bird is a denizen in the summer time of the northern provinces, where for the most part it builds its nest. On the approach of winter it seeks the more southern provinces, migrating about the time of full-moon in October. Then, after pairing, it returns to the north through Austria, about the time of the March full-moon."

[2] It is now an ascertained fact, that though woodcocks arrive here in the autumn, and leave us again in the spring, many remain here to breed.

many of our soft-billed summer birds of passage; and moreover of birds which never leave us, such as all the various sorts of hawks and kites. Old Belon, two hundred years ago, gives a curious account of the incredible armies of hawks and kites which he saw in the spring-time traversing the Thracian Bosphorus from Asia to Europe. Besides the above-mentioned, he remarks that the procession is swelled by whole troops of eagles and vultures.

Now it is no wonder that birds residing in Africa should retreat before the sun as it advances, and retire to milder regions, and especially birds of prey, whose blood being heated with hot animal food, are more impatient of a sultry climate; but then I cannot help wondering why kites and hawks, and such hardy birds as are known to defy all the severity of England, and even of Sweden and all north Europe, should want to migrate from the south of Europe, and be dissatisfied with the winters of Andalusia.

It does not appear to me that much stress may be laid on the difficulty and hazard that birds must run in their migrations, by reason of vast oceans, cross winds, etc.; because, if we reflect, a bird may travel from England to the Equator without launching out and exposing itself to boundless seas, and that by crossing the water at Dover, and again at Gibraltar. And I with the more confidence advance this obvious remark, because my brother has always found that some of his birds, and particularly the swallow kind, are very sparing of their pains in crossing the Mediterranean; for when arrived at Gibraltar they do not

> . . . "Rang'd in figure wedge their way,
> . . . . . and set forth
> Their airy caravan high over seas
> Flying, and over lands with mutual wing
> Easing their flight:" . . . . —MILTON.

but scout and hurry along in little detached parties of six or seven in a company; and sweeping low, just over the surface of the land and water, direct their course to the opposite continent at the narrowest passage they can find. They usually slope across the bay to the south-west, and so pass over opposite to Tangier, which, it seems, is the narrowest space.

In former letters we have considered whether it was probable that woodcocks in moonshiny nights cross the German Ocean from Scandinavia. As a proof that birds of less speed may pass that sea, considerable as it is, I shall relate the following incident, which, though mentioned to have happened so many years ago, was strictly matter of fact:—As some people were shooting in the parish of Trotton, in the county of Sussex, they killed a duck in that dreadful winter, 1708–9, with a silver collar about its neck,[1] on which were engraven the arms of the king of Denmark. This anecdote the rector of Trotton at that time has often told to a near relation of mine; and, to the best of my remembrance, the collar was in the possession of the rector.

At present I do not know anybody near the seaside that will take the trouble to remark at what time of the moon woodcocks first come; if I lived near the sea myself I would soon tell you more of the matter. One thing I used to observe when I was a sportsman, that there were times in which woodcocks were so sluggish and sleepy that they would drop again when flushed just before the spaniels, nay, just at the muzzle of a gun that had been fired at them. Whether this strange laziness was the effect of a recent fatiguing journey I shall not presume to say.

Nightingales not only never reach Northumberland and Scotland, but also, as I have been always told, Devonshire and Cornwall. In those two last counties we cannot attribute the failure of them to the want of warmth; the defect in the west is rather a presumptive argument that these birds come over to us from the Continent at the narrowest passage, and do not stroll so far westward.

Let me hear from your own observation whether skylarks do not dust. I think they do; and if they do, whether they wash also.

The *Alauda pratensis* (or titlark) of Ray was the poor dupe that was educating the booby of a cuckoo mentioned in my letter of October last.

Your letter came too late for me to procure a ring-ousel for Mr. Tunstal during their autumnal visit; but I will endeavour to get him one when they call on us again in April. I am glad that you and that gentleman saw my Andalusian birds; I hope they answered your expectation. Royston, or grey crows, are winter birds that come much about the same time with the woodcock; they, like the fieldfare and redwing, have no apparent reason for migration; for as they fare in the winter like their congeners, so might they in all appearance in

---

[1] I have read a like anecdote of a swan.—W.

the summer. Was not Tenant, when a boy, mistaken? Did he not find a missel-thrush's nest, and take it for the nest of a fieldfare?

The stock-dove, or wood-pigeon, *Œnas Raii*, is the last winter bird of passage which appears with us; it is not seen till towards the end of November: about twenty years ago they abounded in the district of Selborne; and strings of them were seen morning and evening that reached a mile or more; but since the beechen woods have been greatly thinned they are much decreased in number. The ring-dove, *Palumbus Raii*, stays with us the whole year, and breeds several times through the summer.

Before I received your letter of October last I had just remarked in my journal that the trees were unusually green. This uncommon verdure lasted on late into November; and may be accounted for from a late spring, a cool and moist summer; but more particularly from vast armies of chafers, or tree-beetles, which, in many places, reduced whole woods to a leafless naked state. These trees shot again at midsummer, and then retained their foliage till very late in the year.

My musical friend, at whose house I am now visiting, has tried all the owls that are his near neighbours with a pitch-pipe set at concert pitch, and finds they all hoot in B flat. He will examine the nightingales next spring.

LETTER X.

SELBORNE, *Aug. 1st*, 1771.

From what follows, it will appear that neither owls nor cuckoos, keep to one note. A friend remarks that many (most) of his owls hoot in B flat; but that one went almost half a note below A. The pipe he tried their notes by was a common half-crown pitch-pipe, such as masters use for tuning of harpsichords; it was the common London pitch.

A neighbour of mine, who is said to have a nice ear, remarks that the owls about this village hoot in three different keys, in G flat or F sharp, in B flat, and A flat. He heard two hooting to each other, the one in A flat, and the other in B flat. *Query:* Do these different notes proceed from different species, or only from various individuals? The same person finds upon trial that the note of the cuckoo (of which we have but one species) varies in different individuals; for, about Selborne Wood, he found they were mostly in D: he heard two sing together, the one in D, the other in D sharp, who made a disagreeable concert: he afterwards heard one in D sharp, and about Wolmer Forest some in C. As to nightingales, he says that their notes are so short, and their transitions so rapid, that he cannot well ascertain their key. Perhaps in a cage, and in a room, their notes may be more distinguishable. This person has tried to settle the notes of a swift, and of several other small birds, but cannot bring them to any criterion.

As I have often remarked that redwings are some of the first birds that suffer with us in severe weather, it is no wonder at all that they retreat from Scandinavian winters: and much more the *Ordo* of *Grallæ*, who, all to a bird, forsake the northern parts of Europe at the approach of winter. "*Grallæ tanquam conjuratæ, unanimiter in fugam se conjiciunt; ne earum unicam quidem inter nos habitantem invenire possimus; ut enim æstate in australibus degere nequeunt ob defectum lumbricorum, terramque siccam; ita nec in frigidis ob eandem causam,*"[1] says Ekmarck the Swede, in his ingenious little treatise called *Migrationes Avium*, which by all means you ought to read while your thoughts run on the subject of migration. See *Amœnitates Academicæ*, vol. iv., p. 565.

Birds may be so circumstanced as to be obliged to migrate in one country, and not in another: but the *Grallæ* (which procure their food from marshes and boggy grounds) must in winter forsake the more northerly parts of Europe, or perish for want of food.

I am glad you are making inquiries from Linnæus concerning the woodcock: it is expected of him that he should be able to account for the motions and manner of life of the animals of his own *Fauna*.

Faunists, as you observe, are too apt to acquiesce in bare descriptions, and a few synonyms: the reason is plain; because all that may be done at home in a man's study, but the investigation of the life and conversation of animals, is a concern of much more trouble and difficulty, and is not to be attained but by the active and inquisitive, and by those that reside much in the country.

Foreign systematics are, I observe, much too vague in their

[1] "The *Grallæ*, like conspirators, take unanimously to flight; so that we are not able to find a single one left; for as they are not able to live in the south during the summer on account of the want of worms and the hardened earth, so for the same reason they cannot exist in the cold north."

specific differences; which are almost universally constituted by one or two particular marks, the rest of the description running in general terms. But our countryman, the excellent Mr. Ray, is the only describer that conveys some precise idea in every term or word, maintaining his superiority over his followers and imitators in spite of the advantage of fresh discoveries and modern information.

At this distance of years it is not in my power to recollect at what periods woodcocks used to be sluggish or alert when I was a sportsman: but, upon my mentioning this circumstance to a friend, he thinks he has observed them to be remarkably listless against snowy foul weather; if this should be the case, then the inaptitude for flying arises only from an eagerness for food; as sheep are observed to be very intent on grazing against stormy wet evenings.

In his *Observations on Nature*, White has the following remarks on birds in general, which may very well find a place here:—

"In severe weather, fieldfares, redwings, skylarks, and titlarks, resort to watered meadows for food; the latter wades up to its belly in pursuit of the pupæ of insects, and runs along upon the floating grass and weeds. Many gnats are on the snow near the water; these support the birds in part.

"Birds are much influenced in their choice of food by colour, for though white currants are a much sweeter fruit than red, yet they seldom touch the former till they have devoured every bunch of the latter.

"Redstarts, fly-catchers, and black-caps, arrive early in April. If these little delicate beings are birds of passage (as we have reason to suppose they are, because they are never seen in winter), how could they, feeble as they seem, bear up against such storms of snow and rain, and make their way through such meteorous turbulences, as one should suppose would embarrass and retard the most hardy and resolute of the winged nation? Yet they keep their appointed times and seasons; and in spite of frosts and winds return to their stations periodically as if they had met with nothing to obstruct them. The withdrawing and appearance of the short-winged summer birds is a very puzzling circumstance in natural history.

"When the boys bring me wasps' nests, my bantam fowls fare deliciously, and when the combs are pulled to pieces, devour the young wasps in their maggot state with the highest glee and delight. Any insect-eating bird would do the same; and therefore I have wondered that the accurate Mr. Ray should call one species of buzzard *buteo apivorus sive vespivorus*, or the *honey buzzard*, because some combs of wasps happened to be found in one of their nests. The combs were conveyed thither doubtless for the sake of the maggots or nymphs, and not for their honey, since none is to be found in the combs of wasps. Birds of prey occasionally feed on insects; thus have I seen a tame kite picking up the female ants full of eggs, with much satisfaction."

LETTER XI.

SELBORNE, *Feb. 8th*, 1772.

When I ride about in the winter, and see such prodigious flocks of various kinds of birds, I cannot help admiring these congregations, and wishing that it was in my power to account for those appearances almost peculiar to the season. The two great motives which regulate the proceedings of the brute creation are love and hunger; the former incites animals to perpetuate their kind; the latter induces them to preserve individuals: whether either of these should seem to be the ruling passion in the matter of congregating is to be considered. As to love, that is out of the question at a time of the year when that soft passion is not indulged; besides, during the amorous season, such a jealousy prevails between the male birds that they can hardly bear to be together in the same hedge or field. Most of the singing and elation of spirits of that time seem to me to be the effect of rivalry and emulation; and it is to this spirit of jealousy that I chiefly attribute the equal dispersion of birds in the spring over the face of the country.

Now as to the business of food: as these animals are actuated by instinct to hunt for necessary food, they should not, one would suppose, crowd together in pursuit of sustenance at a time when it is most likely to fail; yet such associations do take place in hard weather chiefly, and thicken as the severity increases. As some kind of self-interest and self-defence is no doubt the motive for the proceeding, may it not arise from the helplessness of their state in such rigorous seasons; as men crowd together, when under great calamities, though they know not why? Perhaps approximation may dispel some degree of cold; and a crowd may make each individual appear safer from the ravages of birds of prey and other dangers.

If I admire when I see how much congenerous birds love to congregate, I am the more struck when I see incongruous ones in such strict amity. If we do not much wonder to see a flock of rooks usually attended by a train of daws, yet it is strange that the former should so frequently have a flight of starlings for their satellites. Is it because rooks have a more discerning scent than their attendants, and can lead them to spots more productive of food? Anatomists say that rooks, by reason of two large nerves which run down between the eyes into the upper mandible, have a more delicate feeling in their beaks than other round-billed birds, and can grope for their meat when out of sight. Perhaps, then, their associates attend them on the motive of interest, as greyhounds wait on the motions of their finders; and as lions are said to do on the yelping of jackals. Lapwings and starlings sometimes associate.

LETTER XII.

March 9th, 1772.

As a gentleman and myself were walking on the 4th of last November round the sea-banks at Newhaven, near the mouth of the Lewes river, in pursuit of natural knowledge, we were surprised to see three house-swallows gliding very swiftly by us. That morning was rather chilly, with the wind at north-west; but the tenor of the weather for some time before had been delicate, and the noons remarkably warm. From this incident, and from repeated accounts which I met with, I am more and more induced to believe that many of the swallow kind do not depart from this island, but lay themselves up in holes and caverns; and do, insect-like and bat-like, come forth at mild times, and then retire again to their *latebræ*. Nor make I the least doubt but that, if I lived at Newhaven, Seaford, Brighthelmstone, or any of those towns near the chalk cliffs of the Sussex coast, by proper observations, I should see swallows stirring at periods of the winter, when the noons are soft and inviting, and the sun warm and invigorating. And I am the more of this opinion from what I have remarked during some of our late springs, that though some swallows did make their appearance about the usual time, viz., the 13th or 14th of

April, yet meeting with a harsh reception, and blustering cold north-east winds, they immediately withdrew, absconding for several days, till the weather gave them better encouragement.

LETTER XIII

April 12th, 1772.

While I was in Sussex last autumn my residence was at the village near Lewes, from whence I had formerly the pleasure of writing to you. On the 1st of November I remarked that the old tortoise, formerly mentioned, began first to dig the ground in order to the forming its hybernaculum, which it had fixed on just beside a great tuft of hepaticas. It scrapes out the ground with its fore-feet, and throws it up over its back with its hind; but the motion of its legs is ridiculously slow, little exceeding the hour-hand of a clock; and suitable to the composure of such an animal. Nothing can be more assiduous than this creature night and day in scooping the earth, and forcing its great body into the cavity; but, as the noons of that season proved unusually warm and sunny, it was continually interrupted, and called forth by the heat in the middle of the day; and though I continued there till the 13th of November, yet the work remained unfinished. Harsher weather, and frosty mornings, would have quickened its operations. No part of its behaviour ever struck me more than the extreme timidity it always expresses with regard to rain; for though it has a shell that would secure it against the wheel of a loaded cart, yet does it discover as much solicitude about rain as a lady dressed in all her best attire, shuffling away on the first sprinklings, and running its head up in a corner. If attended to, it becomes an excellent weather-glass; for as sure as it walks elate, and as it were on tiptoe, feeding with great earnestness in a morning, so sure will it rain before night. It is totally a diurnal animal, and never pretends to stir after it becomes dark. The tortoise, like other reptiles, has an arbitrary stomach as well as lungs; and can refrain from eating as well as breathing for a great part of the year. When first awakened it eats nothing; nor again in the autumn before it retires: through the height of the summer it feeds voraciously, devouring all the food that comes in its way. I was much taken with its sagacity in discerning those that do it kind offices; for, as soon as the good old lady comes in sight who has waited on it for more than thirty years, it hobbles towards its benefactress with awkward alacrity; but remains inattentive to strangers. Thus not only "the ox knoweth his owner, and the ass his master's crib",[1] but the most abject reptile and torpid of beings distinguishes the hand that feeds it, and is touched with the feelings of gratitude!

P.S.—In about three days after I left Sussex the tortoise retired into the ground under the hepaticas.

At the end of his *Antiquities of Selborne* White gives the following particulars respecting the old family tortoise, which may be appended here:—

Because (he says) we call this creature an abject reptile, we are too apt to undervalue his abilities, and depreciate his powers of instinct, yet he is, as Mr. Pope says of his lord,

"—— much too wise to walk into a well";

and has so much discernment as not to fall down a haha, but to stop and withdraw from the brink with the readiest precaution.

Though he loves warm weather, he avoids the hot sun; because his thick shell, when once heated, would, as the poet says of solid armour, "scald with safety". He therefore spends the more sultry hours under the umbrella of a large cabbage-leaf, or amidst the waving forests of an asparagus bed.

But, as he avoids heat in the summer, so, in the decline of the year, he improves the faint autumnal beams, by getting within the reflection of a fruit-wall; and, though he never has read that planes inclining to the horizon receive a greater share of warmth, he inclines his shell, by tilting it against the wall, to collect and admit every feeble ray.

Pitiable seems the condition of this poor embarrassed reptile; to be cased in a suit of ponderous armour, which he cannot lay aside; to be imprisoned, as it were, within his own shell, must preclude, we should suppose, all activity and disposition for enterprise. Yet there is a season of the year (usually the beginning of June) when his exertions are remarkable. He then walks on tiptoe, and is stirring by five in the morning; and, traversing the garden, examines every wicket and interstice in the fences, through which he will escape if possible; and often has eluded the care of the gardener, and wandered to some

1 Isaiah i. 3.

distant field. The motives that impel him to undertake these rambles seem to be of the amorous kind; his fancy then becomes intent on sexual attachments, which transport him beyond his usual gravity, and induce him to forget for a time his ordinary solemn deportment.

LETTER XIV.

SELBORNE, *March 26th*, 1773.

The more I reflect on the στοργὴ (parental love) of animals, the more I am astonished at its effects. Nor is the violence of this affection more wonderful than the shortness of its duration. Thus every hen is in her turn the virago of the yard, in proportion to the helplessness of her brood; and will fly in the face of a dog or a sow in defence of those chickens, which in a few weeks she will drive before her with relentless cruelty.

This affection sublimes the passions, quickens the invention, and sharpens the sagacity of the brute creation. Thus a hen, just become a mother, is no longer that placid bird she used to be, but with feathers standing on end, wings hovering, and clocking note, she runs about like one possessed. Dams will throw themselves in the way of the greatest danger in order to avert it from their progeny. Thus a partridge will tumble along before a sportsman in order to draw away the dogs from her helpless covey. In the time of nidification the most feeble birds will assault the most rapacious. All the *Hirundines* of a village are up in arms at the sight of a hawk, whom they will persecute till he leaves that district. A very exact observer has often remarked that a pair of ravens nesting in the rock of Gibraltar would suffer no vulture or eagle to rest near their station, but would drive them from the hill with an amazing fury; even the blue thrush at the season of breeding would dart out from the clefts of the rocks to chase away the kestril, or the sparrow-hawk. If you stand near the nest of a bird that has young, she will not be induced to betray them by an inadvertent fondness, but will wait about at a distance with meat in her mouth for an hour together.

Should I farther corroborate what I have advanced above by some anecdotes which I probably may have mentioned before in conversation, yet you will, I trust, pardon the repetition for the sake of the illustration.

The fly-catcher of the *Zoology* (the *Stoparola* of Ray),

*I have seen this take place on the Mendip Hills.

builds every year in the vines that grow on the walls of my house. A pair of these little birds had one year inadvertently placed their nest on a naked bough, perhaps in a shady time, not being aware of the inconvenience that followed. But a hot sunny season coming on before the brood was half fledged, the reflection of the wall became insupportable, and must inevitably have destroyed the tender young, had not affection suggested an expedient, and prompted the parent birds to hover over the nest all the hotter hours, while with wings expanded, and mouths gaping for breath, they screened off the heat from their suffering offspring.

A farther instance I once saw of notable sagacity in a willow-wren, which had built in a bank in my fields. This bird a friend and myself had observed as she sat in her nest; but were particularly careful not to disturb her, though we saw that she eyed us with some degree of jealousy. Some days after, as we passed that way, we were desirous of remarking how this brood went on; but no nest could be found, till I happened to take a large bundle of long green moss, as it were, carelessly thrown over the nest in order to dodge the eye of any impertinent intruder.

A still more remarkable mixture of sagacity and instinct occurred to me one day as my people were pulling off the lining of a hot-bed, in order to add some fresh dung. From out of the side of this bed leaped an animal with great agility that made a most grotesque figure; nor was it without great difficulty that it could be taken; when it proved to be a large white-bellied field-mouse with three or four young clinging to her teats by their mouths and feet. It was amazing that the desultory and rapid motions of this dam should not oblige her litter to quit their hold, especially when it appeared that they were so young as to be both naked and blind!

To these instances of tender attachment, many more of which might be daily discovered by those that are studious of nature, may be opposed that rage of affection, that monstrous perversion of the στοργὴ, which induces some females of the brute creation to devour their young because their owners have handled them too freely, or removed them from place to place! Swine, and sometimes the more gentle race of dogs and cats, are guilty of this horrid and preposterous murder. When I hear now and then of an abandoned mother that destroys her offspring, I am not so much amazed; since reason perverted, and the bad passions let loose, are capable of any enormity; but why the parental feelings of brutes, that usually flow in one most uniform tenor, should sometimes be so extravagantly diverted, I leave to abler philosophers than myself to determine.

LETTER XV.

SELBORNE, *July 8th*, 1773.

Some young men went down lately to a pond on the verge of Wolmer Forest to hunt flappers, or young wild-ducks, many of which they caught, and, among the rest, some very minute well-fledged wild-fowls alive, which upon examination I found to be teals. I did not know till then that teals ever bred in the south of England, and was much pleased with the discovery: this I look upon as a great stroke in natural history.

We have had, ever since I can remember, a pair of white owls that constantly breed under the eaves of this church. As I have paid good attention to the manner of life of these birds during their season of breeding, which lasts the summer through, the following remarks may not perhaps be unacceptable:— About an hour before sunset (for then the mice begin to run) they sally forth in quest of prey, and hunt all round the hedges of meadows and small inclosures for them, which seem to be their only food. In this irregular country we can stand on an eminence and see them beat the fields over like a setting-dog, and often drop down in the grass or corn. I have minuted these birds with my watch for an hour together, and have found that they return to their nest, the one or the other of them, about once in five minutes; reflecting at the same time on the adroitness that every animal is possessed of as far as regards the well-being of itself and offspring. But a piece of address, which they show when they return loaded, should not, I think, be passed over in silence. As they take their prey with their claws, so they carry it in their claws to their nest; but, as the feet are necessary in their ascent under the tiles, they constantly perch first on the roof of the chancel, and shift the mouse from their claws to their bill, that their feet may be at liberty to take hold of the plate on the wall as they are rising under the eaves.

White owls seem not (but in this I am not positive) to hoot at all; all that clamorous hooting appears to me to come from the wood kinds. The white owl does indeed snore and hiss in a tremendous manner; and these menaces well answer the intention of intimidating; for I have known a whole village up in arms on such an occasion, imagining the churchyard to be full of goblins and spectres. White owls also often scream horribly as they fly along; from this screaming probably arose the common people's imaginary species of screech-owl, which they superstitiously think attends the windows of dying persons. The plumage of the remiges of the wings of every species of owl that I have yet examined is remarkably soft and pliant. Perhaps it may be necessary that the wings of these birds should not make much resistance or rushing, that they may be enabled to steal through the air unheard upon a nimble and watchful quarry.

While I am talking of owls, it may not be improper to mention what I was told by a gentleman of the county of Wilts. As they were grubbing a vast hollow pollard-ash that had been the mansion of owls for centuries, he discovered at the bottom a mass of matter that at first he could not account for. After some examination he found that it was a congeries of the bones of mice (and perhaps of birds and bats) that had been heaping together for ages, being cast up in pellets out of the crops of many generations of inhabitants. For owls cast up the bones, fur, and feathers, of what they devour, after the manner of hawks. He believes, he told me, that there were bushels of this kind of substance.

When brown owls hoot their throats swell as big as a hen's egg. I have known an owl of this species live a full year without any water. Perhaps the case may be the same with all birds of prey. When owls fly they stretch out their legs behind them as a balance to their large heavy heads, for as most nocturnal birds have large eyes and ears they must have large heads to contain them. Large eyes, I presume, are necessary to collect every ray of light, and large concave ears to command the smallest degree of sound or noise.

It will be proper to premise here that the sixteenth, eighteenth, twentieth, and twenty-first letters have been published already in the *Philosophical Transactions*; but as nicer observation has furnished several corrections and additions, it is hoped that the republication of them will not give offence; especially as these sheets would be very imperfect without them, and as they will be new to many readers who had no opportunity of seeing them when they made their first appearance.

The *Hirundines* are a most inoffensive, harmless, entertaining, social, and useful tribe of birds; they touch no fruit in our gardens; delight, all except one species, in attaching themselves to our houses; amuse us with their migrations, songs, and marvellous agility; and clear our outlets from the annoyances of gnats and other troublesome insects. Some districts in the south seas, near Guayaquil,[1] are desolated, it seems, by the infinite swarms of venomous mosquitoes, which fill the air, and render those coasts insupportable. It would be worth inquiring whether any species of *Hirundines* is found in those regions. Whoever contemplates the myriads of insects that sport in the sunbeams of a summer evening in this country, will soon be convinced to what a degree our atmosphere would be choked with them were it not for the friendly interposition of the swallow tribe.

Many species of birds have their peculiar lice; but the *Hirundines* alone seem to be annoyed with dipterous insects, which infest every species, and are so large, in proportion to themselves, that they must be extremely irksome and injurious to them. These are the *Hippoboscæ hirundines*, with narrow subulated wings, abounding in every nest; and are hatched by the warmth of the bird's own body during incubation, and crawl about under its feathers.

A species of them is familiar to horsemen in the south of England under the name of forest-fly; and to some of side-fly, from its running sideways like a crab. It creeps under the tails, and about the groins, of horses, which, at their first coming out of the north, are rendered half frantic by the tickling sensation; while our own breed little regards them.

The curious Réaumur discovered the large eggs, or rather *pupæ*, of these flies as big as the flies themselves, which he hatched in his own bosom. Any person that will take the trouble to examine the old nests of either species of swallows may find in them the black shining cases or skins of the *pupæ* of these insects; but for other particulars, too long for this place, we refer the reader to *L'Histoire d'Insectes* of that admirable entomologist. Tom. iv., pl. ii.

[1] See *Ulloa's Travels.*—W.

LETTER XVI.

SELBORNE, *Nov. 20th*, 1773.

In obedience to your injunctions I sit down to give you some account of the house-martin, or martlet; and if my monography of this little domestic and familiar bird should happen to meet with your approbation, I may probably soon extend my inquiries to the rest of the British *Hirundines*—the swallow, the swift, and the bank-martin.

A few house-martins begin to appear about the 16th April; usually some few days later than the swallow. For some time after they appear the *Hirundines* in general pay no attention to the business of nidification, but play and sport about, either to recruit from the fatigue of their journey, if they do migrate at all, or else that their blood may recover its true tone and texture after it has been so long benumbed by the severities of winter. About the middle of May, if the weather be fine, the martin begins to think in earnest of providing a mansion for its family. The crust or shell of this nest seems to be formed of such dirt or loam as comes most readily to hand, and is tempered and wrought together with little bits of broken straws to render it tough and tenacious. As this bird often builds against a perpendicular wall without any projecting ledge under, it requires its utmost efforts to get the first foundation firmly fixed, so that it may safely carry the superstructure. On this occasion the bird not only clings with its claws, but partly supports itself by strongly inclining its tail against the wall, making that a fulcrum; and thus steadied, it works and plasters the materials into the face of the brick or stone. But then, that this work may not, while it is soft and green, pull itself down by its own weight, the provident architect has prudence and forbearance enough not to advance her work too fast; but by building only in the morning, and by dedicating the rest of the day to food and amusement, gives it sufficient time to dry and harden. About half an inch seems to be a sufficient layer for a day. Thus careful workmen, when they build mud-walls (informed at first perhaps by this little bird), raise but a moderate layer at a time, and then desist, lest the work should become top-heavy, and so be ruined by its own weight. By this method in about ten or twelve days is formed a hemispheric nest with a small aperture towards the top, strong, compact, and warm; and perfectly fitted for all the purposes for which it was intended. But then nothing is more common than for the house-sparrow, as soon as the shell is finished, to seize on it as its own, to eject the owner, and to line it after its own manner.

After so much labour is bestowed in erecting a mansion, as Nature seldom works in vain, martins will breed on for several years together in the same nest, where it happens to be well sheltered and secure from the injuries of weather. The shell or crust of the nest is a sort of rustic work, full of knobs and protuberances on the outside; nor is the inside of those that I have examined smoothed with any exactness at all; but is rendered soft and warm, and fit for incubation, by a lining of small straws, grasses, and feathers, and sometimes by a bed of moss interwoven with wool. In this nest they tread frequently during the time of building; and the hen lays from three to five white eggs.

At first when the young are hatched, and are in a naked and helpless condition, the parent birds, with tender assiduity, carry out what comes away from their young. Was it not for this affectionate cleanliness the nestlings would soon be burnt up, and destroyed in so deep and hollow a nest, by their own caustic excrement. In the quadruped creation the same neat precaution is made use of; particularly among dogs and cats, where the dams lick away what proceeds from their young. But in birds there seems to be a particular provision, that the dung of nestlings is enveloped in a tough kind of jelly, and therefore is the easier conveyed off without soiling or daubing. Yet, as Nature is cleanly in all her ways, the young perform this office for themselves in a little time by thrusting their tails out at the aperture of their nest. As the young of small birds presently arrive at their ἡλικία, or full growth, they soon become impatient of confinement, and sit all day with their heads out at the orifice, where the dams, by clinging to the nest, supply them with food from morning to night. For a time the young are fed on the wing by their parents; but the feat is done by so quick and almost imperceptible a flight that a person must have attended very exactly to their motions before he would be able to perceive it. As soon as the young are able to shift for themselves, the dams immediately turn their thoughts to the business of a second brood; while the first flight, shaken off and rejected by their nurses, congregate in great flocks, and are the birds that are

seen clustering and hovering on sunny mornings and evenings
round towers and steeples, and on the roofs of churches and
houses. These congregatings usually begin to take place
about the first week in August; and therefore we may conclude that by that time the first flight is pretty well over.
The young of this species do not quit their abodes altogether;
but the more forward birds get abroad some days before the
rest. These approaching the eaves of buildings, and playing
about before them, make people think that several old ones
attend one nest. They are often capricious in fixing on a
nesting-place, beginning many edifices, and leaving them
unfinished; but when once a nest is completed in a sheltered
place, it serves for several seasons. Those which breed in a
ready-finished house get the start in hatching of those that
build new by ten days or a fortnight. These industrious
artificers are at their labours in the long days before four in
the morning. When they fix their materials they plaster
them on with their chins, moving their heads with a quick
vibratory motion. They dip and wash as they fly sometimes
in very hot weather; but not so frequently as swallows. It
has been observed that martins usually build to a north-east
or a north-west aspect, that the heat of the sun may not crack
and destroy their nests; but instances are also remembered
where they bred for many years in vast abundance in a hot
stifled inn-yard against a wall facing to the south.

Birds in general are wise in their choice of situation; but
in this neighbourhood every summer is seen a strong proof to
the contrary at a house without eaves in an exposed district,
where some martins build year by year in the corners of the
windows. But, as the corners of these windows (which face
to the south-east and south-west) are too shallow, the nests
are washed down every hard rain; and yet these birds
drudge on to no purpose from summer to summer, without
changing their aspect or house. It is a piteous sight to
see them labouring when half their nest is washed away,
and bringing dirt "to patch the ruins of a fallen house":
. . . "*generis lapsi sarcire ruinas*". Thus is instinct a
most wonderful unequal faculty; in some instances so much
above reason, in other respects so far below it! Martins
love to frequent towns, especially if there are great lakes
and rivers at hand; nay they even affect the close air of
London. And I have not only seen them nesting in the
Borough, but even in the Strand and Fleet Street; but then

it was obvious from the dinginess of their aspect that their feathers partook of the filth of that sooty atmosphere. Martins are by far the least agile of the four species; their wings and tails are short, and therefore they are not capable of such surprising turns and quick and glancing evolutions as the swallow. Accordingly they make use of a placid easy motion in a middle region of the air, seldom mounting to any great height, and never sweeping long together over the surface of the ground or water. They do not wander far for food, but affect sheltered districts, over some lake, or under some hanging wood, or in some hollow vale, especially in windy weather. They breed the latest of all the swallow kind: in 1772 they had nestlings on to October 21st, and are never without unfledged young as late as Michaelmas.

As the summer declines the congregating flocks increase in numbers daily by the constant accession of the second broods; till at last they swarm in myriads upon myriads round the villages on the Thames, darkening the face of the sky as they frequent the aits of that river, where they roost. They retire (the bulk of them, I mean) in vast flocks together about the beginning of October; but have appeared of late years in a considerable flight in this neighbourhood, for one day or two, as late as November 3rd and 6th, after they were supposed to have been gone for more than a fortnight. They therefore withdraw with us the latest of any species. Unless these birds are very short-lived indeed, or unless they do not return to the districts where they are bred, they must undergo vast devastations somehow, and somewhere; for the birds that return yearly bear no manner of proportion to the birds that retire.

House-martins are distinguished from their congeners by having their legs covered with soft downy feathers down to their toes. They are no songsters; but twitter in a pretty inward soft manner in their nests. During the time of breeding they are often greatly molested with fleas.[1]

LETTER XVII.

RINGMER, *near* LEWES, *Dec. 9th*, 1773.

I received your last favour just as I was setting out for this place; and am pleased to find that my monography met with

[1] Reference is made to the parasites of swallows in the previous letter; further allusions to the same subject are made in Letters XX. and XXI.

your approbation. My remarks are the result of many years' observation; and are, I trust, true in the whole; though I do not pretend to say that they are perfectly void of mistake, or that a more nice observer might not make many additions, since subjects of this kind are inexhaustible.

If you think my letter worthy the notice of your respectable society, you are at liberty to lay it before them; and they will consider it, I hope, as it was intended, as a humble attempt to promote a more minute inquiry into natural history; into the life and conversation of animals. Perhaps, hereafter, I may be induced to take the house-swallow under consideration; and from that proceed to the rest of the British *Hirundines*.

Though I have now travelled the Sussex Downs upwards of thirty years, yet I still investigate that chain of majestic mountains with fresh admiration year by year; and I think I see new beauties every time I traverse it. This range, which runs from Chichester eastward as far as Eastbourne, is about sixty miles in length, and is called the South Downs, properly speaking, only round Lewes. As you pass along you command a noble view of the wild, or weald, on one hand, and the broad downs and sea on the other. Mr. Ray used to visit a family[1] just at the foot of these hills, and was so ravished with the prospect from Plumpton Plain, near Lewes, that he mentions those 'scapes in his *Wisdom of God in the Works of the Creation* with the utmost satisfaction, and thinks them equal to anything he had seen in the finest parts of Europe.

For my own part, I think there is somewhat peculiarly sweet and amusing in the shapely-figured aspect of chalk-hills in preference to those of stone, which are rugged, broken, abrupt, and shapeless.

Perhaps I may be singular in my opinion, and not so happy as to convey to you the same idea; but I never contemplate these mountains without thinking I perceive somewhat analogous to growth in their gentle swellings and smooth fungus-like protuberances, their fluted sides, and regular hollows and slopes, that carry at once the air of vegetative dilation and expansion. Or was there ever a time when these immense masses of calcareous matter were thrown into fermentation by some adventitious moisture; were raised and leavened into such shapes by some plastic power; and so made to swell and

[1] Mr. Courthorpe, of Danny.—W

heave their broad backs into the sky so much above the less animated clay of the wild below?

By what I can guess from the admeasurements of the hills that have been taken round my house, I should suppose that these hills surmount the wild at an average of about the rate of five hundred feet.

One thing is very remarkable as to the sheep: from the westward till you get to the river Adur all the flocks have horns, and smooth white faces, and white legs, and a hornless sheep is rarely to be seen; but as soon as you pass that river eastward, and mount Beeding Hill, all the flocks at once become hornless, or as they call them, poll-sheep; and have, moreover, black faces with a white tuft of wool on their foreheads, and speckled and spotted legs, so that you would think that the flocks of Laban were pasturing on one side of the stream, and the variegated breed of his son-in-law Jacob were cantoned along on the other. And this diversity holds good respectively on each side from the valley of Bramber and Beeding to the eastward, and westward all the whole length of the downs. If you talk with the shepherds on this subject, they tell you that the case has been so from time immemorial; and smile at your simplicity if you ask them whether the situation of these two different breeds might not be reversed? However, an intelligent friend of mine near Chichester is determined to try the experiment; and has this autumn, at the hazard of being laughed at, introduced a parcel of black-faced hornless rams among his horned western ewes. The black-faced poll-sheep have the shortest legs and the finest wool.

As I had hardly ever before travelled these downs at so late a season of the year, I was determined to keep as sharp a look-out as possible so near the southern coast, with respect to the summer short-winged birds of passage. We make great inquiries concerning the withdrawing of the swallow kind, without examining enough into the causes why this tribe is never to be seen in winter; for, *entre nous*, the disappearing of the latter is more marvellous than that of the former, and much more unaccountable. The *Hirundines*, if they please, are certainly capable of migration, and yet no doubt are often found in a torpid state; but redstarts, nightingales, whitethroats, black-caps, etc., etc., are very ill provided for long flights; have never been once found, as I ever heard of, in a torpid state, and yet can never be supposed, in such troops, from year to year to dodge and elude the eyes of the curious and inquisitive, which from day to day discern the other small birds that are known to abide our winters. But, notwithstanding all my care, I saw nothing like a summer bird of passage; and what is more strange, not one wheatear, though they abound so in the autumn as to be a considerable perquisite to the shepherds that take them; and though many are to be seen to my knowledge all the winter through in many parts of the south of England. The most intelligent shepherds tell me that some few of these birds appear on the downs in March, and then withdraw to breed probably in warrens and stonequarries: now and then a nest is ploughed up in a fallow on the downs under a furrow, but it is thought a rarity. At the time of wheat-harvest they begin to be taken in great numbers; are sent for sale in vast quantities to Brighthelmstone and Tunbridge; and appear at the tables of all the gentry that entertain with any degree of elegance. About Michaelmas they retire and are seen no more till March. Though these birds are, when in season, in great plenty on the south downs round Lewes, yet at Eastbourne, which is the eastern extremity of those downs, they abound much more. One thing is very remarkable, that though in the height of the season so many hundreds of dozens are taken, yet they never are seen to flock; and it is a rare thing to see more than three or four at a time; so that there must be a perpetual flitting and constant progressive succession. It does not appear that any wheatears are taken to the westward of Houghton Bridge, which stands on the river Arun.

I did not fail to look particularly after my new migration of ring-ousels; and to take notice whether they continued on the downs to this season of the year; as I had formerly remarked them in the month of October all the way from Chichester to Lewes wherever there were any shrubs and covert: but not one bird of this sort came within my observation. I only saw a few larks and whinchats, some rooks, and several kites and buzzards.

About midsummer a flight of crossbills comes to the pinegroves about this house, but never makes any long stay.

The old tortoise, that I have mentioned in a former letter, still continues in this garden; and retired under ground about the 20th of November, and came out again for one day on the 30th: it lies now buried in a wet swampy border under a wall facing to the south, and is enveloped at present in mud and mire!

Here is a large rookery round this house, the inhabitants of which seem to get their livelihood very easily; for they spend the greatest part of the day on their nest-trees when the weather is mild. These rooks retire every evening all the winter from this rookery, where they only call by the way, as they are going to roost in deep woods: at the dawn of day they always revisit their nest-trees, and are preceded a few minutes by a flight of daws, that act, as it were. as their harbingers.

LETTER XVIII.

SELBORNE, Jan. 29th, 1774.

The house-swallow, or chimney-swallow, is undoubtedly the first comer of all the British *Hirundines*; and appears in general on or about 13th of April, as I have remarked from many years observation. Not but now and then a straggler is seen much earlier; and, in particular, when I was a boy I observed a swallow for a whole day together on a sunny warm Shrove Tuesday; which day could not fall out later than the middle of March, and often happened early in February.

It is worth remarking that these birds are seen first about lakes and mill-ponds; and it is also very particular, that if these early visitors happen to find frost and snow, as was the case of the two dreadful springs of 1770 and 1771, they immediately withdraw for a time. A circumstance this much more in favour of hiding than migration; since it is much more probable that a bird should retire to its hybernaculum just at hand, than return for a week or two to warmer latitudes.

The swallow, though called the chimney-swallow, by no means builds altogether in chimneys, but often within barns and out-houses against the rafters; and so she did in Virgil's time:

. . . . "Ante
Garrula quàm tignis nidos suspendat hirundo".
("The twittering swallow suspends its nest from the beams.")

In Sweden she builds in barns, and is called *ladu swala*, the barn swallow. Besides, in the warmer parts of Europe there are no chimneys to houses, except they are English-built: in these countries she constructs her nest in porches, and gateways, and galleries, and open halls.

[handwritten note in margin: w. ho. +]

*[handwritten note at bottom: * Cold weather in nine cases out of ten means a north or northeast wind & this would at once help the flight due south.]*

Here and there a bird may affect some odd, peculiar place; as we have known a swallow build down the shaft of on old well, through which chalk had been formerly drawn up for the purpose of manure: but in general with us this *Hirundo* breeds in chimneys; and loves to haunt those stacks where there is a constant fire, no doubt for the sake of warmth. Not that it can subsist in the immediate shaft where there is a fire; but prefers one adjoining to that of the kitchen, and disregards the perpetual smoke of that funnel, as I have often observed with some degree of wonder.

Five or six or more feet down the chimney does this little bird begin to form her nest about the middle of May, which consists, like that of the house-martin, of a crust or shell composed of dirt or mud, mixed with short pieces of straw to render it tough and permanent; with this difference, that whereas the shell of the martin is nearly hemispheric, that of the swallow is open at the top, and like half a deep dish: this nest is lined with fine grasses, and feathers, which are often collected as they float in the air.

Wonderful is the address which this adroit bird shows all day long in ascending and descending with security through so narrow a pass. When hovering over the mouth of the funnel, the vibrations of her wings acting on the confined air occasion a rumbling like thunder. It is not improbable that the dam submits to this inconvenient situation so low in the shaft, in order to secure her broods from rapacious birds, and particularly from owls, which frequently fall down chimneys, perhaps in attempting to get at these nestlings.

The swallow lays from four to six white eggs, dotted with red specks; and brings out her first brood about the last week in June, or the first week in July. The progressive method by which the young are introduced into life is very amusing: first, they emerge from the shaft with difficulty enough, and often fall down into the rooms below: for a day or so they are fed on the chimney-top, and then are conducted to the dead leafless bough of some tree, where, sitting in a row, they are attended with great assiduity, and may then be called perchers. In a day or two more they become flyers, but are still unable to take their own food; therefore they play about near the place where the dams are hawking for flies; and, when a mouthful is collected, at a certain signal given, the dam and the nestling advance, rising towards each other, and meeting at an angle; the young one all the while uttering such a little quick note of gratitude and complacency, that a person must have paid very little regard to the wonders of Nature that has not often remarked this feat.

The dam betakes herself immediately to the business of a second brood as soon as she is disengaged from her first; which at once associates with the first broods of house-martins; and with them congregates, clustering on sunny roofs, towers, and trees. This *Hirundo* brings out her second brood towards the middle and end of August.

All the summer long is the swallow a most instructive pattern of unwearied industry and affection; for, from morning to night, while there is a family to be supported, she spends the whole day in skimming close to the ground, and executing the most sudden turns and quick evolutions. Avenues, and long walks under hedges, and pasture-fields, and mown meadows where cattle graze, are her delight, especially if there are trees interspersed; because in such spots insects most abound. When a fly is taken a smart snap from her bill is heard, resembling the noise at the shutting of a watch-case; but the motion of the mandibles is too quick for the eye.

The swallow, probably the male bird, is the *excubitor* (or sentinel) to house-martins, and other little birds, announcing the approach of birds of prey. For as soon as a hawk appears, with a shrill alarming note he calls all the swallows and martins about him; who pursue in a body, and buffet and strike their enemy till they have driven him from the village, darting down from above on his back, and rising in a perpendicular line in perfect security. This bird also will sound the alarm, and strike at cats when they climb on the roofs of houses, or otherwise approach the nests. Each species of *Hirundo* drinks as it flies along, sipping the surface of the water; but the swallow alone, in general, washes on the wing, by dropping into a pool for many times together: in very hot weather house-martins and bank-martins dip and wash a little.

The swallow is a delicate songster, and in soft sunny weather sings both perching and flying; on trees in a kind of concert, and on chimney-tops: is also a bold flyer, ranging to distant downs and commons even in windy weather, which the other species seem much to dislike; nay, even frequenting exposed seaport towns, and making little excursions over the salt water. Horsemen on wide downs are often closely attended by a little party of swallows for miles together, which plays before and behind them, sweeping around them, and collecting all the skulking insects that are roused by the trampling of the horses' feet: when the wind blows hard, without this expedient, they are often forced to settle to pick up their lurking prey.

This species feeds much on little *Coleoptera*,[1] as well as on gnats and flies; and often settles on dug ground, or paths, for gravels to grind and digest its food. Before they depart, for some weeks, to a bird, they forsake houses and chimneys, and roost in trees; and usually withdraw about the beginning of October; though some few stragglers may appear on at times till the first week in November.

Some few pairs haunt the new and open streets of London next the fields, but do not enter, like the house-martin, the close and crowded parts of the city.

Both male and female are distinguished from their congeners by the length and forkedness of their tails. They are un-doubtedly the most nimble of all the species: and when the male pursues the female in amorous chase, they then go beyond their usual speed, and exert a rapidity almost too quick for the eye to follow.

After this circumstantial detail of the life and discerning στοργή of the swallow, I shall add, for your farther amusement, an anecdote or two not much in favour of her sagacity.

A certain swallow built for two years together on the handles of a pair of garden-shears, that were stuck up against the boards in an out-house, and therefore must have her nest spoiled whenever that implement was wanted: and, what is stranger still, another bird of the same species built its nest on the wings and body of an owl, that happened by accident to hang dead and dry from the rafter of a barn. This owl, with the nest on its wings, and with eggs in the nest, was brought as a curiosity worthy the most elegant private museum in Great Britain. The owner, struck with the oddity of the sight, furnished the bringer with a large shell, or conch, desiring him to fix it just where the owl hung: the person did as he was ordered, and the following year a pair, probably the same pair, built their nest in the conch, and laid their eggs.

The owl and the conch make a strange grotesque appearance, and are not the least curious specimens in that wonderful collection of art and nature.

Thus is instinct in animals, taken the least out of its way, an undistinguishing, limited faculty; and blind to every circum-

---

[1] *Coleoptera*—A class of insects having an outside covering or sheath, as among the beetles.

stance that does not immediately respect self-preservation, or lead at once to the propagation or support of their species.

LETTER XIX.

SELBORNE, Feb. 14th, 1774.

I received your favour of the 8th, and am pleased to find that you read my little history of the swallow with your usual candour: nor was I the less pleased to find that you made objections where you saw reason.

As to the quotations, it is difficult to say precisely which species of *Hirundo* Virgil might intend in the lines in question, since the ancients did not attend to specific differences like modern naturalists: yet somewhat may be gathered, enough to incline me to suppose that in the two passages quoted the poet had his eye on the swallow.

In the first place the epithet *garrula* suits the swallow well, who is a great songster, and not the martin, which is rather a mute bird; and when it sings is so inward as scarce to be heard. Besides, if *tignum* in that place signifies a rafter rather than a beam, as it seems to me to do, then I think it must be the swallow that is alluded to, and not the martin, since the former does frequently build within the roof against the rafters; while the latter always, as far as I have been able to observe, builds without the roof against eaves and cornices.

As to the simile, too much stress must not be laid on it; yet the epithet *nigra* speaks plainly in favour of the swallow, whose back and wings are very black; while the rump of the martin is milk-white, its back and wings blue, and all its under part white as snow. Nor can the clumsy motions (comparatively clumsy) of the martin well represent the sudden and artful evolutions and quick turns which Juturna gave to her brother's chariot, so as to elude the eager pursuit of the enraged Æneas. The verb *sonat* also seems to imply a bird that is somewhat loquacious.

> "*Nigra* velut magnas domini cum divitis ædes
> Pervolat, et pennis alta atria lustrat hirundo,
> Pabula parva legens, nidisque loquacibus escas:
> Et nunc porticibus vacuis, nunc humida circum
> Stagna *sonat*"[1] . . .

[1] "As the black swallow near the palace plies;
O'er empty courts, and under arches flies;
Now hawks aloft, now skims along the flood,
To furnish her loquacious nests with food."—DRYD. VIRG. ÆN. xii.

We have had a very wet autumn and winter, so as to raise the springs to a pitch beyond anything since 1764; which was a remarkable year for floods and high waters. The land-springs which we call "lavants", break out much on the downs of Sussex, Hampshire, and Wiltshire. The country people say when the lavants rise corn will always be dear; meaning that when the earth is so glutted with water as to send forth springs on the downs and uplands, that the corn-vales must be drowned; and so it has proved for these ten or eleven years past. For land-springs have never obtained more since the memory of man than during that period; nor has there been known a greater scarcity of all sorts of grain, considering the great improvements of modern husbandry. Such a run of wet seasons a century or two ago would, I am persuaded, have occasioned a famine. Therefore pamphlets and newspaper letters, that talk of combinations, tend to inflame and mislead; since we must not expect plenty till Providence sends us more favourable seasons.

The wheat of last year, all round this district, and in the county of Rutland, and elsewhere, yields remarkably bad; and our wheat on the ground, by the continual late sudden vicissitudes from fierce frost to pouring rains, looks poorly; and the turnips rot very fast.

LETTER XX.

SELBORNE, *Feb. 26th*, 1774.

The sand-martin, or bank-martin, is by much the least of any of the British *Hirundines*; and as far as we have ever seen, the smallest known *Hirundo*; though Brisson asserts that there is one much smaller, and that is the *Hirundo esculenta*.

But it is much to be regretted that it is scarce possible for any observer to be so full and exact as he could wish in reciting the circumstances attending the life and conversation of this little bird, since it is *fera naturâ*, at least in this part of the kingdom, disclaiming all domestic attachments, and haunting wild heaths and commons where there are large lakes; while the other species, especially the swallow and house-martin, are remarkably gentle and domesticated, and never seem to think themselves safe but under the protection of man.

Here are in this parish, in the sand-pits and banks of the lakes of Wolmer forest, several colonies of these birds; and yet they are never seen in the village; nor do they at all frequent the cottages that are scattered about in that wild district. The only instance I ever remember where this species haunts any building is at the town of Bishop's Waltham, in this county, where many sand-martins nestle and breed in the scaffold-holes of the back-wall of William of Wykeham's stables; but then this wall stands in a very sequestered and retired inclosure, and faces upon a large and beautiful lake. And indeed this species seems so to delight in large waters, that no instance occurs of their abounding but near vast pools or rivers; and in particular it has been remarked that they swarm in the banks of the Thames in some places below London bridge.

It is curious to observe with what different degrees of architectonic skill Providence has endowed birds of the same genus, and so nearly correspondent in their general mode of life! For while the swallow and the house-martin discover the greatest address in raising and securely fixing crusts or shells of loam as *cunabula* (or cradles) for their young, the bank-martin terebrates a round and regular hole in the sand or earth, which is serpentine, horizontal, and about two feet deep. At the inner end of this burrow does this bird deposit, in a good degree of safety, her rude nest, consisting of fine grasses and feathers, usually goose-feathers, very inartificially laid together.

Perseverance will accomplish anything; though at first one would be disinclined to believe that this weak bird, with her soft and tender bill and claws, should ever be able to bore the stubborn sand-bank without entirely disabling herself; yet with these feeble instruments have I seen a pair of them make great dispatch, and could remark how much they had scooped that day by the fresh sand which ran down the bank, and was of a different colour from that which lay loose and bleached in the sun.

In what space of time these little artists are able to mine and finish these cavities I have not been able to discover, for reasons given above; but it would be a matter worthy of observation, where it falls in the way of any naturalist to make his remarks. This I have often taken notice of, that several holes of different depths are left unfinished at the end of summer. To imagine that these beginnings were intentionally made in order to be in the greater forwardness for next spring is allowing perhaps too much foresight and *rerum prudentia* (prudence in things) to a simple bird. May not the cause of these *latebræ* being left unfinished arise from their meeting in those places with strata too harsh, hard, and solid for their purpose, which they relinquish, and go to a fresh spot that works more freely? Or may they not in other places fall in with a soil as much too loose and mouldering, liable to flounder, and threatening to overwhelm them and their labours?

One thing is remarkable—that, after some years, the old holes are forsaken and new ones bored; perhaps because the old habitations grow foul and fetid from long use, or because they may so abound with fleas as to become untenantable. This species of swallow moreover is strangely annoyed with fleas; and we have seen fleas, bed-fleas (*Pulex irritans*), swarming at the mouths of these holes, like bees on the stools of their hives.

The following circumstance should by no means be omitted— that these birds do not make use of their caverns by way of hybernacula, as might be expected; since banks so perforated have been dug out with care in the winter, when nothing was found but empty nests.

The sand-martin arrives much about the same time with the swallow, and lays, as she does, from four to six white eggs. But as this species is *cryptogame*, carrying on the business of nidification, incubation, and the support of its young in the dark, it would not be so easy to ascertain the time of breeding, were it not for the coming forth of the broods, which appear much about the time, or rather somewhat earlier than those of the swallow. The nestlings are supported in common like those of their congeners, with gnats and other small insects; and sometimes they are fed with *Libellulæ* (dragon-flies) almost as long as themselves. In the last week in June we have seen a row of these sitting on a rail near a great pool as perchers, and so young and helpless as easily to be taken by hand; but whether the dams ever feed them on the wing, as swallows and house-martins do, we have never yet been able to determine; nor do we know whether they pursue and attack birds of prey.

When they happen to breed near hedges and enclosures, they are dispossessed of their breeding-holes by the house-sparrow, which is on the same account a fell adversary to house-martins.

These *Hirundines* are no songsters, but rather mute, making only a little harsh noise when a person approaches their nests. They seem not to be of a sociable turn, never with us congregating with their congeners in the autumn. Undoubtedly they breed a second time, like the house-martin and swallow; and withdraw about Michaelmas.

Though in some particular districts they may happen to abound, yet in the whole, in the south of England at least, is this much the rarest species. For there are few towns or large villages but what abound with house-martins; few churches, towers, or steeples, but what are haunted by some swifts; scarce a hamlet or single cottage-chimney that has not its swallow; while the bank-martins, scattered here and there, live a sequestered life among some abrupt sand-hills, and in the banks of some few rivers.

These birds have a peculiar manner of flying; flitting about with odd jerks, and vacillations, not unlike the motions of a butterfly. Doubtless the flight of all *Hirundines* is influenced by, and adapted to, the peculiar sort of insects which furnish their food. Hence it would be worth inquiry to examine what particular genus of insects affords the principal food of each respective species of swallow.

Notwithstanding what has been advanced above, some few sand-martins, I see, haunt the skirts of London, frequenting the dirty pools in Saint George's Fields, and about White-chapel. The question is where these build, since there are no banks or bold shores in that neighbourhood; perhaps they nestle in the scaffold holes of some old or new deserted building. They dip and wash as they fly sometimes, like the house-martin and swallow.

Sand-martins differ from their congeners in the diminutiveness of their size, and in their colour, which is what is usually called a mouse-colour. Near Valencia, in Spain, they are taken, says Willoughby, and sold in the markets for the table; and are called by the country people, probably from their desultory jerking manner of flight, *Papilon di montagna.*

LETTER XXI.

SELBORNE, *Sept. 28th*, 1774.

As the swift or black-martin is the largest of the British *Hirundines*, so it is undoubtedly the latest comer. For I remember but one instance of its appearing before the last week in April: and in some of our late frosty, harsh springs, it has not been seen till the beginning of May. This species usually arrives in pairs.

The swift, like the sand-martin, is very defective in architecture, making no crust, or shell, for its nest: but forming it of dry grasses and feathers, very rudely and inartificially put together. With all my attention to these birds, I have never been able once to discover one in the act of collecting or carrying in materials; so that I have suspected (since their nests are exactly the same) that they sometimes usurp upon the house-sparrows, and expel them, as sparrows do the house- and sand-martin; well remembering that I have seen them squabbling together at the entrance of their holes, and the sparrows up in arms, and much disconcerted at these intruders. And yet I am assured, by a nice observer in such matters, that they do collect feathers for their nests in Andalusia, and that he has shot them with such materials in their mouths.

Swifts, like sand-martins, carry on the business of nidification quite in the dark, in crannies of castles, and towers, and steeples, and upon the tops of the walls of churches under the roof; and therefore cannot be so narrowly watched as those species that build more openly; but, from what I could ever observe, they begin nesting about the middle of May; and I have remarked, from eggs taken, that they have sat hard by the 9th of June. In general they haunt tall buildings, churches, and steeples, and breed only in such; yet in this village some pairs frequent the lowest and meanest cottages, and educate their young under those thatched roofs. We remember but one instance where they breed out of buildings, and that is in the sides of a deep chalk-pit near the town of Odiham, in this county, where we have seen many pairs entering the crevices, and skimming and squeaking round the precipices.

As I have regarded these amusive birds with no small attention, if I should advance something new and peculiar with respect to them, and different from all other birds, I might perhaps be credited; especially as my assertion is the result of many years' exact observation. The fact that I would advance is, that swifts tread on the wing; and I would wish any nice observer, that is startled at this supposition, to use his own eyes, and I think he will soon be convinced. In another class of animals, viz. the insect, nothing is so common as to see the different species of many genera in conjunction as they fly. The swift is almost continually on the wing; and as it never

K

settles on the ground, on trees, or roofs, would seldom find opportunity for amorous play, was it not enabled so to indulge in the air.

As the swift eats, drinks, and collects materials for its nest, on the wing, it appears to live more in the air than any other bird, and to perform all functions there save those of sleeping and incubation.

This *Hirundo* differs widely from its congeners in laying invariably but two eggs at a time, which are milk-white, long, and peaked at the small end; whereas the other species lay at each brood from four to six. It is a most alert bird, rising very early, and retiring to roost very late: and is on the wing in the height of summer at least sixteen hours. In the longest days it does not withdraw to rest till a quarter before nine in the evening, being the latest of all day-birds. Just before they retire whole groups of them assemble high in the air, and squeak, and shoot about with wonderful rapidity. But this bird is never so much alive as in sultry thundery weather, when it expresses great alacrity, and calls forth all its powers. In hot mornings several, getting together in little parties, dash round the steeples and churches, squeaking as they go in a very clamorous manner; these, by nice observers, are supposed to be males serenading their sitting hens; and not without reason, since they seldom squeak till they come close to the walls or eaves, and since those within utter at the same time a little inward note of complacency.

When the hen has sat hard all day, she rushes forth just as it is almost dark, and stretches and relieves her weary limbs, and snatches a scanty meal for a few minutes, and then returns to her duty of incubation. Swifts, when wantonly and cruelly shot while they have young, discover a little lump of insects in their mouths, which they pouch and hold under their tongue. In general they feed in a much higher district than the other species; a proof that gnats and other insects do also abound to a considerable height in the air; they also range to vast distances, since locomotion is no labour to them who are endowed with such wonderful powers of wing. Their powers seem to be in proportion to their levers; and their wings are longer in proportion than those of almost any other bird. When they mute, or ease themselves in flight, they raise their wings, and make them meet over their backs.

At some certain times in the summer I had remarked that swifts were hawking very low for hours together over pools and streams; and could not help inquiring into the object of their pursuit that induced them to descend so much below their usual range. After some trouble, I found that they were taking *Phryganeæ*, *Ephemeræ*, and *Libellulæ* (caddis-flies, may-flies, and dragon-flies), that were just emerged out of their aurelia (or chrysalis) state. I then no longer wondered that they should be so willing to stoop for a prey that afforded them such plentiful and succulent nourishment.

They bring out their young about the middle or latter end of July; but as these never become perchers, nor, that ever I could discern, are fed on the wing by their dams, the coming forth of the young is not so notorious as in the other species.

On the 30th of last June, I untiled the eaves of a house where many pairs build, and found in each nest only two squab, naked *pulli* (or young); on the 8th July I repeated the same inquiry, and found that they had made very little pro-gress towards a fledged state, but were still naked and helpless. From whence we may conclude that birds whose way of life keeps them perpetually on the wing would not be able to quit their nest till the end of the month. Swallows and martins, that have numerous families, are continually feeding them every two or three minutes; while swifts, that have but two young to maintain, are much at their leisure, and do not attend on their nests for hours together.

Sometimes they pursue and strike at hawks that come in their way; but not with that vehemence and fury that swallows express on the same occasion. They are out all day long in wet days, feeding about, and disregarding still rain: from whence two things may be gathered; first, that many insects abide high in the air, even in rain; and next, that the feathers of these birds must be well preened to resist so much wet. Windy, and particularly windy weather with heavy showers, they dislike; and on such days withdraw, and are scarce ever seen.

There is a circumstance respecting the colour of swifts which seems not to be unworthy of our attention. When they arrive in the spring they are all over of a glossy, dark soot-colour, except their chins, which are white; but, by being all day long in the sun and air, they become quite weather-beaten and bleached before they depart, and yet they return glossy again in the spring. Now, if they pursue the sun into lower latitudes, as some suppose, in order to enjoy a perpetual summer, why do they not return bleached? Do they not rather perhaps retire to rest for a season, and at that juncture moult and change their feathers, since all other birds are known to moult soon after the season of breeding?

Swifts are very anomalous in many particulars, dissenting from all their congeners not only in the number of their young, but in breeding but once in a summer; whereas all the other British *Hirundines* breed invariably twice. It is past all doubt that swifts can breed but once, since they withdraw in a short time after the flight of their young, and some time before their congeners bring out their second broods. We may here remark, that, as swifts breed but once in a summer, and only two at a time, and the other *Hirundines* twice, the latter, who lay from four to six eggs, increase at an average five times as fast as the former.

But in nothing are swifts more singular than in their early retreat. They retire, as to the main body of them, by the 10th of August, and sometimes a few days sooner; and every straggler invariably withdraws by the 20th, while their congeners, all of them, stay till the beginning of October; many of them all through that month, and some occasionally to the beginning of November. This early retreat is mysterious and wonderful, since that time is often the sweetest season in the year. But what is more extraordinary, they begin to retire still earlier in the most southerly parts of Andalusia, where they can be in no ways influenced by any defect of heat; or, as one might suppose, failure of food. Are they regulated in their motions with us by a defect of food, or by a propensity to moulting, or by a disposition to rest after so rapid a life, or by what? This is one of those incidents in natural history that not only baffles our searches, but almost eludes our guesses!

These *Hirundines* never perch on trees or roofs, and so never congregate with their congeners. They are fearless while haunting their nesting-places, and are not to be scared with a gun; and are often beaten down with poles and cudgels as they stoop to go under the eaves. Swifts are much infested with those pests to the genus called *Hippoboscæ hirundinis*; and often wriggle and scratch themselves in their flight to get rid of that clinging annoyance.

Swifts are no songsters, and have only one harsh screaming note; yet there are ears to which it is not displeasing, from an agreeable association of ideas, since that note never occurs but in the most lovely summer weather.

They never can settle on the ground but through accident; and when down, can hardly rise, on account of the shortness of their legs and the length of their wings; neither can they walk, but only crawl; but they have a strong grasp with their feet, by which they cling to walls. Their bodies being flat they can enter a very narrow crevice; and where they cannot pass on their bellies they will turn up edgewise.

The particular formation of the foot discriminates the swift from all the British *Hirundines*; and indeed from all other known birds, the *Hirundo melba*, or great white-bellied swift of Gibraltar, excepted; for it is so disposed as to carry "*omnes quatuor digitos anticos*"—all its four toes forward; besides, the least toe, which should be the back toe, consists of one bone alone, and the other three only of two apiece,—a construction most rare and peculiar, but nicely adapted to the purposes in which their feet are employed. This and some peculiarities attending the nostrils and under mandible, have induced a discerning[1] naturalist to suppose that this species might constitute a genus *per se*.

In London a party of swifts frequent the Tower, playing and feeding over the river just below the bridge; others haunt some of the churches of the Borough, next the fields, but do not venture, like the house-martin, into the close crowded part of the town.

The Swedes have bestowed a very pertinent name on this swallow, calling it "ring swala", from the perpetual rings or circles that it takes round the scene of its nidification.

Swifts feed on *Coleoptera*, or small beetles with hard cases over their wings, as well as on the softer insects; but it does not appear how they can procure gravel to grind their food, as swallows do, since they never settle on the ground. Young ones, overrun with *Hippoboscæ*, are sometimes found, under their nests, fallen to the ground; the number of vermin rendering their abode insupportable any longer. They frequent in this village several abject cottages; yet a succession still haunts the same unlikely roofs,—a good proof this that the same birds return to the same spots. As they must stoop very low to get up under these humble eaves, cats lie in wait, and sometimes catch them on the wing.

On July 5th, 1775, I again untiled part of a roof over the nest of a swift. The dam sat in the nest; but so strongly was she affected by natural στοργη for her brood, which she sup-

[1] John Antony Scopoli, of Carniola, M.D.—W.

posed to be in danger, that, regardless of her own safety, she would not stir, but lay sullenly by them, permitting herself to be taken in hand. The squab young we brought down and placed on the grass-plot, where they tumbled about, and were as helpless as a new-born child. While we contemplated their naked bodies, their unwieldy disproportioned abdomina, and their heads, too heavy for their necks to support, we could not but wonder when we reflected that these shiftless beings in a little more than a fortnight would be able to dash through the air almost with the inconceivable swiftness of a meteor; and perhaps in their emigration must traverse vast continents and oceans as distant as the equator. So soon does Nature advance small birds to their ἡλικια, (prime of life) or state of perfection; while the progressive growth of men and large quadrupeds is slow and tedious!

LETTER XXII.

SELBORNE, *Sept.* 13*th*, 1774.

By means of a straight cottage chimney I had an opportunity this summer of remarking, at my leisure, how swallows ascend and descend through the shaft; but my pleasure in contemplating the address with which this feat was performed to a considerable depth in the chimney, was somewhat interrupted by apprehensions lest my eyes might undergo the same fate with those of Tobit.[1]

Perhaps it may be some amusement to you to hear at what times the different species of *Hirundines* arrived this spring in three very distant counties of this kingdom. With us the swallow was seen first on April 4th, the swift on April 24th, the bank-martin on April 12th, and the house-martin not till April 30th. At South Zele, Devonshire, swallows did not arrive till April 25th, swifts in plenty on May 1st, and house-martins not till the middle of May. At Blackburn, in Lancashire, swifts were seen April 28th, swallows April 29th, house martins May 1st. Do these different dates, in such distant districts, prove anything for or against migration?

A farmer, near Weyhill, fallows his land with two teams of asses; one of which works till noon, and the other in the afternoon. When these animals have done their work, they are penned all night, like sheep, on the fallow. In the winter

[1] Tobit ii. 10.

they are confined and foddered in a yard, and make plenty of dung.

Linnæus says that hawks are disposed to keep the peace with other birds so long as the cuckoo's note is heard: "*pacis-cuntur inducias cum avibus, quamdiu cuculus cuculat*"; but it appears to me, that during that period, many little birds are taken and destroyed by birds of prey, as may be seen by their feathers left in lanes and under hedges.

The missel-thrush is, while breeding, fierce and pugnacious, driving such birds as approach its nest with great fury to a distance. The Welsh call it *pen y llwyn*, the head or master of the coppice. He suffers no magpie, jay, or blackbird, to enter the garden where he haunts; and is, for the time, a good guard to the new-sown legumens. In general, he is very successful in the defence of his family; but once I observed in my garden that several magpies came determined to storm the nest of a missel-thrush: the dams defended their mansion with great vigour, and fought resolutely *pro aris et focis* ("for their altars and their homes"); but numbers at last prevailed, they tore the nest to pieces, and swallowed the young alive.

[Thrushes during long droughts are of great service, in hunting out shell snails, which they pull to pieces for their young, and are thereby very serviceable in gardens. Missel-thrushes do not destroy the fruit in gardens like the other species of turdi, but feed on the berries of misletoe, and in the spring on ivy berries, which then begin to ripen. In the summer, when their young become fledged, they leave neighbourhoods, and retire to sheep-walks and wild commons.

The magpies, when they have young, destroy the broods of missel-thrushes, though the dams are fierce birds, and fight boldly in defence of their nests. It is probably to avoid such insults, that this species of thrush, though wild at other times, delights to build near houses, and in frequented walks and gardens.—*Observations on Nature*.]

In the season of nidification the wildest birds are comparatively tame. Thus the ring-dove breeds in my fields, though they are continually frequented; and the missel-thrush, though most shy and wild in the autumn and winter, builds in my garden close to a walk where people are passing all day long.

Wall-fruit abounds with me this year; but my grapes, that used to be forward and good, are at present backward beyond all precedent: and this is not the worst of the story; for the same ungenial weather, the same black cold solstice, has injured the more necessary fruits of the earth, and discoloured and blighted our wheat. The crop of hops promises to be very large.

Frequent returns of deafness incommode me sadly, and half disqualify me for a naturalist; for, when those fits are upon me, I lose all the pleasing notices and little intimations arising from rural sounds; and May is to me as silent and mute with respect to the notes of birds, etc., as August. My eyesight is, thank God, quick and good; but with respect to the other sense, I am, at times, disabled:

"And Wisdom at one entrance quite shut out".

LETTER XXIII.

SELBORNE, *June 8th*, 1775.

On September 21st, 1741, being then on a visit, and intent on field diversions, I rose before daybreak: when I came into the enclosures, I found the stubbles and clover grounds matted all over with a thick coat of cobweb, in the meshes of which a copious and heavy dew hung so plentifully that the whole face of the country seemed, as it were, covered with two or three setting-nets drawn one over another. When the dogs attempted to hunt, there eyes were so blinded and hood-winked that they could not proceed, but were obliged to lie down and scrape the incumbrances from their faces with their fore-feet, so that, finding my sport interrupted, I returned home musing in my mind on the oddness of the occurrence.

As the morning advanced the sun became bright and warm, and the day turned out one of those most lovely ones which no season but the autumn produces; cloudless, calm, serene, and worthy of the south of France itself.

About nine an appearance very unusual began to demand our attention, a shower of cobwebs falling from very elevated regions, and continuing without any interruption till the close of the day. These webs were not single filmy threads, floating in the air in all directions, but perfect flakes or rags; some near an inch broad, and five or six long, which fell with a degree of velocity that showed they were considerably heavier than the atmosphere.

On every side as the observer turned his eyes might he behold a continual succession of fresh flakes falling into his sight, and twinkling like stars as they turned their sides towards the sun.

How far this wonderful shower extended would be difficult to say; but we know that it reached Bradley, Selborne, and Alresford, three places which lie in a sort of a triangle, the shortest of whose sides is about eight miles in extent.

At the second of those places there was a gentleman (for whose veracity and intelligent turn we have the greatest veneration) who observed it the moment he got abroad; but concluded that, as soon as he came upon the hill above his house, where he took his morning rides, he should be higher than this meteor, which he imagined might have been blown, like thistle-down, from the common above; but, to his great astonishment, when he rode to the most elevated part of the down, three hundred feet above his fields, he found the webs in appearance still as much above him as before; still descending into sight in a constant succession, and twinkling in the sun, so as to draw the attention of the most incurious.

Neither before nor after was any such fall observed; but on this day the flakes hung in the trees and hedges so thick that a diligent person sent out might have gathered baskets full.

The remark that I shall make on these cobweb-like appearances, called gossamer, is, that, strange and superstitious as the notions about them were formerly, nobody in these days doubts but that they are the real production of small spiders, which swarm in the fields in fine weather in autumn, and have a power of shooting out webs from their tails so as to render themselves buoyant, and lighter than air. But why these apterous insects should that day take such a wonderful aërial excursion, and why their webs should at once become so gross and material as to be considerably more weighty than air, and to descend with precipitation, is a matter beyond my skill. If I might be allowed to hazard a supposition, I should imagine that those filmy threads, when first shot, might be entangled in the rising dew, and so drawn up, spiders and all, by a brisk evaporation, into the regions where clouds are formed: and if the spiders have a power of coiling and thickening their webs in the air, as Dr. Lister says they have, then, when they were become heavier than the air, they must fall.

Every day in fine weather, in autumn chiefly, do I see those spiders shooting out their webs and mounting aloft: they will go off from your finger if you will take them in your hand.

Last summer one alighted on my book as I was reading in the parlour; and, running to the top of the page, and shooting out a web, took its departure from thence. But what I most wondered at was, that it went off with considerable velocity in a place where no air was stirring; and I am sure that I did not assist it with my breath. So that these little crawlers seem to have, while mounting, some locomotive power without the use of wings, and to move in the air faster than the air itself.

LETTER XXIV.

Selborne, Aug. 15th, 1775.

There is a wonderful spirit of sociality in the brute creation, independent of sexual attachment: the congregating of gregarious birds in the winter is a remarkable instance.

Many horses, though quiet with company, will not stay one minute in a field by themselves: the strongest fences cannot restrain them. My neighbour's horse will not only not stay by himself abroad, but he will not bear to be left alone in a strange stable without discovering the utmost impatience, and endeavouring to break the rack and manger with his fore feet. He has been known to leap out at a stable-window, through which dung was thrown, after company; and yet in other respects is remarkably quiet. Oxen and cows will not fatten by themselves; but will neglect the finest pasture that is not recommended by society. It would be needless to instance sheep, which constantly flock together.

But this propensity seems not to be confined to animals of the same species; for we know a doe, still alive, that was brought up from a little fawn with a dairy of cows; with them it goes a-field, and with them it returns to the yard. The dogs of the house take no notice of this deer, being used to her; but, if strange dogs come by, a chase ensues; while the master smiles to see his favourite securely leading her pursuers over hedge, or gate, or stile; till she returns to the cows, who, with fierce lowings and menacing horns, drive the assailants quite out of the pasture.

Even great disparity of kind and size does not always prevent social advances and mutual fellowship. For a very intelligent and observant person has assured me that, in the former part of his life, keeping but one horse, he happened also on a time to have but one solitary hen. These two incongruous animals spent much of their time together in a lonely orchard, where they saw no creature but each other. By degrees an apparent regard began to take place between these two sequestered individuals. The fowl would approach the quadruped with notes of complacency, rubbing herself gently against his legs: while the horse would look down with satisfaction, and move with the greatest caution and circumspection, lest he should trample on his diminutive companion. Thus, by mutual good offices, each seemed to console the vacant hours of the other: so that Milton, when he puts the following sentiment in the mouth of Adam, seems to be somewhat mistaken:

> "Much less can bird with beast, or fish with fowl,
> So well converse; nor with the ox the ape."

LETTER XXV.

SELBORNE, *Oct. 2nd*, 1775.

We have two gangs or hordes of gypsies which infest the south and west of England, and come round in their circuit two or three times in the year. One of these tribes calls itself by the noble name of Stanley, of which I have nothing particular to say; but the other is distinguished by an appellative somewhat remarkable. As far as their harsh gibberish can be understood, they seem to say that the name of their clan is Curleople; now the termination of this word is apparently Grecian, and as Mezeray and the gravest historians all agree that these vagrants did certainly migrate from Egypt and the East, two or three centuries ago, and so spread by degrees over Europe, may not this family-name, a little corrupted, be the very name they brought with them from the Levant? It would be matter of some curiosity, could one meet with an intelligent person among them, to inquire whether, in their jargon, they still retain any Greek words; the Greek radicals will appear in hand, foot, head, water, earth, etc. It is possible that amidst their cant and corrupted dialect many mutilated remains of their native language might still be discovered.

With regard to those peculiar people, the gypsies, one thing is very remarkable, and especially as they came from warmer climates; and that is, that while other beggars lodge in barns, stables, and cow-houses, these sturdy savages seem to pride themselves in braving the severities of winter, and in living *sub dio* (in the open air) the whole year round. Last September was as wet a month as ever was known; and yet during those deluges did a young gypsy girl lie in the midst of one of our hop-gardens, on the cold ground, with nothing over her but a piece of a blanket extended on a few hazel-rods bent hoop-fashion, and stuck into the earth at each end, in circumstances too trying for a cow in the same condition; yet within this garden there was a large hop-kiln, into the chambers of which she might have retired, had she thought shelter an object worthy her attention.

Europe itself, it seems, cannot set bounds to the rovings of these vagabonds; for Mr. Bell, in his return from Pekin, met a gang of these people on the confines of Tartary, who were endeavouring to penetrate those deserts, and try their fortune in China.[1]

Gypsies are called in French, Bohemians; in Italian and modern Greek, Zingari.

LETTER XXVI.

SELBORNE, *Nov. 1st*, 1775.

" Hic . . .   tædæ pingues, hic plurimus ignis
Semper, et assiduâ postes fuligine nigri."—*Virg.*, Ecl. vii.

(" Here are greasy torches, here ever abundant fire,
And with constant soot the posts of the door are blackened.")

I shall make no apology for troubling you with the detail of a very simple piece of domestic economy, being satisfied that you think nothing beneath your attention that tends to utility; the matter alluded to is the use of rushes instead of candles, which I am well aware prevails in many districts besides this; but as I know there are countries also where it does not obtain, and as I have considered the subject with some degree of exactness, I shall proceed in my humble story, and leave you to judge of the expediency.

The proper species of rush for this purpose seems to be the *Juncus conglomeratus,* or common soft rush, which is to be found in most moist pastures, by the sides of streams, and under hedges. These rushes are in best condition in the height of summer; but may be gathered, so as to serve the purpose

---

[1] See BELL'S *Travels in China.*—W.

well, quite on to autumn. It would be needless to add that the largest and longest are best. Decayed labourers, women, and children make it their business to procure and prepare them. As soon as they are cut, they must be flung into water, and kept there, for otherwise they will dry and shrink, and the peel will not run. At first a person would find it no easy matter to divest a rush of its peel or rind, so as to leave one regular, narrow, even rib from top to bottom that may support the pith; but this, like other feats, soon becomes familiar even to children; and we have seen an old woman, stone blind, performing this business with great despatch, and seldom failing to strip them with the nicest regularity. When these *Junci* are thus far prepared, they must lie out on the grass to be bleached, and take the dew for some nights, and afterwards be dried in the sun.

Some address is required in dipping these rushes in the scalding fat or grease; but this knack also is to be attained by practice. The careful wife of an industrious Hampshire labourer obtains all her fat for nothing; for she saves the scummings of her bacon-pot for this use; and, if the grease abounds with salt, she causes the salt to precipitate to the bottom, by setting the scummings in a warm oven. Where hogs are not much in use, and especially by the sea-side, the coarser animal-oils will come very cheap. A pound of common grease may be procured for fourpence, and about six pounds of grease will dip a pound of rushes, and one pound of rushes may be bought for one shilling; so that a pound of rushes, medicated and ready for use, will cost three shillings. If men that keep bees will mix a little wax with the grease, it will give it a consistency, and render it more cleanly, and make the rushes burn longer; mutton-suet would have the same effect.

A good rush, which measured in length two feet four inches and a half, being minuted, burnt only three minutes short of an hour; and a rush of still greater length has been known to burn one hour and a quarter.

These rushes give a good clear light. Watch-lights (coated with tallow), it is true, shed a dismal one, "darkness visible"; but then the wick of those have two ribs of the rind, or peel, to support the pith, while the wick of the dipped rush has but one. The two ribs are intended to impede the progress of the flame, and make the candle last.

In a pound of dry rushes, avoirdupois, which I caused to be

weighed and numbered, we found upwards of one thousand
six hundred individuals. Now suppose each of these burns,
one with another, only half an hour, then a poor man will
purchase eight hundred hours of light, a time exceeding thirty-
three entire days, for three shillings. According to this account
each rush, before dipping, costs one-thirty-third of a farthing,
and one-eleventh afterwards. Thus a poor family will enjoy
five and a half hours of comfortable light for a farthing. An
experienced old housekeeper assures me that one pound and
a half of rushes completely supplies his family the year round
since working people burn no candles in the long days, because
they rise and go to bed by daylight.

Little farmers use rushes much in the short days both morning and evening, in the dairy and kitchen; but the very poor,
who are always the worst economists, and therefore must continue very poor, buy a halfpenny candle every evening, which
in their blowing, open rooms, does not burn much more than
two hours. Thus have they only two hours' light for their
money instead of eleven.

While on the subject of rural economy, it may not be improper to mention a pretty implement of housewifery that we
have seen nowhere else; that is, little neat besoms which our
foresters make from the stalks of the *Polytricum commune*, or
great golden maiden hair, which they call silk-wood, and find
plenty in the bogs. When this moss is well combed and dressed,
and divested of its outer skin, it becomes of a beautiful bright-
chestnut colour; and, being soft and pliant, is very proper for
the dusting of beds, curtains, carpets, hangings, &c. If these
besoms were known to the brush-makers in town, it is probable
they might come much in use for the purpose above-mentioned.

LETTER XXVII.

SELBORNE, *Dec.* 12th, 1775.

We had in this village more than twenty years ago an idiot
boy, whom I well remember, who, from a child, showed a strong
propensity to bees; they were his food, his amusement, his
sole object. And as people of this cast have seldom more than
one point in view, so this lad exerted all his few faculties on
this one pursuit. In the winter he dozed away his time,
within his father's house, by the fireside, in a kind of torpid
state, seldom departing from the chimney-corner; but in the

summer he was all alert, and in quest of his game in the fields,
and on sunny banks.　Honey-bees, humble-bees, and wasps,
were his prey wherever he found them; he had no apprehensions from their stings, but would seize them *nudis manibus* (with
bare hands), and at once disarm them of their weapons, and suck
their bodies for the sake of their honey-bags.　Sometimes he
would fill his bosom between his shirt and his skin with a
number of these captives, and sometimes would confine them
in bottles.　He was a very *Merops apiaster*, or bee-bird, and very
injurious to men that kept bees; for he would slide into their
bee-gardens, and sitting down before the stools, would rap
with his finger on the hives, and so take the bees as they
came out.　He has been known to overturn hives for the
sake of honey, of which he was passionately fond.　Where
metheglin was making he would linger round the tubs and
vessels, begging a draught of what he called bee-wine.　As
he ran about he used to make a humming noise with his lips,
resembling the buzzing of bees.　This lad was lean and sallow,
and of a cadaverous complexion; and, except in his favourite
pursuit, in which he was wonderfully adroit, discovered no
manner of understanding.　Had his capacity been better,
and directed to the same object, he had perhaps abated much
of our wonder at the feats of a more modern exhibitor of
bees; and we may justly say of him now,—

> "　.　.　.　.　Thou,
> Had thy presiding star propitious shone,
> Shouldst Wildman be　.　.　"

When a tall youth he was removed from hence to a distant
village, where he died, as I understand, before he arrived at
manhood.

LETTER XXVIII.

SELBORNE, *Jan. 8th,* 1776.

It is the hardest thing in the world to shake off superstitious
prejudices: they are sucked in, as it were, with our mother's
milk; and, growing up with us at a time when they take the
fastest hold, and make the most lasting impressions, become
so interwoven into our very constitutions, that the strongest
good sense is required to disengage ourselves from them.
No wonder, therefore, that the lower people retain them their
whole lives through, since their minds are not invigorated by

a liberal education, and therefore not enabled to make any efforts adequate to the occasion.

Such a preamble seems to be necessary before we enter on the superstitions of this district, lest we should be suspected of exaggeration in a recital of practices too gross for this enlightened age.

But the people of Tring, in Hertfordshire, would do well to remember, that no longer ago than the year 1751, and within twenty miles of the capital, they seized on two superannuated wretches, crazed with age, and overwhelmed with infirmities, on a suspicion of witchcraft; and, by trying experiments, drowned them in a horse-pond.

In a farm-yard near the middle of this village stands, at this day, a row of pollard-ashes, which, by the seams and long cicatrices down their sides, manifestly show that, in former times, they had been cleft asunder. These trees, when young and flexible, were severed and held open by wedges, while ruptured children, stripped naked, were pushed through the apertures, under a persuasion that, by such a process, the poor babes would be cured of their infirmity. As soon as the feat was over, the tree, in the suffering part, was plastered with loam, and carefully swathed up. If the parts coalesced and soldered together, as usually fell out, where the feat was performed with any adroitness at all, the party was cured; but, where the cleft continued to gape, the operation, it was supposed, would prove ineffectual. Having occasion to enlarge my garden not long since, I cut down two or three such trees, one of which did not grow together.

We have several persons now living in the village, who, in their childhood, were supposed to be healed by this superstitious ceremony, derived down perhaps from our Saxon ancestors, who practised it before their conversion to Christianity.

At the fourth corner of the Plestor, or area, near the church, there stood, about twenty years ago, a very old grotesque hollow pollard-ash, which for ages had been looked on with no small veneration as a shrew-ash. Now a shrew-ash is an ash whose twigs or branches, when gently applied to the limbs of cattle, will immediately relieve the pains which a beast suffers from the running of a shrew-mouse over the part affected; for it is supposed that a shrew-mouse is of so baneful and deleterious a nature, that wherever it creeps over a beast, be it horse, cow, or sheep, the suffering animal is afflicted with cruel anguish, and threatened with the loss of the use of the

limb. Against this accident, to which they were continually
liable, our provident forefathers always kept a shrew-ash at
hand, which, when once medicated, would maintain its virtue
for ever. A shrew-ash was made thus[1]:—Into the body of
the tree a deep hole was bored with an auger, and a poor
devoted shrew-mouse was thrust in alive, and plugged in, no
doubt, with several quaint incantations long since forgotten.
As the ceremonies necessary for such a consecration are no
longer understood, all succession is at an end, and no such
tree is known to subsist in the manor, or hundred.

As to that on the Plestor,

> "The late vicar stubb'd and burnt it"

when he was way-warden, regardless of the remonstrances of
the bystanders, who interceded in vain for its preservation,
urging its power and efficacy, and alleging that it had been
"guarded through many years by the piety of our forefathers":

> "Religione patrum multos servata per annos."

LETTER XXIX.

SELBORNE, *Feb. 7th*, 1776.

In heavy fogs, on elevated situations especially, trees are
perfect alembics; and no one that has not attended to such
matters can imagine how much water one tree will distil in a
night's time, by condensing the vapour, which trickles down
the twigs and boughs, so as to make the ground below quite
in a float. In Newton Lane, in October, 1775, on a misty
day, a particular oak in leaf dropped so fast that the cart-way
stood in puddles and the ruts ran with water, though the
ground in general was dusty.

In some of our smaller islands in the West Indies, if I
mistake not, there are no springs or rivers: but the people are
supplied with that necessary element, water, merely by the
dripping of some large tall trees, which, standing in the
bosom of a mountain, keep their heads constantly enveloped
with fogs and clouds, from which they dispense their kindly
never-ceasing moisture; and so render those districts habitable
by condensation alone.

Trees in leaf have such a vast proportion more of surface
than those that are naked, that, in theory, their condensations

---

[1] For a similar practice, see Plot's *Staffordshire.*—W.

should greatly exceed those that are stripped of their leaves; but, as the former imbibe also a great quantity of moisture, it is difficult to say which drip most; but this I know, that deciduous trees that are entwined with much ivy seem to distil the greatest quantity. Ivy-leaves are smooth, and thick, and cold, and therefore condense very fast; and besides, evergreens imbibe very little. These facts may furnish the intelligent with hints concerning what sorts of trees they should plant round small ponds that they would wish to be perennial; and show them how advantageous some trees are in preference to others.

Trees perspire profusely, condense largely, and check evaporation so much, that woods are always moist; no wonder, therefore, that they contribute much to pools and streams.

That trees are great promoters of lakes and rivers appears from a well-known fact in North America; for, since the woods and forests have been grubbed and cleared, all bodies of water are much diminished; so that some streams, that were very considerable a century ago, will not now drive a common mill.[1] Besides, most woodlands, forests, and chases with us abound with pools and morasses; no doubt for the reason given above.

To a thinking mind few phenomena are more strange than the state of little ponds on the summits of chalk-hills, many of which are never dry in the most trying droughts of summer. On chalk-hills, I say, because in many rocky and gravelly soils springs usually break out pretty high on the sides of elevated grounds and mountains; but no person acquainted with chalky districts will allow that they ever saw springs in such a soil but in valleys and bottoms, since the waters of so pervious a stratum as chalk all lie on one dead level, as well-diggers have assured me again and again.

Now we have many such little round ponds in this district; and one in particular on our sheep-down, three hundred feet above my house; which, though never above three feet deep in the middle, and not more than thirty feet in diameter, and containing perhaps not more than two or three hundred hogsheads of water, yet never is known to fail, though it affords drink for three hundred or four hundred sheep, and for at least twenty head of large cattle beside. This pond, it is true, is overhung with two moderate beeches, that doubtless at times afford it much supply: but then we have others

---

[1] *Vide* Kahn's *Travels in North America.*—W.

as small, that, without the aid of trees, and in spite of evaporation from sun and wind, and perpetual consumption by cattle, yet constantly maintain a moderate share of water, without overflowing in the wettest seasons, as they would do if supplied by springs. By my journal of May, 1775, it appears that "the small and even considerable ponds in the vales are now dried up, while the small ponds on the very tops of hills are but little affected". Can this difference be accounted for from evaporation alone, which certainly is more prevalent in bottoms? or rather have not those elevated pools some unnoticed recruits, which in the night-time counterbalance the waste of the day; without which the cattle alone must soon exhaust them? And here it will be necessary to enter more minutely into the cause. Dr. Hales, in his *Vegetable Statics*, advances, from experiment, that "the moister the earth is the more dew falls on it in a night; and more than a double quantity of dew falls on a surface of water than there does on an equal surface of moist earth". Hence we see that water, by its coolness, is enabled to assimilate to itself a large quantity of moisture nightly by condensation; and that the air, when loaded with fogs and vapours, and even with copious dews, can alone advance a considerable and never-failing resource. Persons that are much abroad, and travel early and late, such as shepherds, fishermen, etc., can tell what prodigious fogs prevail in the night on elevated downs, even in the hottest parts of summer; and how much the surfaces of things are drenched by those swimming vapours, though, to the senses, all the while, little moisture seems to fall.

LETTER XXX.

SELBORNE, *April 3rd*, 1776.

Monsieur Herissant, a French anatomist, seems persuaded that he has discovered the reason why cuckoos do not hatch their own eggs; the impediment, he supposes, arises from the internal structure of their parts, which incapacitates them for incubation. According to this gentleman, the crop, or craw, of a cuckoo does not lie before the sternum at the bottom of the neck, as in poultry (*Gallinæ*), pigeons (*Columbæ*), etc., but immediately behind it, on and over the bowels, so as to make a large protuberance in the belly.[1]

[1] *Histoire de l'Académie Royale*, 1752.

Induced by this assertion, we procured a cuckoo; and, cutting open the breastbone, and exposing the intestines to sight, found the crop lying as mentioned above. This stomach was large and round, and stuffed hard, like a pin-cushion, with food, which, upon nice examination, we found to consist of various insects; such as small scarabs, spiders, and dragon-flies; the last of which we have seen cuckoos catching on the wing as they were just emerging out of the aurelia state. Among this farrago also were to be seen maggots, and many seeds, which belonged either to gooseberries, currants, cran-berries, or some such fruit; so that these birds apparently subsist on insects and fruits; nor was there the least appear-ance of bones, feathers, or fur, to support the idle notion of their being birds of prey.

The sternum in this bird seemed to us to be remarkably short, between which and the anus lay the crop, or craw, and immediately behind that the bowels against the backbone.

It must be allowed, as this anatomist observes, that the crop placed just upon the bowels must, especially when full, be in a very uneasy situation during the business of incubation; yet the test will be to examine whether birds that are actually known to sit for certain are not formed in a similar manner. This inquiry I proposed to myself to make with a fern-owl, or goat-sucker, as soon as opportunity offered: because, if their formation proves the same, the reason for incapacity in the cuckoo will be allowed to have been taken up somewhat hastily.

Not long after a fern-owl was procured, which, from its habit and shape, we suspected might resemble the cuckoo in its internal construction. Nor were our suspicions ill-grounded; for, upon dissection, the crop, or craw, also lay behind the sternum, immediately on the viscera, between them and the skin of the belly. It was bulky, and stuffed hard with large *Phalænæ*, moths of several sorts, and their eggs, which no doubt had been forced out of those insects by the action of swallowing.

Now, as it appears that this bird, which is so well known to practise incubation, is formed in a similar manner with cuckoos, Monsieur Herissant's conjecture, that cuckoos are incapable of incubation from the disposition of their intestines, seems to fall to the ground; and we are still at a loss for the cause of that strange and singular peculiarity in the instance of the *Cuculus canorus*.

We found the case to be the same with the ring-tailed hawk, in respect to formation; and, as far as I can recollect, with the swift; and probably it is so with many more sorts of birds that are not granivorous.

LETTER XXXI.

SELBORNE, *April 29th*, 1776.

On August 4th, 1775, we surprised a large viper, which seemed very heavy and bloated, as it lay in the grass basking in the sun. When we came to cut it up, we found that the abdomen was crowded with young, fifteen in number; the shortest of which measured full seven inches, and were about the size of full-grown earth-worms. This little fry issued into the world with the true viper-spirit about them, showing great alertness as soon as disengaged from the dam: they twisted and wriggled about, and set themselves up, and gaped very wide when touched with a stick, showing manifest tokens of menace and defiance, though as yet they had no manner of fangs that we could find, even with the help of our glasses.

To a thinking mind nothing is more wonderful than that early instinct which impresses young animals with a notion of the situation of their natural weapons, and of using them properly in their own defence, even before those weapons subsist or are formed. Thus a young cock will spar at his adversary before his spurs are grown; and a calf or a lamb will push with their heads before their horns are sprouted. In the same manner did these young adders attempt to bite before their fangs were in being. The dam, however, was furnished with very formidable ones, which we lifted up (for they fold down when not used), and cut them off with the point of our scissors.

There was little room to suppose that this brood had ever been in the open air before; and that they were taken in for refuge, at the mouth of the dam, when she perceived that danger was approaching; because then probably we should have found them somewhere in the neck, and not in the abdomen.

LETTER XXXII.

The natural term of a hog's life is little known, and the reason is plain—because it is neither profitable nor convenient to keep that turbulent animal to the full extent of its time: however, my neighbour, a man of substance, who had no occasion to study every little advantage to a nicety, kept a half-bred bantam-sow, who was as thick as she was long, and whose belly swept on the ground, till she was advanced to her seventeenth year, at which period she showed some tokens of age by the decay of her teeth and the decline of her fertility.

For about ten years this prolific mother produced two litters in the year of about ten at a time, and once above twenty at a litter; but, as there were near double the number of pigs to that of teats, many died. At the age of about fifteen her litters began to be reduced to four or five; and such a litter she exhibited when in her fatting-pen. She proved, when fat, good bacon, juicy, and tender; the rind, or sward, was remarkably thin. At a moderate computation she was allowed to have been the fruitful parent of three hundred pigs: a prodigious instance of fecundity in so large a quadruped! She was killed in spring 1775.

LETTER XXXIII.

SELBORNE, *May 9th*, 1776.

" . . . admôrunt ubera tigres."[1]

We have remarked in a former letter[2] how much incongruous animals in a lonely state may be attached to each other from a spirit of sociality; in this it may not be amiss to recount a different motive which has been known to create as strange a fondness.

My friend had a little helpless leveret brought to him, which the servants fed with milk in a spoon, and about the same time his cat kittened and the young were despatched and buried. The hare was soon lost, and supposed to be gone the way of most fondlings, to be killed by some dog or cat. However, in about a fortnight, as the master was sitting in his garden in the dusk of the evening, he observed his cat, with tail erect, trotting towards him, and calling with little short inward notes of complacency, such as they use towards their kittens, and something gamboling after, which proved to be the leveret that the cat had supported with her milk, and continued to support with great affection.

[1] "By tigers suckled."   [2] Letter XXIV.

Thus was a graminivorous animal nurtured by a carnivorous and predaceous one!

Why so cruel and sanguinary a beast as a cat, of the ferocious genus of *Felis*, the *Murium leo*, as Linnæus calls it, should be affected with any tenderness towards an animal which is its natural prey, is not so easy to determine.

This strange affection probably was occasioned by that *desiderium*, those tender maternal feelings, which the loss of her kittens had awakened in her breast; and by the complacency and ease she derived to herself from the procuring her teats to be drawn, which were too much distended with milk, till, from habit, she became as much delighted with this foundling as if it had been her real offspring.

This incident is no bad solution of that strange circumstance which grave historians as well as the poets assert, of exposed children being sometimes nurtured by female wild beasts that probably had lost their young. For it is not one whit more marvellous that Romulus and Remus, in their infant state, should be nursed by a she-wolf, than that a poor little sucking leveret should be fostered and cherished by a bloodthirsty grimalkin.

> "   .   .   .   viridi fœtam Mavortis in antro
> Procubuisse lupam: geminos huic ubera circum
> Ludere pendentes pueros, et lambere matrem
> Impavidos: illam tereti cervice reflexam
> Mulcere alternos, et corpora fingere linguâ." [1]

LETTER XXXIV.

SELBORNE, *May 20th*, 1777.

Lands that are subject to frequent inundations are always poor; and probably the reason may be because the worms are drowned. The most insignificant insects and reptiles are of much more consequence, and have much more influence in the economy of Nature, than the incurious are aware of; and are mighty in their effect, from their minuteness, which renders them less an object of attention; and from their numbers and

---

[1] "The cave of Mars was dressed with mossy greens:
There by the wolf were laid the martial twins,
Intrepid on her swelling dugs they hung;
The foster dam loll'd out her fawning tongue:
They suck'd secure, while bending back her head,
She lick'd their tender limbs, and formed them as they fed."
—DRYD. VIRG.

fecundity. Earth-worms, though in appearance a small and despicable link in the chain of Nature, yet, if lost, would make a lamentable chasm. For to say nothing of half the birds, and some quadrupeds, which are almost entirely supported by them, worms seem to be the great promoters of vegetation, which would proceed but lamely without them, by boring, perforating, and loosening the soil, and rendering it pervious to rains and the fibres of plants, by drawing straws and stalks of leaves and twigs into it; and, most of all, by throwing up such infinite numbers of lumps of earth called worm-casts, which, being their excrement, is a fine manure for grain and grass. Worms probably provide new soil for hills and slopes where the rain washes the earth away; and they affect slopes, probably to avoid being flooded. Gardeners and farmers express their detestation of worms; the former because they render their walks unsightly, and make them much work; and the latter because, as they think, worms eat their green corn. But these men would find that the earth without worms would soon become cold, hard-bound, and void of fermentation, and consequently sterile; and besides, in favour of worms, it should be hinted that green corn, plants, and flowers, are not so much injured by them as by many species of *Coleoptera* (scarabs), and *Tipulæ* (long-legs) in their larva, or grub state; and by unnoticed myriads of small shell-less snails, called slugs, which silently and imperceptibly make amazing havoc in the field and garden.[1]

These hints we think proper to throw out in order to set the inquisitive and discerning to work.

A good monography of worms would afford much entertainment and information at the same time, and would open a large and new field in natural history. Worms work most in the spring; but by no means lie torpid in the dead months: are out every mild night in the winter, as any person may be convinced that will take the pains to examine his grass-plots with a candle; are hermaphrodites, and much addicted to venery, and consequently very prolific.

[1] Farmer Young, of Norton Farm, says, that this spring (1777) about four acres of his wheat in one field were entirely destroyed by slugs, which swarmed on the blades of corn, and devoured it as fast as it sprang.

LETTER XXXV.

SELBORNE, *Nov.* 22*nd*, 1777.

You cannot but remember that the 26th and 27th of last March were very hot days,—so sultry that everybody complained and were restless under those sensations to which they had not been reconciled by gradual approaches.

This sudden summer-like heat was attended by many summer coincidences; for on those two days the thermometer rose to 66° in the shade; many species of insects revived and came forth; some bees swarmed in this neighbourhood; the old tortoise, near Lewes, in Sussex, awakened and came forth out of its dormitory; and, what is most to my present purpose, many house-swallows appeared and were very alert in many places, and particularly at Chobham, in Surrey.

But as that short warm period was succeeded as well as preceded by harsh severe weather, with frequent frosts and ice, and cutting winds, the insects withdrew, the tortoise retired again into the ground, and the swallows were seen no more until the 10th of April, when, the rigour of the spring abating, a softer season began to prevail.

Again: it appears by my journals for many years past that house-martins retire, to a bird, about the beginning of October; so that a person not very observant of such matters would conclude that they had taken their last farewell; but then it may be seen in my diaries also that considerable flocks have discovered themselves again in the first week of November, and often on the fourth day of that month only for one day; and that not as if they were in actual migration, but playing about at their leisure and feeding calmly, as if no enterprise of moment at all agitated their spirits. And this was the case in the beginning of this very month; for on the 4th November, more than twenty house-martins, which, in appearance, had all departed about the 7th of October, were seen again, for that one morning only, sporting between my fields and the Hanger, and feasting on insects which swarmed in that sheltered district. The preceding day was wet and blustering, but the 4th was dark, and mild, and soft, the wind at south-west, and the thermometer at 58½°; a pitch not common at that season of the year. Moreover, it may not be amiss to add in this place, that whenever the thermometer is above 50°, the bat comes flitting out in every autumnal and winter month.

From all these circumstances laid together, it is obvious that torpid insects, reptiles, and quadrupeds, are awakened from their profoundest slumbers by a little untimely warmth; and therefore that nothing so much promotes its death-like stupor as a defect of heat. And farther, it is reasonable to suppose that two whole species, or at least many individuals of those two species of British *Hirundines* do never leave this island at all, but partake of the same benumbed state; for we cannot suppose, that after a month's absence, house-martins can return from southern regions to appear for one morning in November, or that house-swallows should leave the districts of Asia to enjoy in March the transient summer of a couple of days.

Bad logic & bad observation.

LETTER XXXVI.

SELBORNE, *Jan. 8th*, 1778.

There was in this village several years ago a miserable pauper, who from his birth was afflicted with a leprosy, as far as we are aware of a singular kind, since it affected only the palms of his hands and the soles of his feet. This scaly eruption usually broke out twice in the year, at the spring and fall; and, by peeling away, left the skin so thin and tender that neither his hands nor feet were able to perform their functions; so that the poor object was half his time on crutches, incapable of employ, and languishing in a tiresome state of indolence and inactivity. His habit was lean, lank and cadaverous. In this sad plight he dragged on a miserable existence, a burden to himself and his parish, which was obliged to support him till he was relieved by death at more than thirty years of age.

The good women, who love to account for every defect in children by the doctrine of longing, said that his mother felt a violent propensity for oysters, which she was unable to gratify; and that the black rough scurf on his hands and feet were the shells of that fish. We knew his parents, neither of whom were lepers; his father in particular lived to be far advanced in years.

In all ages the leprosy has made dreadful havoc among mankind. The Israelites seem to have been greatly afflicted with it from the most remote times, as appears from the peculiar and repeated injunctions given them in the Levitical law.[1] Nor was the rancour of this foul disorder much abated

[1] See Lev. xiii. and xiv.

in the last period of their commonwealth, as may be seen in many passages of the New Testament.

Some centuries ago this horrible distemper prevailed all Europe over: and our forefathers were by no means exempt, as appears by the large provision made for objects labouring under this calamity. There was an hospital for female lepers in the diocese of Lincoln; a noble one near Durham; three in London and Southwark; and perhaps many more in or near our great towns and cities. Moreover, some crowned heads, and other wealthy and charitable personages, bequeathed large legacies to such poor people as languished under this hopeless infirmity.

It must, therefore, in these days be to a humane and thinking person a matter of equal wonder and satisfaction, when he contemplates how nearly this pest is eradicated, and observes that a leper now is a rare sight. He will, moreover, when engaged in such a train of thought naturally inquire for the reason. This happy change, perhaps, may have originated and been continued from the much smaller quantity of salted meat and fish now eaten in these kingdoms; from the use of linen next the skin; from the plenty of better bread; and from the profusion of fruits, roots, legumes, and greens, so common in every family. Three or four centuries ago, before there were any enclosures, sown-grasses, field-turnips, or field-carrots, or hay, all the cattle which had grown fat in summer, and were not killed for winter use, were turned out soon after Michaelmas to shift as they could through the dead months; so that no fresh meat could be had in winter or spring. Hence the marvellous account of the vast stores of salted flesh found in the larder of the eldest Spencer[1] in the days of Edward II., even so late in the spring as the 3rd of May. It was from magazines like these that the turbulent barons supported in idleness their riotous swarms of retainers ready for any disorder or mischief. But agriculture is now arrived at such a pitch of perfection that our best and fattest meats are killed in the winter; and no man need eat salted flesh, unless he prefers it, that has money to buy fresh.

One cause of this distemper might be, no doubt, the quantity of wretched fresh and salt fish consumed by the commonalty at all seasons as well as in Lent; which our poor now would hardly be persuaded to touch.

The use of linen changes, shirts or shifts, in the room of

[1] Viz. six hundred bacons, eighty carcasses of beef, and six hundred muttons.—W

sordid and filthy woollen, long worn next the skin, is a matter of neatness comparatively mcdern; but must prove a great means of preventing cutaneous ails. At this very time woollen, instead of linen, prevails among the poorer Welsh, who are subject to foul eruptions.

The plenty of good wheaten bread that now is found among all ranks of people in the south, instead of that miserable sort which used in old days to be made of barley or beans, may contribute not a little to the sweetening their blood and correcting their juices; for the inhabitants of mountainous districts to this day are still liable to the itch and other cutaneous disorders, from a wretchedness and poverty of diet.

As to the produce of a garden, every middle-aged person of observation may perceive, within his own memory, both in town and country, how vastly the consumption of vegetables is increased. Green-stalls in cities now support multitudes in a comfortable state, while gardeners get fortunes. Every decent labourer also has his garden, which is half his support, as well as his delight; and common farmers provide plenty of beans, peas, and greens, for their hinds to eat with their bacon· and those few that do not are despised for their sordid parsimony, and looked upon as regardless of the welfare of their dependants. Potatoes have prevailed in this little district by means of premiums within these twenty years only; and are much esteemed here now by the poor, who would scarce have ventured to taste them in the last reign.

Our Saxon ancestors certainly had some sort of cabbage, because they call the month of February "Sprout-cale"; but long after their days the cultivation of gardens was little attended to. The religious, being men of leisure, and keeping up a constant correspondence with Italy, were the first people among us that had gardens and fruit-trees in any perfection within the wall of their abbeys[1] and priories. The barons neglected every pursuit that did not lead to war or tend to the pleasure of the chase.

It was not till gentlemen took up the study of horticulture themselves that the knowledge of gardening made such hasty advances. Lord Cobham, Lord Ila, and Mr. Waller, of Beaconsfield, were some of the first people of rank that promoted the elegant science of ornamenting without despising the superintendence of the kitchen quarters and fruit walls.

[1] "In monasteries the lamp of knowledge continued to burn, however dimly. In them men of business were formed for the state: the art of writing was cultivated by

A remark made by the excellent Mr. Ray, in his *Tour of Europe*, at once surprises us, and corroborates what has been advanced above; for we find him observing so late as his days, that, "the Italians use several herbs for sallets, which are not yet, or have not been but lately, used in England, viz., *selleri* (celery), which is nothing else but the sweet smallage; the young shoots whereof, with a little of the head of the root cut off, they eat raw with oil and pepper". And further adds: "Curled endive blanched is much used beyond seas; and for a raw sallet, seemed to excel lettuce itself". Now this journey was undertaken no longer ago than in the year 1663.

LETTER XXXVII.

SELBORNE, *Feb.* 12*th*, 1778.

" Fortè puer, comitum seductus ab agmine fido,
  Dixerat, ecquis adest? et, adest, responderat echo,
  Hic stupet; utque aciem partes divisit in omnes;
  Voce, veni, clamat magnâ.   Vocat illa vocantem."[1]

In a district so diversified as this, so full of hollow vales and hanging woods, it is no wonder that echoes should abound. Many we have discovered that return the cry of a pack of dogs, the notes of a hunting-horn, a tunable ring of bells, or the melody of birds very agreeably; but we were still at a loss for a polysyllabical articulate echo, till a young gentleman, who had parted from his company in a summer evening walk, and was calling after them, stumbled upon a very curious one in a spot where it might least be expected. At first he was much surprised, and could not be persuaded but that he was mocked by some boy; but repeating his trials in several languages, and finding his respondent to be a very adroit polyglot, he then discerned the deception.

This echo in an evening, before rural noises cease, would repeat ten syllables most articulately and distinctly, especially if quick dactyls were chosen. The last syllables of

" Tityre, tu patulæ recubans   .   .   ."[2]

the monks; they were the only proficients in mechanics, gardening, and architecture."—DALRYMPLE'S *Annals of Scotland.*—W.

[1] "By chance, the youth, being separated from the trusty company of his attendants, cries out, ' Is there anyone here?' and Echo answers ' Here!' He is amazed; and when he has cast his eyes on every side, he cries out with a loud voice, ' Come!' Whereon she calls the youth who calls."

[2] " Beneath the shade which beechen boughs diffuse,
    You, Tityrus, entertain your sylvan muse."—DRYDEN'S VIRG. *Ecl.* I

were as audibly and intelligibly returned as the first; and there is no doubt, could trial have been made, but that at midnight, when the air is very elastic, and a dead stillness prevails, one or two syllables more might have been obtained; but the distance rendered so late an experiment very inconvenient.

Quick dactyls, we observed, succeeded best; for when we came to try its powers in slow, heavy, embarrassed spondees of the same number of syllables,

"Monstrum horrendum, informe, ingens . . ."[1]

we could perceive a return but of four or five.

All echoes have some one place to which they are returned stronger and more distinct than to any other; and that is always the place that lies at right angles with the object of repercussion, and is not too near, nor too far off. Buildings, or naked rocks, re-echo much more articulately than hanging woods or vales; because in the latter the voice is as it were entangled, and embarrassed in the covert, and weakened in the rebound.

The true object of this echo, as we found by various experiments, is the stone-built, tiled hop-kiln in Gally-lane, which measures in front forty feet, and from the ground to the eaves twelve feet. The true *centrum phonicum*, or just distance, is one particular spot in the King's field, in the path to Nore-hill, on the very brink of the steep balk above the hollow cart-way. In this case there is no choice of distance; but the path, by mere contingency, happens to be the lucky, the identical spot, because the ground rises or falls so immediately, if the speaker either retires or advances, that his mouth would at once be above or below the object.

We measured this polysyllabical echo with great exactness, and found the distance to fall very short of Dr. Plot's rule for distinct articulation; for the Doctor, in his history of Oxfordshire, allows a hundred and twenty feet for the return of each syllable distinctly; hence this echo, which gives ten distinct syllables, ought to measure four hundred yards, or one hundred and twenty feet to each syllable; whereas our distance is only two hundred and fifty-eight yards, or near seventy-five feet, to each syllable. Thus our measure falls short of the Doctor's, as five to eight; but then it must be acknowledged that this candid philosopher was convinced afterwards, that

[1] "A monster grim, tremendous, vast and high."—DRYDEN'S VIRG. *Æn.* iii.

some latitude must be admitted of in the distance of echoes according to time and place.

When experiments of this sort are making, it should always be remembered that weather and the time of day have a vast influence on an echo; for a dull, heavy, moist air deadens and clogs the sound; and hot sunshine renders the air thin and weak, and deprives it of all its springiness, and a ruffling wind quite defeats the whole. In a still, clear, dewy evening the air is most elastic; and perhaps the later the hour the more so.

Echo has always been so amusing to the imagination that the poets have personified her; and in their hands she has been the occasion of many a beautiful fiction. Nor need the gravest man be ashamed to appear taken with such a phenomenon, since it may become the subject of philosophical or mathematical inquiries.

One should have imagined that echoes, if not entertaining, must at least have been harmless and inoffensive; yet, Virgil advances a strange notion, that they are injurious to bees. After enumerating some probable and reasonable annoyances, such as prudent owners would wish far removed from their bee-gardens, he adds—

———"aut ubi concava pulsu
Saxa sonant, vocisque offensa resultat imago."[1]

This wild and fanciful assertion will hardly be admitted by the philosophers of these days, especially as they all now seem agreed that insects are not furnished with any organs of hearing at all. But if it should be urged, that though they cannot hear, yet perhaps they may feel the repercussions of sounds, I grant it is possible they may. Yet that these impressions are distasteful or hurtful, I deny, because bees, in good summers, thrive well in my outlet, where the echoes are very strong; for this village is another Anathoth, a place of responses and echoes. Besides, it does not appear from experiment that bees are in any way capable of being affected by sounds; for I have often tried my own with a large speaking-trumpet held close to their hives, and with such an exertion of voice as would have hailed a ship at the distance of a mile, and still these insects pursued their various employments undisturbed, and without showing the least sensibility or resentment.

[1] "Nor place them where too deep a water flows,

Nor hollow rocks that render back the sound,
Nor double images of the voice rebound."—DRYDEN'S VIRG. *Georg.* iv.

Some time since its discovery this echo is become totally silent, though the object, or hop-kiln, remains; nor is there any mystery in this defect; for the field between is planted as a hop-garden, and the voice of the speaker is totally absorbed and lost among the poles and entangled foliage of the hops. And when the poles are removed in autumn the disappointment is the same; because a tall quick-set hedge, nurtured up for the purpose of shelter to the hop ground, entirely interrupts the impulse and repercussion of the voice; so that till those obstructions are removed no more of its garrulity can be expected.

Should any gentleman of fortune think an echo in his park or outlet a pleasing incident, he might build one at little or no expense. For whenever he had occasion for a new barn, stable, dog-kennel, or the like structure, it would be only needful to erect this building on the gentle declivity of a hill, with a like rising opposite to it, at a few hundred yards distance; and perhaps success might be the easier ensured could some canal, lake, or stream intervene. From a seat at the *centrum phonicum* he and his friends might amuse themselves sometimes of an evening with the prattle of this loquacious nymph; of whose complacency and decent reserve more may be said than can with truth of every individual of her sex; since she is "neither backward in her discourse, nor too obtrusive with it".

" ———quæ nec reticere loquenti,
Nec prior ipsa loqui didcit resonabilis echo."

The classic reader will, I trust, pardon the following lovely quotation, so finely describing echoes, and so poetically accounting for their causes from popular superstition:—

" Quæ benè quom videas, rationem reddere possis
Tute tibi atque aliis, quo pacto per loca sola
Saxa paries formas verborum ex ordine reddant,
Palanteis comites quom monteis inter opacos
Quærimus, et magna dispersos voce ciemus.
Sex etiam, aut septem loca vidi reddere voces
Unam quom jaceres : ita colles collibus ipsis
Verba repulsantes iterabant dicta referre.
Hæc loca capripedes Satyros, Nymphasque tenere
Finitimi fingunt, et Faunos esse loquuntur;
Quorum noctivago strepitu, ludoque jocanti
Adfirmant volgo taciturna silentia rumpi,
Chordarumque sonos fieri, dulceisque querelas,
Tibia quas fundit digitis pulsata canentum :

Et genus agricolûm latè sentiscere, quom Pan
Pinea semiferi capitis velamina quassans,
Unco sæpe labro calamos percurrit hianteis,
Fistula silvestrem ne cesset fundere musam." [1]

LUCRETIUS, lib. iv.

LETTER XXXVIII.

SELBORNE, *May* 13*th*, 1778.

Among the many singularities attending those amusing birds
the swifts, I am now confirmed in the opinion that we have
every year the same number of pairs invariably; at least the
result of my inquiry has been exactly the same for a long time
past. The swallows and martins are so numerous, and so
widely distributed over the village, that it is hardly possible
to recount them; while the swifts, though they do not build
in the church, yet so frequently haunt it, and play and
rendezvous round it, that they are easily enumerated. The
number that I constantly find are eight pairs; about half of
which reside in the church, and the rest build in some of the
lowest and meanest thatched cottages. Now as these eight
pairs, allowance being made for accidents, breed yearly eight
pairs more, what becomes annually of this increase; and what
determines every spring which pairs shall visit us, and reoccupy
their ancient haunts?

Ever since I have attended to the subject of ornithology, I
have always supposed that that sudden reverse of affection,
that strange αντιστοργη (parental dislike), which immediately suc
ceeds in the feathered kind to the most passionate fondness, is
the occasion of an equal dispersion of birds over the face of the

---

[1] This passage in Creech's translation runs as follows:—
'This shows thee why, whilst men, through caves and groves
Call their lost friends, or mourn unhappy loves,
The pitying rocks, the groaning caves return
Their sad complaints again, and seem to mourn:
This all observe, and I myself have known
Both rocks and hills return six words for one:
The dancing words from hill to hill rebound,
They all receive, and all restore the sound:
The vulgar and the neighbours think, and tell,
That there the Nymphs, and Fauns, and Satyrs dwell;
And that their wanton sport, their loud delight,
Breaks through the quiet silence of the night:
Their music's softest airs fill all the plains,
And mighty Pan delights the list'ning swains:
The goat-faced Pan, whose flocks securely feed;
With long-hung lip he blows his oaten reed;
The horned, the half-beast god, when brisk and gay,
With pine leaves crowned, provokes the swains to play."

earth.   Without this provision one favourite district would be
crowded with inhabitants, while others would be destitute and
forsaken.   But the parent birds seem to maintain a jealous
superiority, and to oblige the young to seek for new abodes;
and the rivalry of the males, in many kinds, prevents their
crowding the one on the other.   Whether the swallows and
house-martins return in the same exact number annually is not
easy to say, for reasons given above; but it is apparent, as I
have remarked before in my Monographies, that the numbers
returning bear no manner of proportion to the numbers retiring.

LETTER XXXIX.

SELBORNE, *June 2nd,* 1778.

The standing objection to botany has always been, that it is
a pursuit that amuses the fancy and exercises the memory,
without improving the mind or advancing any real knowledge;
and, where the science is carried no farther than a mere systematic classification, the charge is but too true.   But the
botanist that is desirous of wiping off this aspersion should be
by no means content with a list of names; he should study
plants philosophically, should investigate the laws of vegetation,
should examine the powers and virtues of efficacious herbs,
should promote their cultivation; and graft the gardener, the
planter, and the husbandman, on the phytologist.   Not that
system is by any means to be thrown aside; without system
the field of Nature would be a pathless wilderness; but system
should be subservient to, not the main object of, pursuit.

Vegetation is highly worthy of our attention; and in itself
is of the utmost consequence to mankind, and productive of
many of the greatest comforts and elegancies of life.   To plants
we owe timber, bread, beer, honey, wine, oil, linen, cotton, &c.,
what not only strengthens our hearts, and exhilarates our
spirits, but what secures us from inclemencies of weather and
adorns our persons.   Man, in his true state of nature, seems
to be subsisted by spontaneous vegetation; in middle climes,
where grasses prevail, he mixes some animal food with the
produce of the field and garden; and it is towards the polar
extremes only that, like his kindred bears and wolves, he
gorges himself with flesh alone, and is driven to what hunger
has never been known to compel the very beasts, to prey on
his own species.

The productions of vegetation have had a vast influence on the commerce of nations, and have been the great promoters of navigation, as may be seen in the articles of sugar, tea, tobacco, opium, ginseng,[1] betel, paper, &c. As every climate has its peculiar produce, our natural wants bring on a mutual intercourse; so that by means of trade each distinct part is supplied with the growth of every latitude. But, without the knowledge of plants and their culture, we must have been content with our hips and haws, without enjoying the delicate fruits of India and the salutiferous drugs of Peru.

Instead of examining the minute distinctions of every various species of each obscure genus, the botanist should endeavour to make himself acquainted with those that are useful. You shall see a man readily ascertain every herb of the field, yet hardly know wheat from barley, or at least one sort of wheat or barley from another. But of all sorts of vegetation the grasses seem to be most neglected; neither the farmer nor the grazier seem to distinguish the annual from the perennial, the hardy from the tender, nor the succulent and nutritive from the dry and juiceless.

The study of grasses would be of great consequence to a northerly, and grazing kingdom. The botanist that could improve the sward of the district where he lived would be an useful member of society: to raise a thick turf on a naked soil would be worth volumes of systematic knowledge; and he would be the best commonwealth's man that could occasion the growth of "two blades of grass where one alone was seen before".

LETTER XL.

SELBORNE, *July 3rd*, 1778.

In a district so diversified with such a variety of hill and dale, aspects, and soils, it is no wonder that great choice of plants should be found. Chalks, clays, sands, sheep-walks and downs, bogs, heaths, woodlands, and champaign fields, cannot but furnish an ample Flora. The deep rocky lanes abound with *Filices*, and the pastures and moist woods with *Fungi*. If in any branch of botany we may seem to be wanting, it must be in the large aquatic plants, which are not to be ex-

[1] Ginseng—a plant whose root, of an aromatic flavour, is greatly esteemed as a medicine by the Chinese.

pected on a spot far removed from rivers, and lying up amidst the hill country at the spring heads. To enumerate all the plants that have been discovered within our limits would be a needless work; but a short list of the more rare, and the spots where they are to be found, may be neither unacceptable nor unentertaining:—

Helleborus fœtidus, stinking hellebore, bear's foot, or setter-worth,—all over the High-wood and Coney-croft Hanger: this continues a great branching plant the winter through, blossoming about January, and is very ornamental in shady walks and shrubberies. The good women give the leaves powdered to children troubled with worms; but it is a violent remedy, and ought to be administered with caution.

Helleborus viridis, green hellebore,—in the deep stony lane on the left hand just before the turning to Norton Farm, and at the top of Middle Dorton under the hedge: this plant dies down to the ground early in autumn, and springs again about February, flowering almost as soon as it appears above the ground.

Vaccinium oxycoccos, creeping bilberries, or cranberries,—in the bogs of Bin's Pond.

Vaccinium myrtillus, whortle, or bleaberries,—on the dry hillocks of Wolmer Forest.

Drosera rotundifolia, round-leaved sundew,—in the bogs of Bin's Pond.

Drosera longifolia, long-leaved sundew,— in the bogs of Bin's Pond.

Comarum palustre, purple comarum, or marsh cinquefoil,—in the bogs of Bin's Pond.

Hypericum androsæmum, tutsan, or St. John's Wort,—in the stony, hollow lanes.

Vinca minor, lesser periwinkle,—in Selborne Hanger and Shrubwood.

Monotropa hypopithys, yellow monotropa, or birds' nest,—in Selborne Hanger under the shady beeches, to whose roots it seems to be parasitical, at the north-west end of the Hanger.

Chlora perfoliata, *Blackstonia perfoliata*, *Hudsonii*, perfoliated yellow-wort,—on the banks in the King's Field.

Paris quadrifolia, herb Paris, true-love, or one-berry,—in the Church Litten Coppice.

Chrysosplenium oppositifolium, opposite golden saxifrage,—in the dark and rocky hollow lanes.

Gentiana amarella, autumnal gentian, or fellwort,—on the Zigzag and Hanger.

Lathrœa squamaria, tooth-wort,—in the Church Litten Coppice under some hazels near the foot-bridge, in Trimming's garden hedge, and on the dry wall opposite Grange Yard.

Dipsacus pilosus, small teasel,—in the Short and Long Lith.

Lathyrus sylvestris, narrow-leaved, or wild lathyrus,—in the bushes at the foot of the Short Lith, near the path.

Ophrys spiralis, ladies' traces,—in the Long Lith, and towards the south corner of the common.

Ophrys nidus avis, birds' nest ophrys,—in the Long Lith under the shady beeches among the dead leaves; in Great Dorton among the bushes, and on the Hanger plentifully.

Serapias latifolia, helleborine,—in the High Wood under the shady beeches.

Daphne laureola, spurge laurel,—in Selborne Hanger and the High Wood.

Daphne mezereum, the mezereon, in Selborne Hanger among the shrubs, at the south-east end above the cottages.

Lycoperdon tuber, truffles,—in the Hanger and High Wood.

Sambucus ebulus, dwarf elder, walwort, or danewort—among the rubbish and ruined foundations of the Priory.

Of all the propensities of plants, none seem more strange than their different periods of blossoming. Some produce their flowers in the winter, or very first dawnings of spring; many when the spring is established; some at midsummer, and some not till autumn. When we see the *Helleborus fœtidus* and *Helleborus niger* blowing at Christmas, the *Helleborus hyemalis* in January, and the *Helleborus viridis* as soon as ever it emerges out of the ground, we do not wonder, because they are kindred plants that we expect should keep pace the one with the other; but other congenerous vegetables differ so widely in their time of flowering, that we cannot but admire. I shall only instance at present in the *Crocus sativus*, the vernal and the autumnal crocus, which have such an affinity, that the best botanists only make them varieties of the same genus, of which there is only one species, not being able to discern any difference in the corolla, or in the internal structure. Yet the vernal crocus expands its flowers by the beginning of March at farthest, and often in very rigorous weather; and cannot be retarded but by some violence offered; while the autumnal (the saffron) defies the influence of the spring and summer, and will not blow till most plants begin to fade and run to seed. This circumstance is one of the wonders of the creation, little noticed because a common occurrence; yet ought not to be overlooked on account of its familiarity, since it would be as difficult to be explained as the most stupendous phenomenon in nature.

> "Say, what impels, amidst surrounding snow
> Congeal'd, the crocus' flamy bud to glow?
> Say, what retards, amidst the summer's blaze,
> Th' autumnal bulb, till pale, declining days?
> The GOD OF SEASONS; whose pervading power
> Controls the sun, or sheds the fleecy shower:
> He bids each flower His quickening word obey,
> Or to each lingering bloom enjoins delay."

LETTER XLI.

SELBORNE, *Aug. 7th*, 1778.

"Omnibus animalibus reliquis certus et uniusmodi, et in suo cuique genere incessus est: aves solæ vario meatu feruntur, et in terrâ, et in äere."— PLIN. *Nat. Hist.*, lib. x. cap. 38.[1]

A good ornithologist should be able to distinguish birds by their air as well as by their colours and shape; on the ground as well as on the wing; and in the bush as well as in the hand. For, though it must not be said that every species of birds has a manner peculiar to itself, yet there is somewhat in most genera at least, that at first sight discriminates them, and enables a judicious observer to pronounce upon them with some certainty. Put a bird in motion "and it is truly betrayed by its walk ".

"—— Et verâ incessu patuit ——"

Thus kites and buzzards sail round in circles with wings expanded and motionless; and it is from their gliding manner that the former are still called in the north of England gleads, from the Saxon verb *glidan*, to glide. The kestrel, or windhover, has a peculiar mode of hanging in the air in one place,

[1] "All animals have a certain definite gait peculiar to their species; birds alone bear themselves in a varied manner both on the ground and in the air."

his wings all the while being briskly agitated. Hen-harriers fly low over heaths or fields of corn, and beat the ground regularly like a pointer or setting-dog. Owls move in a buoyant manner, as if lighter than the air; they seem to want ballast. There is a peculiarity belonging to ravens that must draw the attention even of the most incurious—they spend all their leisure time in striking and cuffing each other on the wing in a kind of playful skirmish; and, when they move from one place to another, frequently turn on their backs with a loud croak, and seem to be falling to the ground. When this odd gesture betides them, they are scratching themselves with one foot, and thus lose the centre of gravity. Rooks sometimes dive and tumble in a frolicsome manner; crows and daws swagger in their walk; woodpeckers fly *volatu undoso* (in an undulating manner), opening and closing their wings at every stroke, and so are always rising or falling in curves. All of this genus use their tails, which incline downward, as a support while they run up trees. Parrots, like all other hooked-clawed birds, walk awkwardly, and make use of their bill as a third foot, climbing and descending with ridiculous caution. All the *Gallinæ* parade and walk gracefully, and run nimbly; but fly with difficulty, with an impetuous whirring, and in a straight line. Magpies and jays flutter with powerless wings, and make no despatch; herons seem encumbered with too much sail for their light bodies, but these vast hollow wings are necessary in carrying burdens such as large fishes and the like; pigeons, and particularly the sort called smiters, have a way of clashing their wings the one against the other over their backs with a loud snap; another variety, called tumblers, turn themselves over in the air. Some birds have movements peculiar to the season of love: though strong and rapid at other times, yet in the spring hang about on the wing in a toying and playful manner; thus the cock-snipe while breeding, forgetting his former flight, fans the air like the wind-hover; and the greenfinch in particular, exhibits such languishing and faltering gestures as to appear like a wounded and dying bird; the kingfisher darts along like an arrow; fern-owls, or goatsuckers, glance in the dusk over the tops of trees like a meteor; starlings as it were swim along, while missel-thrushes use a wild and desultory flight; swallows sweep over the surface of the ground and water, and distinguish themselves by rapid turns and quick evolutions; swifts dash round in circles; and the bank-martin moves with frequent vacillations

like a butterfly. Most of the small birds fly by jerks, rising
and falling as they advance. Most small birds hop; but wagtails and larks walk, moving their legs alternately. Skylarks
rise and fall perpendicularly as they sing; woodlarks hang
poised in the air; and titlarks rise and fall in large curves,
singing in their descent. The white-throats use odd jerks
and gestulations over the tops of hedges and bushes. All the
duck kind waddle; divers and auks walk as if fettered, and
stand erect on their tails: these are the *compedes* of Linnæus.
Geese and cranes, and most wild fowls, move in figured flights,
often changing their position. The secondary *remiges* of
Tringæ, wild-ducks, and some others, are very long, and give
their wings, when in motion, a hooked appearance. Dabchicks,
moor-hens, and coots, fly erect, with their legs hanging down,
and hardly make any despatch; the reason is plain, their wings
are placed too forward out of the true centre of gravity; as the
legs of auks and divers are situated too backward

LETTER XLII.

SELBORNE, *Sept. 9th*, 1778.

From the motion of birds, the transition is natural enough
to their notes and language, of which I shall say something.
Not that I would pretend to understand their language like
the vizier; who, by the recital of a conversation which passed
between two owls, reclaimed a sultan, before delighting in
conquest and devastation[1]; but I would be thought only to
mean that many of the winged tribes have various sounds and
voices adapted to express their various passions, wants, and
feelings; such as anger, fear, love, hatred, hunger, and the like.
All species are not equally eloquent; some are copious and
fluent as it were in their utterance, while others are confined
to a few important sounds: no bird, like the fish kind, is
quite mute, though some are rather silent. The language of
birds is very ancient, and, like other ancient modes of speech,
very elliptical; little is said, but much is meant and understood.

The notes of the eagle kind are shrill and piercing; and
about the season of nidification much diversified, as I have
been often assured by a curious observer of Nature who long

[1] See *Spectator*, vol. vii. no. 512.

resided at Gibraltar, where eagles abound. The notes of our hawks much resemble those of the king of birds. Owls have very expressive notes; they hoot in a fine vocal sound, much resembling the *vox humana*, and reducible by a pitch-pipe to a musical key.[1] This note seems to express complacency and rivalry among the males; they use also a quick call and a horrible scream; and can snore and hiss when they mean to menace. Ravens, besides their loud croak, can exert a deep and solemn note that makes the woods to echo; the amorous sound of a crow is strange and ridiculous; rooks, in the breeding season, attempt sometimes in the gaiety of their hearts to sing, but with no great success; the parrot kind have many modulations of voice, as appears by their aptitude to learn human sounds; doves coo in an amorous and mournful manner, and are emblems of despairing lovers; the woodpecker sets up a sort of loud and hearty laugh; the fern-owl, or goat-sucker, from the dusk till daybreak, serenades his mate with the clattering of castanets. All the tuneful *Passeres* express their complacency by sweet modulations, and a variety of melody. The swallow, as has been observed in a former letter, by a shrill alarm bespeaks the attention of the other *Hirundines*, and bids them be aware the hawk is at hand. Aquatic and gregarious birds, especially the nocturnal, that shift their quarters in the dark, are very noisy and loquacious; as cranes, wild-geese, wild-ducks, and the like; their perpetual clamour prevents them from dispersing and losing their companions.

In so extensive a subject, sketches and outlines are as much as can be expected; for it would be endless to instance in all the infinite variety of the feathered nation. We shall therefore confine the remainder of this letter to the few domestic fowls of our yards, which are most known, and therefore best understood. And first the peacock, with his gorgeous train, demands our attention; but, like most of the gaudy birds, his notes are grating and shocking to the ear: the yelling of cats, and the braying of an ass, are not more disgustful. The voice of the goose is trumpet-like, and clanking; and once saved the Capitol at Rome, as grave historians assert; the hiss, also, of the gander, is formidable and full of menace, and "protective of his young". Among ducks the sexual distinction of voice is remarkable; for, while the quack of the female is loud and sonorous, the voice of the drake is inward and harsh, and feeble, and scarce discernible. The cock turkey struts and

---

[1] The brown owl hoots; the white owl screams.—W.

gobbles to his mistress in a most uncouth manner; he hath
also a pert and petulant note when he attacks his adversary.
When a hen turkey leads forth her young brood she keeps a
watchful eye; and if a bird of prey appear, though ever so
high in the air, the careful mother announces the enemy with
a little inward moan, and watches him with a steady and
attentive look; but, if he approach, her note becomes earnest
and alarming, and her outcries are redoubled.

No inhabitants of a yard seem possessed of such a variety of
expression and so copious a language as common poultry.
Take a chicken of four or five days old, and hold it up to a
window where there are flies, and it will immediately seize its
prey, with little twitterings of complacency; but if you tender
it a wasp or a bee, at once its note becomes harsh, and expressive of disapprobation and a sense of danger. When a pullet
is ready to lay she intimates the event by a joyous and easy
soft note. Of all the occurrences of their life that of laying
seems to be the most important; for no sooner has a hen dis-
burdened herself, than she rushes forth with a clamorous kind
of joy, which the cock and the rest of his mistresses immediately adopt. The tumult is not confined to the family
concerned, but catches from yard to yard, and spreads to every
homestead within hearing, till at last the whole village is in an
uproar. As soon as a hen becomes a mother her new relation
demands a new language; she then runs clocking and screaming about, and seems agitated as if possessed. The father of
the flock has also a considerable vocabulary; if he finds food,
he calls a favourite concubine to partake; and if a bird of prey
passes over, with a warning voice he bids his family beware.
The gallant chanticleer has, at command, his amorous phrases
and his terms of defiance. But the sound by which he is best
known is his crowing: by this he has been distinguished in all
ages as the countryman's clock or larum, as the watchman
that proclaims the divisions of the night. Thus the poet
elegantly styles him:

> "——the crested cock, whose clarion sounds
> The silent hours".

A neighbouring gentleman one summer had lost most of his
chickens by a sparrow-hawk, that came gliding down between
a faggot pile and the end of his house to the place where the
coops stood. The owner, inwardly vexed to see his flock thus
diminished, hung a setting net adroitly between the pile and

the house, into which the caitiff dashed, and was entangled.
Resentment suggested the law of retaliation; he therefore
clipped the hawk's wings, cut off his talons, and, fixing a cork
on his bill, threw him down among the brood-hens.   Imagination cannot paint the scene that ensued; the expressions that
fear, rage, and revenge inspired, were new, or at least such as
had been unnoticed before: the exasperated matrons upbraided,
they execrated, they insulted, they triumphed.   In a word,
they never desisted from buffeting their adversary till they had
torn him in a hundred pieces.

LETTER XLIII.

SELBORNE.

"————Monstrent
*   *   *   *   *
Quid tantem Oceano properent se tingere soles
Hyberni; vel quæ tardis mora noctibus obstet."[1]

Gentlemen who have outlets might contrive to make ornament subservient to utility: a pleasing eye-trap might also
contribute to promote science: an obelisk in a garden or park
might be both an embellishment and a heliotrope.

Any person that is curious, and enjoys the advantage of a
good horizon, might, with little trouble, make two heliotropes;
the one for the winter, the other for the summer solstice: and
the two erections might be constructed with very little expense;
for two pieces of timber frame-work, about ten or twelve feet
high, and four feet broad at the base, and close lined with
plank, would answer the purpose.

The erection for the former should, if possible, be placed
within sight of some window in the common sitting-parlour;
because men, at that dead season of the year, are usually
within doors at the close of the day; while that for the latter
might be fixed for any given spot in the garden or outlet;
whence the owner might contemplate, in a fine summer's
evening, the utmost extent that the sun makes to the northward at the season of the longest days.   Now nothing would
be necessary but to place these two objects with so much

[1] "*Teach me* the various labours of the moon

What shakes the solid earth; *what cause delays
The summer nights, what shortens winter days.*"
—DRYDEN'S VIRG. *Georg.* ii.

exactness, that the westerly limb of the sun, at setting, might but just clear the winter heliotrope to the west of it on the shortest day; and that the whole disc of the sun, at the longest day, might exactly at setting also clear the summer heliotrope to the north of it.

By this simple expedient it would soon appear that there is no such thing, strictly speaking, as a solstice; for, from the shortest day, the owner would, every clear evening, see the disc advancing at its setting, to the westward of the object; and, from the longest day, observe the sun retiring backwards every evening at its setting, towards the object westward, till, in a few nights, it would set quite behind it, and so by degrees, to the west of it: for when the sun comes near the summer solstice, the whole disc of it would at first set behind the object; after a time the northern limb would first appear, and so every night gradually more, till at length the whole dia- meter would set northward of it for about three nights; but on the middle night of the three, sensibly more remote than the former or following. When beginning its recess from the summer tropic, it would continue more and more to be hidden every night, till at length it would descend quite behind the object again; and so nightly more and more to the westward.

LETTER XLIV.

SELBORNE.

" ————Mugire videbis
Sub pedibus terram, et descendere montibus ornos."[1]—VIRG. Æn. iv.

When I was a boy I used to read, with astonishment and implicit assent, accounts in *Baker's Chronicle* of walking hills and travelling mountains. John Philips, in his *Cyder*, alludes to the credit that was given to such stories with a delicate but quaint vein of humour peculiar to the author of the *Splendid Shilling*.

"I nor advise, nor reprehend the choice
  Of Marcely Hill; the apple no where finds
  A kinder mould: yet 'tis unsafe to trust
  Deceitful ground: who knows but that once more
  This mount may journey, and his present site
  Forsaken, to thy neighbour's bound transfer

[1] " Behold, the earth beneath her footsteps groans,
   And from the hills the wild ash trees descend."

Thy goodly plants, affording matter strange
For law debates?"

But, when I came to consider better, I began to suspect that though our hills may never have journeyed far, yet that the ends of many of them have slipped and fallen away at distant periods, leaving the cliffs bare and abrupt. This seems to have been the case with Nore and Whetham Hills; and especially with the ridge between Harteley Park and Wardleham, where the ground has slid into vast swellings and furrows; and lies still in such romantic confusion as cannot be accounted for from any other cause. A strange event, that happened not long since, justifies our suspicions; which though it befell not within the limits of this parish, yet as it was within the hundred of Selborne, and as the circumstances were singular, may fairly claim a place in a work of this nature.

The months of January and February, in the year 1774, were remarkable for great melting snows and vast gusts of rain; so that by the end of the latter month the land-springs, or lavants, began to prevail, and to be near as high as in the memorable winter of 1764. The beginning of March also went on in the same tenor; when, in the night between the 8th and 9th of that month, a considerable part of the great woody hanger at Hawkley was torn from its place, and fell down, leaving a high freestone cliff naked and bare, and resembling the steep side of a chalk-pit. It appears that this huge fragment, being perhaps sapped and undermined by waters, foundered, and was ingulfed, going down in a perpendicular direction; for a gate which stood in the field, on the top of the hill, after sinking with its posts for thirty or forty feet, remained in so true and upright a position as to open and shut with great exactness, just as in its first situation. Several oaks are still standing, and in a state of vegetation, after taking the same desperate leap. That great part of this prodigious mass was absorbed in some gulf below, is plain also from the inclining ground at the bottom of the hill, which is free and unencumbered; but would have been buried in heaps of rubbish, had the fragment parted and fallen forward. About a hundred yards from the foot of this hanging coppice stood a cottage by the side of a lane; and two hundred yards lower, on the other side of the lane, was a farmhouse, in which lived a labourer and his family; and, just by, a stout new barn. The cottage was inhabited by an old woman and her son, and his wife. These people in the evening, which was very dark and tempestuous, observed that the brick floors of their kitchens began to heave and part; and that the walls seemed to open, and the roofs to crack; but they all agree that no tremor of the ground, indicating an earthquake, was ever felt; only that the wind continued to make a most tremendous roaring in the woods and hangers. The miserable inhabitants, not daring to go to bed, remained in the utmost solicitude and confusion, expecting every moment to be buried under the ruins of their shattered edifices. When daylight came they were at leisure to contemplate the devastations of the night: they then found that a deep rift, or chasm, had opened under their houses, and torn them, as it were, in two; and that one end of the barn had suffered in a similar manner: that a pond near the cottage had undergone a strange reverse, becoming deep at the shallow end and so *vice versâ*; that many large oaks were removed out of their perpendicular, some thrown down, and some fallen into the heads of neighbouring trees; and that a gate was thrust forward, with its hedge, full six feet, so as to require a new track to be made to it. From the foot of the cliff the general course of the ground, which is pasture, inclines in a moderate descent for half a mile, and is interspersed with small hillocks, which were rifted, in every direction, as well towards the great woody hanger, as from it. In the first pasture the deep clefts began; and running across the lane, and under the building, made such vast shelves that the road was impassable for some time; and so over to an arable field on the other side, which was strangely torn and disordered. The second pasture-field, being more soft and spongy, was protruded forward without many fissures in the turf, which was raised in long ridges resembling graves, lying at right angles to the motion. At the bottom of this inclosure the soil and turf rose many feet against the bodies of some oaks that obstructed their farther course, and terminated this awful commotion.

The perpendicular height of the precipice in general is twenty-three yards; the length of the lapse or slip as seen from the fields below, one hundred and eighty-one; and a partial fall, concealed in the coppice, extends seventy yards more; so that the total length of this fragment that fell was two hundred and fifty-one yards. About fifty acres of land suffered from this violent convulsion; two houses were entirely destroyed; one end of a new barn was left in ruins, the walls being cracked through the very stones that composed them; a hanging coppice was changed into a naked rock; and some grass grounds and an arable field so broken and rifted by the chasms as to be rendered for a time neither fit for the plough nor safe for pasturage, till considerable labour and expense had been bestowed in levelling the surface and filling up gaping fissures.

LETTER XLV.

SELBORNE

" ———— resonant arbusta ————."[1]—VIRG. *Ecl.* ii.

There is a steep abrupt pasture field and interspersed with furze close to the back of this village, well known by the name of Short Lithe, consisting of a rocky dry soil, and inclining to the afternoon sun. This spot abounds with the *Gryllus campestris*, or field-cricket; which, though frequent in these parts, is by no means a common insect in many other counties.

As their cheerful summer cry cannot but draw the attention of a naturalist, I have often gone down to examine the economy of these *grylli*, and study their mode of life; but they are so shy and cautious that it is no easy matter to get a sight of them; for feeling a person's footsteps as he advances, they stop short in the midst of their song, and retire backward nimbly into their burrows, where they lurk till all suspicion of danger is over.

At first we attempted to dig them out with a spade, but without any great success; for either we could not get to the bottom of the hole, which often terminated under a great stone; or else in breaking up the ground we inadvertently squeezed the poor insect to death. Out of one so bruised we took a multitude of eggs, which were long and narrow, of a yellow colour, and covered with a very tough skin. By this accident we learned to distinguish the male from the female; the former of which is shining black, with a golden stripe across his shoulders; the latter is more dusky, more capacious about the abdomen, and carries a long sword-shaped weapon at her tail, which probably is the instrument with which she deposits her eggs in crannies and safe receptacles.

Where violent methods will not avail, more gentle means will often succeed; and so it proved in the present case; for, though a spade be too boisterous and rough an implement, a

[1] "The groves resound."

pliant stalk of grass, gently insinuated into the caverns, will probe their windings to the bottom, and quickly bring out the inhabitant; and thus the humane inquirer may gratify his curiosity without injuring the object of it. It is remarkable, that though these insects are furnished with long legs behind, and brawny thighs for leaping, like grasshoppers; yet when driven from their holes they show no activity, but crawl along in a shiftless manner, so as easily to be taken; and again, though provided with a curious apparatus of wings, yet they never exert them when there seems to be the greatest occasion. The males only make that shrilling noise, perhaps, out of rivalry and emulation, as is the case with many animals which exert some sprightly note during their breeding-time. It is raised by a brisk friction of one wing against the other. They are solitary beings, living singly male and female, each as it may happen; but there must be a time when the sexes have some intercourse, and then the wings may be useful perhaps during the hours of night. When the males meet they will fight fiercely, as I found by some which I put into the crevices of a dry stone wall, where I should have been glad to have made them settle. For though they seemed distressed by being taken out of their knowledge; yet the first that got possession of the chinks would seize on any other that were intruded upon them with a vast row of serrated fangs. With their strong jaws, toothed like the shears of a lobster's claws, they perforate and round their curious regular cells, having no fore-claws to dig, like the mole-cricket. When taken in hand I could not but wonder that they never offered to defend themselves, though armed with such formidable weapons. Of such herbs as grow before the mouths of their burrows they eat indiscriminately, and on a little platform which they make just by, they drop their dung; and never, in the daytime, seem to stir more than two or three inches from home. Sitting in the entrance of their caverns they chirp all night as well as day from the middle of the month of May to the middle of July; and in hot weather, when they are most vigorous, they make the hills echo, and in the stiller hours of darkness may be heard to a considerable distance. In the beginning of the season their notes are more faint and inward; but become louder as the summer advances, and so die away again by degrees.

Sounds do not always give us pleasure according to their sweetness and melody; nor do harsh sounds always displease.

We are more apt to be captivated or disgusted with the associations which they promote than with the notes themselves. Thus the shrilling of the field-cricket, though sharp and stridulous, yet marvellously delights some hearers, filling their minds with a train of summer ideas of everything that is rural, verdurous, and joyous.

About the 10th of March the crickets appear at the mouths of their cells, which they then open and bore, and shape very elegantly. All that ever I have seen at that season were in their pupa state, and had only the rudiments of wings, lying under a skin or coat, which must be cast before the insect can arrive at its perfect state;[1] from whence I should suppose that the old ones of last year do not always survive the winter. In August their holes begin to be obliterated, and the insects are seen no more till spring.

Not many summers ago I endeavoured to transplant a colony to the terrace in my garden, by boring deep holes in the sloping turf. The new inhabitants stayed some time, and fed and sung; but wandered away by degrees, and were heard at a farther distance every morning, so that it appears that on this emergency they made use of their wings in attempting to return to the spot from which they were taken.

One of these crickets when confined in a paper cage and set in the sun, and supplied with plants moistened with water, will feed and thrive, and become so merry and loud as to be irksome in the same room where a person is sitting; if the plants are not wetted it will die.

LETTER XLVI.

SELBORNE.

" Far from all resort of mirth
Save the cricket on the hearth."
—MILTON'S *Il Penseroso*.

While many other insects must be sought after in fields, and woods, and waters, the *Gryllus domesticus*, or house-cricket, resides altogether within our dwellings, intruding itself upon our notice whether we will or no. This species delights in new-built houses, being, like the spider, pleased with the moisture of the walls; and besides, the softness of the mortar

------

[1] We have observed that they cast their skins in April, which are then seen lying at the mouths of their holes.—W.

enables them to burrow and mine between the joints of the bricks or stones, and to open communications from one room to another. They are particularly fond of kitchens and baker's ovens, on account of their perpetual warmth.

Tender insects that live abroad either enjoy only the short period of one summer, or else dose away the cold uncomfortable months in profound slumbers; but these, residing as it were in a torrid zone, are always alert and merry: a good Christmas fire is to them like the heats of the dog-days. Though they are frequently heard by day, yet is their natural time of motion only in the night. As soon as it grows dusk, the chirping increases, and they come running forth, and are from the size of a flea to that of their full stature. As one should suppose, from the burning atmosphere which they inhabit, they are a thrifty race, and show a great propensity for liquids, being found frequently drowned in pans of water, milk, broth, or the like. Whatever is moist they affect; and therefore often gnaw holes in wet woollen stockings and aprons that are hung to the fire: they are the housewife's barometer, foretelling her when it will rain, and are prognostic sometimes, she thinks, of ill or good luck, of the death of a near relation, or the approach of an absent lover. By being the constant companions of her solitary hours they naturally become the objects of her superstition. These crickets are not only very thrifty, but very voracious; for they will eat the scummings of pots, and yeast, salt, and crumbs of bread, and any kitchen offal or sweepings. In the summer we have observed them to fly when it became dusk out of the windows, and over the neighbouring roofs. This feat of activity accounts for the sudden manner in which they often leave their haunts, as it does for the method by which they come to houses where they were not known before. It is remarkable that many sorts of insects seem never to use their wings but when they have a mind to shift their quarters and settle new colonies. When in the air they move *volatu undoso*, in waves or curves, like woodpeckers, opening and shutting their wings at every stroke, and so are always rising or sinking.

When they increase to a great degree, as they did once in the house where I am now writing, they become noisome pests, flying into the candles, and dashing into people's faces; but may be blasted and destroyed by gunpowder discharged into their crevices and crannies. In families at such times they are like Pharaoh's plague of frogs,—"in their bedchambers, and upon their beds, and in their ovens, and in their kneading troughs ".[1] Their shrilling noise is occasioned by a brisk attrition of their wings. Cats catch hearth-crickets, and, playing with them as they do with mice, devour them. Crickets may be destroyed, like wasps, by phials half filled with beer, or any liquid, and set in their haunts; for being always eager to drink, they will crowd in till the bottles are full.[2]

LETTER XLVII.

How diversified are the modes of life not only of incongruous but even of congenerous animals; and yet their specific distinctions are not more various than their propensities. Thus, while the field-cricket delights in sunny dry banks, and the house-cricket rejoices amidst the glowing heat of the kitchen hearth or oven, the *Gryllus gryllotalpa* (the mole-cricket) haunts moist meadows, and frequents the sides of ponds and banks of streams, performing all its functions in a swampy wet soil. With a pair of fore-feet, curiously adapted to the purpose, it burrows and works under ground like the mole, raising a ridge as it proceeds, but seldom throwing up hillocks.

As mole-crickets often infest gardens by the sides of canals, they are unwelcome guests to the gardener, raising up ridges in their subterranean progress, and rendering the walks unsightly. If they take to the kitchen quarters they occasion great damage among the plants and roots, by destroying whole beds of cabbages, young legumes, and flowers. When dug out they seem very slow and helpless, and make no use of their wings by day; but at night they come abroad, and make long excursions, as I have been convinced by finding stragglers, in a morning, in improbable places. In fine weather, about the middle of April, and just at the close of day, they begin to solace themselves with a low, dull, jarring note, continued for a long time without interruption, and not unlike the chattering of the fern-owl, or goat-sucker, but more inward.

About the beginning of May they lay their eggs, as I was

[1] Exod. viii. 3.

[2] Further notes respecting the house-cricket will be found in *Observations on Nature* at the end of the book.

once an eye-witness; for a gardener at a house where I was on a visit, happening to be mowing, on the sixth of that month, by the side of a canal, his scythe struck too deep, pared off a large piece of turf, and laid open to view a curious scene of domestic economy:—

> "———Ingentem lato dedit ore fenestram:
> Apparet domus intus, et atria longa patescunt:
> Apparent——penetralia." [1]—Virg. Æn. ii.

There were many caverns and winding passages leading to a kind of chamber, neatly smoothed and rounded, and about the size of a moderate snuff-box. Within this secret nursery were deposited near a hundred eggs of a dirty yellow colour, and enveloped in a tough skin, but too lately excluded to contain any rudiments of young, being full of a viscous substance. The eggs lay but shallow, and within the influence of the sun, just under a little heap of fresh-moved mould, like that which is raised by ants.

When mole-crickets fly they move *cursu undoso*, rising and falling in curves, like the other species mentioned before. In different parts of this kingdom people call them fen-crickets, churr-worms, and eve-churrs, all very apposite names.

Anatomists, who have examined the intestines of these insects, astonish me with their accounts; for they say that, from the structure, position, and number of their stomachs, or maws, there seems to be good reason to suppose that this and the two former species ruminate or chew the cud like many quadrupeds!

LETTER XLVIII.

SELBORNE, *May 7th*, 1779.

It is now more than forty years that I have paid some attention to the ornithology of this district, without being able to exhaust the subject: new occurrences still arise as long as any inquiries are kept alive.

In the last week of last month five of those most rare birds, too uncommon to have obtained an English name, but known to naturalists by the terms of *Himantopus*, or *Loripes*, and

---

[1] "A yawning breach of monstrous size he made:
The inmost house is now to light displayed:
The admitted light with sudden lustre falls
On the long galleries and the splendid halls."—DRYDEN.

Charadrius himantopus, were shot upon the verge of Frinsham
Pond, a large lake belonging to the Bishop of Winchester, and
lying between Wolmer Forest and the town of Farnham,
in the county of Surrey. The pond keeper says there were
three brace in the flock: but, that after he had satisfied his
curiosity, he suffered the sixth to remain unmolested. One
of these specimens I procured, and found the length of the
legs to be so extraordinary, that, at first sight, one might
have supposed the shanks had been fastened on to impose on
the credulity of the beholder; they were legs in *caricatura*;
and had we seen such proportions on a Chinese or Japan
screen we should have made large allowances for the fancy of
the draughtsman. These birds are of the plover family, and
might with propriety be called the stilt plovers. Brisson,
under that idea, gives them the apposite name of *l'échasse.*
My specimen, when drawn and stuffed with pepper, weighed
only four ounces and a quarter, though the naked part of the
thigh measured three inches and a half, and the legs four
inches and a half. Hence we may safely assert that these
birds exhibit, weight for inches, incomparably the greatest
length of legs of any known bird. The flamingo, for instance,
is one of the most long-legged birds, and yet it bears no
manner of proportion to the *Himantopus;* for a cock flamingo
weighs, at an average, about four pounds avoirdupois; and his
legs and thighs measure usually about twenty inches. But
four pounds are fifteen times and a fraction more than four
ounces, and one quarter; and if four ounces and a quarter have
eight inches of legs, four pounds must have one hundred and
twenty inches and a fraction of legs; viz., somewhat more
than ten feet; such a monstrous proportion as the world never
saw! If you should try the experiment in still larger birds
the disparity would still increase. It must be matter of
great curiosity to see the stilt plover move; to observe how it
can wield such a length of lever with such feeble muscles as
the thighs seem to be furnished with. At best one should
expect it to be but a bad walker: but what adds to the
wonder is, that it has no back toe. Now without that steady
prop to support its steps it must be liable, in speculation,
to perpetual vacillations, and seldom able to preserve the
true centre of gravity.

The old name of *Himantopus* is taken from Pliny; and, by
an awkward metaphor, implies that the legs are as slender and
pliant as if cut out of a thong of leather. Neither Willughby

nor Ray, in all their curious researches, either at home or abroad, ever saw this bird. Mr. Pennant never met with it in all Great Britain, but observed it often in the cabinets of the curious at Paris. Hasselquist says that it migrates to Egypt in the autumn: and a most accurate observer of Nature has assured me that he has found it on the banks of the streams in Andalusia.

Our writers record it to have been found only twice in Great Britain. From all these relations it plainly appears that these long-legged plovers are birds of South Europe, and rarely visit our island; and when they do, are wanderers and stragglers, and impelled to make so distant and northern an excursion from motives or accidents for which we are not able to account. One thing may fairly be deduced, that these birds come over to us from the Continent, since nobody can suppose that a species not noticed once in an age, and of such a remarkable make, can constantly breed unobserved in this kingdom.

LETTER XLIX.

SELBORNE, *April 21st*, 1780.

The old Sussex tortoise, that I have mentioned to you so often, is become my property. I dug it out of its winter dormitory in March last, when it was enough awakened to express its resentments by hissing; and, packing it in a box with earth, carried it eighty miles in post-chaises. The rattle and hurry of the journey so perfectly roused it that, when I turned it out on a border, it walked twice down to the bottom of my garden; however, in the evening, the weather being cold, it buried itself in the loose mould, and continues still concealed.

As it will be under my eye, I shall now have an opportunity of enlarging my observations on its mode of life, and propensities; and perceive already that, towards the time of coming forth, it opens a breathing place in the ground near its head, requiring, I conclude, a freer respiration as it becomes more alive. This creature not only goes under the earth from the middle of November to the middle of April, but sleeps great part of the summer: for it goes to bed in the longest days at four in the afternoon, and often does not stir in the morning till late. Besides, it retires to rest for every shower; and does not move at all in wet days.

When one reflects on the state of this strange being, it is a matter of wonder to find that Providence should bestow such a profusion of days, such a seeming waste of longevity, on a reptile that appears to relish it so little as to squander more than two-thirds of its existence in a joyless stupor, and be lost to all sensation for months together in the profoundest of slumbers.

While I was writing this letter, a moist and warm afternoon, with the thermometer at 50°, brought forth troops of shell-snails; and, at the same juncture, the tortoise heaved up the mould and put out its head; and the next morning came forth, as it were, raised from the dead; and walked about till four in the afternoon. This was a curious coincidence! a very amusing occurrence! to see such a similarity of feelings between the two φερεοικοι!—house-bearers—for so the Greeks called both the shell-snail and the tortoise.

Summer birds are, this cold and backward spring, unusually late: I have seen but one swallow yet. This conformity with the weather convinces me more and more that they sleep in the winter.

LETTER L.

SELBORNE, *Sept. 3rd*, 1781.

I have now read your Miscellanies through with much care and satisfaction; and am to return you my best thanks for the honourable mention made in them of me as a naturalist, which I wish I may deserve.

In some former letters I expressed my suspicions that many of the house-martins do not depart in the winter far from this village. I therefore determined to make some search about the south-east end of the hill, where I imagined they might slumber out the uncomfortable months of winter. But supposing that the examination would be made to the best advantage in the spring, and observing that no martins had appeared by the 11th of April last, on that day I employed some men to explore the shrubs and cavities of the suspected spot. The persons took pains, but without any success; however, a remarkable incident occurred in the midst of our pursuit: while the labourers were at work a house-martin, the first that had been seen this year, came down the village in the sight of several people, and went at once into a nest, where it stayed a short time, and then flew over the houses; for some days after no martins were observed, not till the 16th of April, and then only a pair. Martins in general were remarkably late this year.

LETTER LI.

SELBORNE, *Sept. 9th*, 1781.

I have just met with a circumstance respecting swifts, which furnishes an exception to the whole tenor of my observations ever since I have bestowed any attention on that species of *Hirundines*. Our swifts, in general, withdrew this year about the first day of August, all save one pair, which in two or three days was reduced to a single bird. The perseverance of this individual made me suspect that the strongest of motives, that of an attachment to her young, could alone occasion so late a stay. I watched therefore till the 24th of August, and then discovered that, under the eaves of the church, she attended upon two young, which were fledged, and now put out their white chins from a crevice. These remained till the 27th, looking more alert every day, and seeming to long to be on the wing. After this day they were missing at once; nor could I ever observe them with their dam coursing round the church in the act of learning to fly, as the first broods evidently do. On the 31st I caused the eaves to be searched, but we found in the nest only two callow, dead, stinking swifts, on which a second nest had been formed. This double nest was full of the black shining cases of the *Hippoboscæ hirundinis*.

The following remarks on this unusual incident are obvious. The first is, that though it may be disagreeable to swifts to remain beyond the beginning of August, yet that they can subsist longer is undeniable. The second is, that this uncommon event, as it was owing to the loss of the first brood, so it corroborates my former remark, that swifts breed regularly but once; since, was the contrary the case, the occurrence above could neither be new nor rare.

P.S.—One swift was seen at Lyndon, in the county of Rutland, in 1782, so late as the 3rd of September.

LETTER LII.

As I have sometimes known you make inquiries about several kinds of insects, I shall here send you an account of one sort which I little expected to have found in this kingdom. I had often observed that one particular part of a vine growing on the walls of my house was covered in the autumn with a black dust-like appearance, on which the flies fed eagerly; and that the shoots and leaves thus affected did not thrive; nor did the fruit ripen. To this substance I applied my glasses; but could not discover that it had anything to do with animal life, as I at first expected: but, upon a closer examination behind the larger boughs, we were surprised to find that they were coated over with husky shells, from whose sides proceeded a cotton-like substance, surrounding a multitude of eggs. This curious and uncommon production put me upon recollecting what I have heard and read concerning the *Coccus vitis viniferæ* of Linnæus, which, in the south of Europe, infests many vines, and is a horrid and loathsome pest. As soon as I had turned to the accounts given of this insect, I saw at once that it swarmed on my vine; and did not appear to have been at all checked by the preceding winter, which had been uncommonly severe.

Not being then at all aware that it had anything to do with England, I was much inclined to think that it came from Gibraltar among the many boxes and packages of plants and birds which I had formerly received from thence; and especially as the vine infested grew immediately under my study-window, where I usually kept my specimen. True it is that I had received nothing from thence for some years: but as insects, we know, are conveyed from one country to another in a very unexpected manner, and have a wonderful power of maintaining their existence till they fall into a *nidus*, or nest, proper for their support and increase, I cannot but suspect still that these *Cocci* came to me originally from Andalusia. Yet, all the while, candour obliges me to confess that Mr. Lightfoot has written me word that he once, and but once, saw these insects on a vine at Weymouth in Dorsetshire; which, it is here to be observed, is a seaport town to which the *Coccus* might be conveyed by shipping.

As many of my readers may possibly never have heard of

this strange and unusual insect, I shall here transcribe a passage from a natural history of Gibraltar, written by the Reverend John White, late vicar of Blackburn in Lancashire, but not yet published:—

"In the year 1770 a vine, which grew on the east side of my house, and which had produced the finest crops of grapes for years past, was suddenly overspread on all the woody branches with large lumps of a white fibrous substance resembling spiders' webs, or rather raw cotton. It was of a very clammy quality, sticking fast to everything that touched it, and capable of being spun into long threads. At first I suspected it to be the product of spiders, but could find none. Nothing was to be seen connected with it but many brown oval husky shells, which by no means looked like insects, but rather resembled bits of the dry bark of the vine. The tree had a plentiful crop of grapes set, when this pest appeared upon it; but the fruit was manifestly injured by this foul encumbrance. It remained all the summer, still increasing, and loaded the woody and bearing branches to a vast degree. I often pulled off great quantities by handfuls; but it was so slimy and tenacious that it could by no means be cleared. The grapes never filled to their natural perfection, but turned watery and vapid. Upon perusing the works afterwards of M. de Réaumur, I found this matter perfectly described and accounted for. Those husky shells, which I had observed, were no other than the female *Coccus*, from whose side this cotton-like substance exudes, and serves as a covering and security for their eggs."

To this account I think proper to add, that, though the female *Cocci* are stationary, and seldom remove from the place to which they stick, yet the male is a winged insect; and that the black dust which I saw was undoubtedly the excrement of the females, which is eaten by ants as well as flies. Though the utmost severity of our winter did not destroy these insects, yet the attention of the gardener in a summer or two has entirely relieved my vine from this filthy annoyance.

As we have remarked above that insects are often conveyed from one country to another in a very unaccountable manner, I shall here mention an emigration of small *Aphides* which was observed in the village of Selborne no longer ago than August 1st, 1785.

About three o'clock in the afternoon of that day, which was very hot, the people of this village were surprised by a shower of *Aphides*, or smother-flies, which fell in these parts. Those

that were walking in the street at that juncture found themselves covered with these insects, which settled also on the
hedges and gardens, blackening all the vegetables where they
alighted. My annuals were discoloured with them, and the
stalks of a bed of onions were quite coated over for six days
after. These armies were then, no doubt, in a state of emigration, and shifting their quarters; and might have come, as
far as we know, from the great hop plantations of Kent or
Sussex, the wind being all that day in the easterly quarter.
They were observed at the same time in great clouds about
Farnham, and all along the vale from Farnham to Alton.[1]

LETTER LIII.

When I happen to visit a family where gold and silver
fishes are kept in a glass bowl, I am always pleased with the
occurrence, because it offers me an opportunity of observing
the actions and propensities of those beings with whom we
can be little acquainted in their natural state. Not long since
I spent a fortnight at the house of a friend where there was
such a vivary, to which I paid no small attention, taking
every occasion to remark what passed within its narrow
limits. It was here that I first observed the manner in which
fishes die. As soon as the creature sickens, the head sinks
lower and lower, and it stands as it were on its head; till,
getting weaker, and losing all poise, the tail turns over, and
at last it floats on the surface of the water with its belly upper-
most. The reason why fishes, when dead, swim in that
manner is very obvious; because, when the body is no longer
balanced by the fins of the belly, the broad muscular back
preponderates by its own gravity, and turns the belly upper-
most, as lighter from its being a cavity, and because it contains
the swimming-bladders, which contribute to render it buoyant.
Some that delight in gold and silver fishes have adopted a
notion that they need no aliment. True it is that they will
subsist for a long time without any apparent food but what
they can collect from pure water frequently changed; yet
they must draw some support from animalcula, and other
nourishment supplied by the water; because, though they
seem to eat nothing, yet the consequences of eating often drop

[1] For various methods by which insects shift their quarters, see Derham's *Physico-
Theology.*—W.

from them. That they are best pleased with such jejune diet may easily be confuted, since if you toss them crumbs they will seize them with great readiness, not to say greediness; however, bread should be given sparingly, lest, turning sour, it corrupt the water. They will also feed on the water-plant called *Lemna* (ducks' meat), and also on small fry.

When they want to move a little, they gently protrude themselves with their *pinnæ pectorales*; but it is with their strong muscular tails only that they and all fishes shoot along with such inconceivable rapidity. It has been said that the eyes of fishes are immovable; but these apparently turn them forward or backward in their sockets as occasions require. They take little notice of a lighted candle, though applied close to their heads, but flounce and seem much frightened by a sudden stroke of the hand against the support whereon the bowl is hung; especially when they have been motionless, and are perhaps asleep. As fishes have no eyelids, it is not easy to discern when they are sleeping or not, because their eyes are always open.

Nothing can be more amusing than a glass bowl containing such fishes; the double refractions of the glass and water represent them, when moving, in a shifting and changeable variety of dimensions, shades, and colours; while the two mediums, assisted by the concavo-convex shape of the vessel, magnify and distort them vastly; not to mention that the introduction of another element and its inhabitants into our parlours engages the fancy in a very agreeable manner.

Gold and silver fishes, though originally natives of China and Japan, yet are become so well reconciled to our climate as to thrive and multiply very fast in our ponds and stews. Linnæus ranks this species of fish under the genus of *Cyprinus*, or carp, and calls it *Cyprinus auratus*.

Some people exhibit this sort of fish in a very fanciful way; for they cause a glass bowl to be blown with a large hollow space within, that does not communicate with it. In this cavity they put a bird occasionally; so that you may see a goldfinch or a linnet hopping as it were in the midst of the water, and the fishes swimming in a circle round it. The simple exhibition of the fishes is agreeable and pleasant; but in so complicated a way becomes whimsical and unnatural, and liable to the objection due to him, "who strangely likes to vary every single thing":

"Qui variare cupit rem prodigialitér unam."—HOR. *Ars Poet.*

LETTER LIV.

October 10th, 1781.

I think I have observed before that much of the most considerable part of the house-martins withdraw from hence about the first week in October; but that some, the latter broods I am now convinced, linger on till towards the middle of that month; and that at times, once perhaps in two or three years, a flight, for one day only, has shown itself in the first week in November.

Having taken notice, in October, 1780, that the last flight was numerous, amounting perhaps to one hundred and fifty; and that the season was soft and still; I was resolved to pay uncommon attention to these late birds, to find, if possible, where they roosted, and to determine the precise time of their retreat. The mode of life of these latter *Hirundines* is very favourable to such a design; for they spend the whole day in the sheltered district, between me and the Hanger, sailing about in a placid, easy manner, and feasting on those insects which love to haunt a spot so secure from ruffling winds. As my principal object was to discover the place of their roosting, I took care to wait on them before they retired to rest, and was much pleased to find that for several evenings together, just at a quarter-past five in the afternoon, they all scudded away in great haste towards the south-east, and darted down among the low shrubs above the cottages at the end of the hill. This spot in many respects seemed to be well calculated for their winter residence; for in many parts it is as steep as the roof of any house, and therefore secure from the annoyances of water; and it is moreover clothed with beechen shrubs, which, being stunted and bitten by sheep, make the thickest covert imaginable; and are so entangled as to be impervious to the smallest spaniel; besides, it is the nature of underwood beech never to cast its leaf all the winter; so that, with the leaves on the ground and those on the twigs, no shelter can be more complete. I watched them on the 13th and 14th of October, and found their evening retreat was exact and uniform; but after this they made no regular appearance. Now and then a straggler was seen; and on the 22nd of October, I observed two in the morning over the village, and with them my remarks for the season ended.

From all these circumstances put together, it is more than probable that this lingering flight, at so late a season of the year, never departed from the island. Had they indulged me that autumn with a November visit, as I much desired, I presume that, with proper assistants, I should have settled the matter past all doubt; but though the 3rd of November was a sweet day, and in appearance exactly suited to my wishes, yet not a martin was to be seen; and so I was forced, reluctantly, to give up the pursuit.

I have only to add that were the bushes, which cover some acres, and are not my own property, to be grubbed and carefully examined, probably those late broods, and perhaps the whole aggregate body of the house-martins of this district, might be found there, in different secret dormitories; and that, so far from withdrawing into warmer climes, it would appear that they never depart three hundred yards from the village.

LETTER LV.

They who write on natural history cannot too frequently advert to instinct, that wonderful limited faculty, which in some instances raises the brute creation, as it were, above reason, and in others leaves them so far below it. Philosophers have defined instinct to be that secret influence by which every species is compelled naturally to pursue, at all times, the same way or track, without any teaching or example; whereas reason, without instruction, would often vary and do that by many methods which instinct effects by one alone. Now this maxim must be taken in a qualified sense; for there are instances in which instinct does vary and conform to the circumstances of place and convenience.

It has been remarked that every species of bird has a mode of nidification peculiar to itself, so that a schoolboy would at once pronounce on the sort of nest before him. This is the case among fields and woods, and wilds; but, in the villages round London, where mosses and gossamer, and cotton from vegetables, are hardly to be found, the nest of the chaffinch has not that elegant finished appearance, nor is it so beautifully studded with lichens, as in a more rural district; and the wren is obliged to contruct its house with straws and dry grasses, which do not give it that rotundity and compactness so remarkable in the edifices of that little architect. Again, the regular nest of the house-martin is hemispheric; but where a rafter, or a joist, or a cornice, may happen to stand in the way, the nest is so contrived as to conform to the obstruction, and becomes flat, or compressed.

In the following instances instinct is perfectly uniform and consistent. There are three creatures, the squirrel, the field-mouse, and the bird called the nut-hatch (*Sitta Europæa*), which live much on hazel-nuts; and yet they open them each in a different way. The first, after rasping off the small end, splits the shell in two with his long fore-teeth, as a man does with his knife; the second nibbles a hole with his teeth, so regular as if drilled with a wimble, and yet so small that one could wonder how the kernel can be extracted through it; while the last picks an irregular ragged hole with its bill: but as this artist has no paws to hold the nut firm while he pierces it, like an adroit workman, he fixes it, as it were, in a vice, in some cleft of a tree, or in some crevice; when standing over it, he perforates the stubborn shell. We have often placed nuts in the chink of a gate-post where nut-hatches have been known to haunt, and have always found that those birds have readily penetrated them. While at work they make a rapping noise that may be heard at a considerable distance.

You that understand both the theory and practical part of music may best inform us why harmony or melody should so strangely assist some men, as it were by recollection, for days after the concert is over. What I mean the following passage will most readily explain:—

"Præhabebat porrò vocibus humanis, instrumentisque harmonicis musicam illam avium: non quod aliâ quoque non delectaretur: sed quod ex musicâ humanâ relinqueretur in animo continens quædam, attentionemque et somnum conturbans agitatio; dum ascensus, exscensus, tenores, ac mutationes illæ sonorum, et consonantiarum euntque, redeuntque per phantasiam:—cum nihil tale relinqui possit ex modulationibus avium, quæ, quod non sunt perinde a nobis imitabiles, non possunt perinde internam facultatem commovere."[1]—*Gassendus in Vitâ Peireskii.*

[1] "He preferred the harmony of birds to either the human voice or instrumental music; not that he did not take pleasure in any other; but because after human music something is left in the mind which causes agitation and disturbs the attention and sleep, whilst the varied imitations of sound and harmony come and go in the imagination, whereas nothing of the sort can be produced by the modulations of birds, since, as they are not equally imitable by us, they cannot equally excite in us the internal faculty."

This curious quotation strikes me much by so well representing my own case, and by describing what I have so often felt, but never could so well express. When I hear fine music I am haunted with passages therefrom night and day; and especially at first waking, which, by their importunity, give me more uneasiness than pleasure; elegant lessons still tease my imagination, and recur irresistibly to my recollection at seasons, and even when I am desirous of thinking of more serious matters.

LETTER LVI.

A rare, and I think a new, little bird frequents my garden, which I have great reason to think is the pettichaps: it is common in some parts of the kingdom; and I have received formerly several dead specimens from Gibraltar. This bird much resembles the whitethroat, but has a more white or rather silvery breast and belly; is restless and active, like the willow-wrens, and hops from bough to bough, examining every part for food; it also runs up the stems of the crown-imperials, and, putting its head into the bells of those flowers, sips the liquor which stands in the nectarium of each petal. Sometimes it feeds on the ground like the hedge-sparrow, by hopping about on the grass-plots and mown walks.[1]

One of my neighbours, an intelligent and observing man, informs me that, in the beginning of May, and about ten minutes before eight o'clock in the evening, he discovered a great cluster of house-swallows, thirty, at least, he supposes, perching on a willow that hung over the verge of James Knight's upper-pond. His attention was first drawn by the twittering of these birds, which sat motionless in a row on the bough, with their heads all one way, and, by their weight, pressing down the twig so that it nearly touched the water. In this situation he watched them till he could see no longer. Repeated accounts of this sort, spring and fall, induce us greatly to suspect that house-swallows have some strong attachment to water, independent of the matter of food; and, though they may not retire into that element, yet they may conceal themselves in the banks of pools and rivers during the uncomfortable months of winter.

[1] This description agrees more with the lesser whitethroat.

One of the keepers of Wolmer Forest sent me a peregrine falcon, which he shot on the verge of that district as it was devouring a wood-pigeon. The *Falco peregrinus*, or haggard-falcon, is a noble species of hawk seldom seen in the southern counties. In winter 1767, one was killed in the neighbouring parish of Farringdon, and sent by me to Mr. Pennant into North Wales.[1] Since that time I have met with none till now. The specimen mentioned above was in fine preservation, and not injured by the shot: it measured forty-two inches from wing to wing, and twenty-one from beak to tail, and weighed two pounds and a half standing weight. This species is very robust, and wonderfully formed for rapine; its breast was plump and muscular; its thighs long, thick, and brawny; and its legs remarkably short and well set: the feet were armed with most formidable, sharp, long talons: the eyelids and cere of the bill were yellow; but the irides of the eyes dusky; the beak was thick and hooked, and of a dark colour, and had a jagged process near the end of the upper mandible on each side: its tail, or train, was short in proportion to the bulk of its body; yet the wings, when closed, did not extend to the end of the train. From its large and fair proportions it might be supposed to have been a female; but I was not permitted to cut open the specimen. For one of the birds of prey, which are usually lean, this was in high case: in its craw were many barley-corns, which probably came from the crop of the wood-pigeon, on which it was feeding when shot; for voracious birds do not eat grain, but, when devouring their quarry, with un-distinguishing vehemence swallow bones and feathers, and all matters, indiscriminately. This falcon was probably driven from the mountains of North Wales or Scotland, where they are known to breed, by rigorous weather and deep snows that had lately fallen.

LETTER LVII.

My near neighbour, a young gentleman in the service of the East India Company, has brought home a dog and a bitch of the Chinese breed from Canton, such as are fattened in that country for the purpose of being eaten: they are about the size of a moderate spaniel; of a pale yellow colour, with coarse

---

[1] See my tenth, eleventh, and twelfth letters to that gentleman.

bristling hairs on their backs; sharp upright ears, and peaked heads, which give them a very fox-like appearance. Their hind legs are unusually straight, without any bend at the hock or ham, to such a degree as to give them an awkward gait when they trot. When they are in motion their tails are curved high over their backs like those of some hounds, and have a bare place each on the outside from the tip midway, that does not seem to be matter of accident, but somewhat singular. Their eyes are jet-black, small, and piercing; the insides of their lips and mouths of the same colour, and their tongues blue. The bitch has a dew-claw on each hind leg; the dog has none. When taken out into a field the bitch showed some disposition for hunting, and dwelt on the scent of a covey of patridges till she sprung them, giving her tongue all the time. The dogs in South America are dumb; but these bark much in a short thick manner like foxes, and have a surly, savage demeanour like their ancestors, which are not domesticated, but bred up in sties, where they are fed for the table with rice-meal and other farinaceous food. These dogs, having been taken on board as soon as weaned, could not learn much from their dam; yet they did not relish flesh when they came to England. In the islands of the Pacific Ocean the dogs are bred upon vegetables, and would not eat flesh when offered them by our circumnavigators.

We believe that all dogs, in a state of nature, have sharp, upright, fox-like ears; and that hanging ears, which are esteemed so graceful, are the effect of choice breeding and cultivation. Thus in the *Travels of Ysbrandt Ides from Muscovy to China*, the dogs which draw the Tartars on snow-sledges, near the river Oby, are engraved with prick-ears, like those from Canton. The Kamschatdales also train the same sort of sharp-eared, peak-nosed dogs to draw their sledges; as may be seen in an elegant print engraved for Captain Cook's last voyage round the world.

Now we are upon the subject of dogs, it may not be impertinent to add that spaniels, as all sportsmen know, though they hunt partridges and pheasants as it were by instinct, and with much delight and alacrity, yet will hardly touch their bones when offered as food; nor will a mongrel dog of my own, though he is remarkable for finding that sort of game. But, when we came to offer the bones of partridges to the two Chinese dogs, they devoured them with much greediness, and licked the platter clean.

No sporting dogs will flush woodcocks till inured to the scent and trained to the sport, which they then pursue with vehemence and transport; but then they will not touch their bones, but turn from them with abhorrence, even when they are hungry.

Now, that dogs should not be fond of the bones of such birds as they are not disposed to hunt is no wonder; but why they reject and do not care to eat their natural game is not so easily accounted for, since the end of hunting seems to be, that the chase pursued should be eaten. Dogs again will not devour the more rancid water-fowls, nor indeed the bones of any wild-fowls; nor will they touch the fœtid bodies of birds that feed on offal and garbage; and indeed there may be somewhat of providential instinct in this circumstance of dislike; for vultures,[1] and kites, and ravens, and crows, &c., were intended to be messmates with dogs over their carrion; and seem to be appointed by nature as fellow-scavengers to remove all cadaverous nuisances from the face of the earth.

LETTER LVIII.

The fossil wood buried in the bogs of Wolmer Forest is not yet all exhausted; for the peat-cutters now and then stumble upon a log. I have just seen a piece which was sent by a labourer of Oakhanger to a carpenter of this village; this was the butt-end of a small oak, about five feet long, and about five inches in diameter. It had apparently been severed from the ground by an axe, was very ponderous, and as black as ebony. Upon asking the carpenter for what purpose he had procured it, he told me that it was to be sent to his brother, a joiner at Farnham, who was to make use of it in cabinet-work, by inlaying it along with whiter woods.

Those that are much abroad on evenings after it is dark, in spring, and summer, frequently hear a nocturnal bird passing by on the wing, and repeating often a short quick note. This bird I have remarked myself, but never could make out till lately. I am assured now that it is the stone-curlew (*Charadrius œdicnemus*). Some of them pass over or near my house

---

[1] "Hasselquist, in his *Travels to the Levant*, observes that the dogs and vultures at Grand Cairo maintain such a friendly intercourse as to bring up their young together in the same place."

almost every evening after it is dark, from the uplands of the hill and North Fields, away down towards Dorton, where, among the streams and meadows, they find a greater plenty of food. Birds that fly by night are obliged to be noisy; their notes often repeated become signals or watch-words to keep them together, that they may not stray or lose each the other in the dark.

The evening proceedings and manœuvres of the rooks are curious and amusing in the autumn. Just before dusk they return in long strings from the foraging of the day, and rendezvous by thousands over Selborne Down, where they wheel round in the air, and sport and dive in a playful manner, all the while exerting their voices, and making a loud cawing, which, being blended and softened by the distance that we at the village are below them, becomes a confused noise or chiding; or rather a pleasing murmur, very engaging to the imagination, and not unlike the cry of a pack of hounds in hollow, echoing woods, or the rush of the wind in tall trees, or the tumbling of the tide upon a pebbly shore. When this ceremony is over, with the last gleam of day, they retire for the night to the deep beechen woods of Tisted and Ropley. We remember a little girl who, as she was going to bed, used to remark on such an occurrence, in the true spirit of physico-theology, that the rooks were saying their prayers; and yet this child was much too young to be aware that the scriptures have said of the Deity—that "He feedeth the ravens who call upon Him."

LETTER LIX

In reading Dr. Huxham's *Observationes de Aëre*, &c., written at Plymouth, I find by those curious and accurate remarks, which contain an account of the weather from the year 1727 to the year 1748, inclusive, that though there is frequent rain in that district of Devonshire, yet the quantity falling is not great; and that some years it has been very small: for in 1731 the rain measured only 17·266 in.; and in 1741, 20·354 in.; and again, in 1743, only 20·908 in. Places near the sea have frequent scuds, that keep the atmosphere moist, yet do not reach far up into the country; making thus the maritime situations appear wet, when the rain is not considerable. In the wettest years at Plymouth the doctor measured only once 36; and again once, viz., 1734, 37·114 in.—a quantity of rain that has twice been exceeded at Selborne in the short period of my observations. Dr. Huxham remarks that frequent small rains keep the air moist, while heavy ones render it more dry, by beating down the vapours. He is also of opinion that the dingy, smoky appearance in the sky, in very dry seasons, arises from the want of moisture sufficient to let the light through, and render the atmosphere transparent; because he had observed several bodies more diaphanous when wet than dry; and did never recollect that the air had that look in rainy seasons.

My friend, who lives just beyond the top of the down, brought his three swivel guns to try them in my outlet, with their muzzles towards the Hanger, supposing that the report would have had a great effect; but the experiment did not answer his expectation. He then removed them to the alcove on the Hanger, when the sound, rushing along the Lythe and Comb Wood, was very grand; but it was at the hermitage that the echoes and repercussions delighted the hearers; not only filling the Lythe with the roar, as if all the beeches were tearing up by the roots; but, turning to the left, they pervaded the vale above Comb Wood ponds; and after a pause seemed to take up the crash again, and to extend round Hartley Hangers, and to die away at last among the coppices and coverts of Wardleham. It has been remarked before that this district is an Anathoth, a place of responses or echoes, and therefore proper for such experiments: we may farther add that the pauses in echoes, when they cease and yet are taken up again, like the pauses in music, surprise the hearers, and have a fine effect on the imagination.

The gentleman above-mentioned has just fixed a barometer in his parlour at Newton Valence. The tube was first filled here (at Selborne) twice with care, when the mercury agreed and stood exactly with my own; but, being filled twice again at Newton, the mercury stood, on account of the great elevation of that house, three-tenths of an inch lower than the barometers at this village, and so continues to do, be the weight of the atmosphere what it may. The plate of the barometer at Newton is figured as low as 27°; because in stormy weather the mercury there will sometimes descend below 28°. We have supposed Newton House to stand two hundred feet higher than this house: but if the rule holds good, which says that mercury in a barometer sinks one-tenth of an inch for every hundred feet elevation, then the Newton barometer, by standing three-tenths lower than that of Selborne, proves that Newton House must be three hundred feet higher than that in which I am writing, instead of two hundred.

It may not be impertinent to add that the barometers at Selborne stand three-tenths of an inch lower than the barometers at South Lambeth: whence we may conclude that the former place is about three hundred feet higher than the latter; and with good reason, because the streams that rise with us run into the Thames at Weybridge, and so to London. Of course therefore there must be lower ground all the way from Selborne to South Lambeth; the distance between which, all the windings and indentings of the streams considered, cannot be less than a hundred miles.

LETTER LX.

Since the weather of a district is undoubtedly part of its natural history, I shall make no further apology for the four following letters, which will contain many particulars concerning some of the great frosts, and a few respecting some very hot summers, that have distinguished themselves from the rest during the course of my observations.

As the frost in January 1768 was, for the small time it lasted, the most severe that we had then known for many years, and was remarkably injurious to evergreens, some account of its rigour, and reason of its ravages, may be useful, and not unacceptable to persons that delight in planting and ornamenting; and may particularly become a work that professes never to lose sight of utility.

For the last two or three days of the former year there were considerable falls of snow, which lay deep and uniform on the ground without any drifting, wrapping up the more humble vegetation in perfect security. From the first day to the fifth of the new year more snow succeeded; but from that day the air became entirely clear; and the heat of the sun about noon had a considerable influence in sheltered situations.

It was in such an aspect that the snow on the author's evergreens was melted every day, and frozen intensely every night;

so that the laurustines, bays, laurels, and arbutuses looked, in three or four days, as if they had been burnt in the fire; while a neighbour's plantation of the same kind, in a high cold situation, where the snow was never melted at all, remained uninjured.

From hence I would infer that it is the repeated melting and freezing of the snow that is so fatal to vegetation, rather than the severity of the cold. Therefore it highly behoves every planter, who wishes to escape the cruel mortification of losing in a few days the labour and hopes of years, to bestir himself on such emergencies; and if his plantations are small, to avail himself of mats, cloths, pease-haum, straw, reeds, or any such covering, for a short time; or, if his shrubberies are extensive, to see that his people go about with prongs and forks, and carefully dislodge the snow from the boughs: since the naked foliage will shift much better for itself, than where the snow is partly melted and frozen again.

It may perhaps appear at first like a paradox; but doubtless the more tender trees and shrubs should never be planted in hot aspects; not only for the reason assigned above, but also because, thus circumstanced, they are disposed to shoot earlier in the spring, and to grow on later in the autumn than they would otherwise do, and so are sufferers by lagging or early frosts. For this reason also plants from Siberia will hardly endure our climate; because, on the very first advances of spring, they shoot away, and so are cut off by the severe nights of March or April.

Dr. Fothergill and others have experienced the same inconvenience with respect to the more tender shrubs from North America, which they therefore plant under north walls. There should also perhaps be a wall to the east to defend them from the piercing blasts from that quarter.

This observation might without any impropriety be carried into animal life; for discerning bee-masters now find that their hives should not in the winter be exposed to the hot sun, because such unseasonable warmth awakens the inhabitants too early from their slumbers; and, by putting their juices into motion too soon, subjects them afterwards to inconveniences when rigorous weather returns.

The coincidents attending this short but intense frost were, that the horses fell sick with an epidemic distemper, which injured the winds of many, and killed some; that colds and coughs were general among the human species; that it froze under people's beds for several nights; that meat was so hard frozen that it could not be spitted, and could not be secured but in cellars; that several redwings and thrushes were killed by the frost; and that the large titmouse continued to pull straws lengthwise from the eaves of thatched houses and barns in a most adroit manner, for a purpose that has been explained already.[1]

On the 3rd January, Benjamin Martin's thermometer within doors, in a close parlour where there was no fire, fell in the night to 20°, and on the 4th, to 18°, and on the 7th, to $17\frac{1}{2}$°, a degree of cold which the owner never since saw in the same situation; and he regrets much that he was not able at that juncture to attend his instrument abroad. All this time the wind continued north and north-east; and yet on the 8th, roost-cocks, which had been silent, began to sound their clarions, and crows to clamour, as prognostic of milder weather; and, moreover, moles began to heave and work, and a manifest thaw took place. From the latter circumstance we may conclude that thaws often originate under ground from warm vapours which arise; else how should subterraneous animals receive such early intimations of their approach? Moreover, we have often observed that cold seems to descend from above; for, when a thermometer hangs abroad in a frosty night, the intervention of a cloud shall immediately raise the mercury 10°; and a clear sky shall again compel it to descend to its former guage.

And here it may be proper to observe, on what has been said above, that though frosts advance to their utmost severity by somewhat of a regular gradation, yet thaws do not usually come on by as regular a declension of cold; but often take place immediately from intense freezing; as men in sickness often mend at once from a paroxysm.

To the great credit of Portugal laurels and American junipers, be it remembered that they remained untouched amidst the general havoc: hence men should learn to ornament chiefly with such trees as are able to withstand accidental severities, and not subject themselves to the vexation of a loss which may befall them once perhaps in ten years, yet may hardly be recovered through the whole course of their lives.

As it appeared afterwards, the ilexes were much injured, the cypresses were half destroyed, the arbutuses lingered on, but never recovered; and the bays, laurustines, and laurels,

[1] See Letter XLI. to Pennant.

were killed to the ground; and the very wild hollies, in hot aspects, were so much affected that they cast all their leaves.

By the 14th January the snow was entirely gone; the turnips emerged not damaged at all, save in sunny places; the wheat looked delicately, and the garden plants were well preserved; for snow is the most kindly mantle that infant vegetation can be wrapped in: were it not for that friendly meteor no vegetable life could exist at all in northerly regions. Yet in Sweden the earth in April is not divested of snow for more than a fortnight before the face of the country is covered with flowers.

LETTER LXI.

There were some circumstances attending the remarkable frost in January 1776, so singular and striking, that a short detail of them may not be unacceptable.

The most certain way to be exact will be to copy the passages from my journal, which were taken from time to time, as things occurred. But it may be proper previously to remark that the first week in January was uncommonly wet, and drowned with vast rains from every quarter: from whence may be inferred, as there is great reason to believe is the case, that intense frosts seldom take place till the earth is perfectly glutted and chilled with water;[1] and hence dry autumns are seldom followed by rigorous winters.

January 7th.—Snow driving all the day, which was followed by frost, sleet, and some snow, till the 12th, when a prodigious mass overwhelmed all the works of men, drifting over the tops of the gates and filling the hollow lanes.

On the 14th the writer was obliged to be much abroad; and thinks he never before or since has encountered such rugged Siberian weather. Many of the narrow roads were now filled above the tops of the hedges; through which the snow was driven into most romantic and grotesque shapes, so striking to the imagination as not to be seen without wonder and pleasure. The poultry dared not to stir out of their roosting-places; for cocks and hens are so dazzled and confounded by

---

[1] The autumn preceding January, 1768, was very wet, and particularly the month of September, during which there fell at Lyndon, in the county of Rutland, six inches and a half of rain. And the terrible long frost in 1739-40 set in after a rainy season, and when the springs were very high.—W.

the glare of snow that they would soon perish without assistance. The hares also lay sullenly in their seats, and would not move till compelled by hunger; being conscious—poor animals—that the drifts and heaps treacherously betray their footsteps, and prove fatal to numbers of them.

From the 14th the snow continued to increase, and began to stop the road waggons and coaches, which could no longer keep on their regular stages; and especially on the western roads, where the fall appears to have been deeper than in the south. The company at Bath, that wanted to attend the Queen's birthday, were strangely incommoded: many carriages of persons, who got in their way to town from Bath as far as Marlborough, after strange embarrassments, here met with a *ne plus ultra*. The ladies fretted, and offered large rewards to labourers if they would shovel them a track to London; but the relentless heaps of snow were too bulky to be removed; and so the 18th passed over, leaving the company in very uncomfortable circumstances at the Castle and other inns.

On the 20th the sun shone out for the first time since the frost began; a circumstance that has been remarked before much in favour of vegetation. All this time the cold was not very intense, for the thermometer stood at 29°, 28°, 25°, and thereabout; but on the 21st it descended to 20°. The birds now began to be in a very pitiable and starving condition. Tamed by the season, skylarks settled in the streets of towns, because they saw the ground was bare; rooks frequented dunghills close to houses; and crows watched horses as they passed, and greedily devoured what dropped from them; hares now came into men's gardens, and, scraping away the snow, devoured such plants as they could find.

On the 22nd the author had occasion to go to London through a sort of Laplandian scene, very wild and grotesque indeed. But the metropolis itself exhibited a still more singular appearance than the country; for, being bedded deep in snow, the pavement of the streets could not be touched by the wheels or the horses' feet, so that the carriages ran about without the least noise. Such an exemption from din and clatter was strange, but not pleasant; it seemed to convey an uncomfortable idea of desolation—"a silence that terrified":—

"—— ipsa silentia terrent".

On the 27th much snow fell all day, and in the evening the frost became very intense. At South Lambeth, for the four following nights, the thermometer fell to 11°, 7°, 6°, 6°; and at Selborne to 7°, 6°, 10°; and on the 31st January, just before sunrise, with rime on the trees and on the tube of the glass, the quicksilver sunk exactly to zero, being 32° below the freezing point; but by eleven in the morning, though in the shade, it sprang up to $16\frac{1}{2}$°[1],—a most unusual degree of cold this for the south of England. During these four nights the cold was so penetrating that it occasioned ice in warm chambers and under beds; and in the day the wind was so keen that persons of robust constitutions could scarcely endure to face it. The Thames was at once so frozen over both above and below bridge that crowds ran about on the ice. The streets were now strangely encumbered with snow, which crumbled and trod dusty; and, turning grey, resembled bay-salt; what had fallen on the roofs was so perfectly dry that, from first to last, it lay twenty-six days on the houses in the city: a longer time than had been remembered by the oldest housekeepers living. According to all appearances we might now have expected the continuance of this rigorous weather for weeks to come, since every night increased in severity; but behold, without any apparent cause, on the 1st February a thaw took place, and some rain followed before night, making good the observation above, that frosts often go off as it were at once, without any gradual declension of cold. On the 2nd of February the thaw persisted; and on the 3rd swarms of little insects were frisking and sporting in a courtyard at South Lambeth, as if they had felt no frost. Why the juices in the small bodies and smaller limbs of such minute beings are not frozen is a matter of curious inquiry.

Severe frosts seem to be partial, or to run in currents; for at the same juncture, as the author was informed by accurate correspondents, at Lyndon, in the county of Rutland, the thermometer stood at 19°; at Blackburn, in Lancashire, at 19°; and at Manchester, at 21°, 20°, and 18°. Thus does some unknown circumstance strangely overbalance latitude, and render the cold sometimes much greater in the southern than the northern parts of this kingdom.

The consequences of this severity were, that in Hampshire, at the melting of the snow, the wheat looked well, and the

---

[1] At Selborne the cold was greater than at any other place that the author could hear of with certainty: though some reported at the time that at a village in Kent the thermometer fell two degrees below zero; viz. thirty-four degrees below the freezing point.

The thermometer used at Selborne was graduated by Benjamin Martin.—W.

turnips came forth little injured. The laurels and laurustines were somewhat damaged, but only in hot aspects. No evergreens were quite destroyed; and not half the damage sustained that befell in January 1768. Those laurels that were a little scorched on the south sides were perfectly untouched on their north sides. The care taken to shake the snow day by day from the branches seemed greatly to avail the author's evergreens. A neighbour's laurel-hedge, in a high situation, and facing to the north, was perfectly green and vigorous; and the Portugal laurels remained unhurt.

As to the birds, the thrushes and blackbirds were mostly destroyed; and the partridges, by the weather and poachers, were so thinned that few remained to breed the following year.

LETTER LXII.

As the frost in December 1784 was very extraordinary, you, I trust, will not be displeased to hear the particulars; and especially when I promise to say no more about the severities of winter after I have finished this letter.

The first week in December was very wet, with the barometer very low. On the 7th, with the barometer at 28·5°, came on a vast snow, which continued all that day and the next, and most part of the following night; so that by the morning of the 9th the works of men were quite overwhelmed, the lanes filled so as to be impassable, and the ground covered twelve or fifteen inches without any drifting. In the evening of the 9th the air began to be so very sharp that we thought it would be curious to attend to the motions of a thermometer; we therefore hung out two, one made by Martin and one by Dollond, which soon began to show us what we were to expect; for by ten o'clock they fell to 21°, and at eleven to 4°, when we went to bed. On the 10th, in the morning, the quicksilver of Dollond's glass was down to half a degree below zero; and that of Martin's, which was absurdly graduated only to four degrees above zero, sunk quite into the brass guard of the ball; so that when the weather became most interesting this was useless. On the 10th, at eleven at night, though the air was perfectly still, Dollond's glass went down to one degree below zero! This strange severity of the weather made me very desirous to know what degree of cold there might be in

such an exalted and near situation as Newton. We had, therefore, on the morning of the 10th, written to Mr. ——, and
entreated him to hang out his thermometer, made by Adams,
and to pay some attention to it morning and evening, expecting wonderful phenomena, in so elevated a region, at two
hundred feet or more above my house. But, behold! on the
10th, at eleven at night, it was down only to 17°, and the next
morning at 22°, when mine was at 10°! We were so disturbed
at this unexpected reverse of comparative local cold, that we
sent one of my glasses up, thinking that of Mr. —— must,
somehow, be wrongly constructed. But, when the instruments
came to be confronted, they went exactly together; so that,
for one night at least, the cold at Newton was 18° less than at
Selborne, and, through the whole frost, 10° or 12°; and indeed,
when we came to observe consequences, we could readily credit
this; for all my laurustines, bays, ilexes, arbutuses, cypresses,
and even my Portugal laurels, and (which occasions more
regret) my fine sloping laurel-hedge, were scorched up; while,
at Newton, the same trees have not lost a leaf.

We had steady frost on the 25th, when the thermometer in
the morning was down to 10° with us, and at Newton only to
21°. Strong frost continued till the 31st, when some tendency
to thaw was observed; and, by January 3rd, 1785, the thaw
was confirmed, and some rain fell.

A circumstance that I must not omit, because it was new to
us, is, that on Friday, December 10th, being bright sunshine,
the air was full of icy *spiculæ*, floating in all directions, like
atoms in a sunbeam let into a dark room. We thought them
at first particles of the rime falling from my tall hedges; but
were soon convinced to the contrary, by making our observations in open places where no rime could reach us. Were
they watery particles of the air frozen as they floated, or were
they evaporations from the snow frozen as they mounted?

We were much obliged to the thermometers for the early
information they gave us; and hurried our apples, pears,
onions, potatoes, &c., into the cellar, and warm closets; while
those who had not, or neglected such warnings, lost all their
store of roots and fruits, and had their very bread and cheese
frozen.

I must not omit to tell you that, during these two Siberian
days, my parlour cat was so electric, that had a person stroked
her, and been properly insulated, the shock might have been
given to a whole circle of people.

I forgot to mention before that, during the two severe days, two men, who were tracing hares in the snow, had their feet frozen, and two men, who were much better employed, had their fingers so affected by the frost, while they were thrashing in a barn, that a mortification followed, from which they did not recover for many weeks.

This frost killed all the furze and most of the ivy, and in many places stripped the hollies of all their leaves. It came at a very early time of the year, before old November ended; and yet may be allowed from its effects to have exceeded any since 1730–40.

LETTER LXIII.

As the effects of heat are seldom very remarkable in the northerly climate of England, where the summers are often so defective in warmth and sunshine as not to ripen the fruits of the earth so well as might be wished, I shall be more concise in my account of the severity of a summer season, and so make a little amends for the prolix account of the degrees of cold, and the inconveniences that we suffered from some late rigorous winters.

The summers of 1781 and 1783 were unusually hot and dry; to them therefore I shall turn back in my journals, without recurring to any more distant period. In the former of these years my peach and nectarine trees suffered so much from the heat that the rind on the bodies was scalded and came off; since which the trees have been in a decaying state. This may prove a hint to assiduous gardeners to fence and shelter their wall-trees with mats or boards, as they may easily do, because such annoyance is seldom of long continuance. During that summer also, I observed that my apples were coddled, as it were, on the trees; so that they had no quickness of flavour, and would not keep in the winter. This circumstance put me in mind of what I have heard travellers assert, that they never ate a good apple or apricot in the south of Europe, where the heats were so great as to render the juices vapid and insipid.

The great pests of a garden are wasps, which destroy all the finer fruits just as they are coming into perfection. In 1781 we had none; in 1783 there were myriads; which would have

devoured all the produce of my garden, had not we set the
boys to take the nests, and caught thousands with hazel-twigs
tipped with bird-lime: we have since employed the boys to take
and destroy the large breeding wasps in the spring. Such ex-
pedients have a great effect on these marauders, and will keep
them under. Though wasps do not abound but in hot summers,
yet they do not prevail in every hot summer, as I have in-
stanced in the two years above-mentioned.

In the sultry season of 1783, honey-dews were so frequent
as to deface and destroy the beauties of my garden. My
honeysuckles, which were one week the most sweet and lovely
objects that the eye could behold, became the next the most
loathsome; being enveloped in a viscous substance, and loaded
with black aphides, or smother-flies. The occasion of this
clammy appearance seems to be this, that in hot weather the
effluvia of flowers in fields and meadows and gardens are drawn
up in the day by a brisk evaporation, and then in the night
fall down again with the dews, in which they are entangled;
that the air is strongly scented, and therefore impregnated
with the particles of flowers in summer weather, our senses
will inform us; and that this clammy sweet substance is of the
vegetable kind we may learn from bees, to whom it is very
grateful: and we may be assured that it falls in the night,
because it is always first seen in warm still mornings.[1]

On chalky and sandy soils, and in the hot villages about
London, the thermometer has been often observed to mount as
high as 83° or 84°; but with us, in this hilly and woody district, I have hardly ever seen it exceed 80°; nor does it often
arrive at that pitch. The reason, I conclude, is, that our
dense clayey soil, so much shaded by trees, is not so easily
heated through as those above-mentioned; and, besides, our
mountains cause currents of air and breezes; and the vast
effluvia from our woodlands temper and moderate our heats.

LETTER LXIV.

The summer of the year 1783 was an amazing and por-
tentous one, and full of horrible phenomena; for, besides the

[1] This explanation of the origin of honey-dew is incorrect. It is now known to be
exuded by aphides, a genus of insects of the order *Hemiptera*. Honey-dew is a
favourite food of ants.

alarming meteors and tremendous thunder-storms that affrighted
and distressed the different counties of this kingdom, the
peculiar haze, or smoky fog, that prevailed for many weeks in
this island, and in every part of Europe, and even beyond its
limits, was a most extraordinary appearance, unlike anything
known within the memory of man. By my journal I find that
I had noticed this strange occurrence from June 23rd to July
20th inclusive, during which period the wind varied to every
quarter without making any alteration in the air. The sun,
at noon, looked as blank as a clouded moon, and shed a rust-
coloured ferruginous light on the ground and floors of rooms;
but was particularly lurid and blood-coloured at rising and
setting. All the time the heat was so intense that butchers'
meat could hardly be eaten on the day after it was killed;
and the flies swarmed so in the lanes and hedges that they
rendered the horses half frantic, and riding irksome. The
country people began to look with a superstitious awe at the
red, louring aspect of the sun; and indeed there was reason
for the most enlightened person to be apprehensive; for, all
the while, Calabria and part of the Isle of Sicily, were torn
and convulsed with earthquakes; and about that juncture a
volcano sprang out of the sea on the coast of Norway. On
this occasion Milton's noble simile of the sun, in his first book
of *Paradise Lost*, frequently occurred to my mind; and it is
indeed particularly applicable, because, towards the end, it
alludes to a superstitious kind of dread, with which the minds
of men are always impressed by such strange and unusual
phenomena.

> "——— As when the sun, new risen,
> Looks through the horizontal, misty air,
> Shorn of his beams; or from behind the moon,
> In dim eclipse, disastrous twilight sheds
> On half the nations, and with fear of change
> Perplexes monarchs———."

LETTER LXV.

We are very seldom annoyed with thunder-storms; and it is
no less remarkable than true, that those which arise in the
south have hardly been known to reach this village; for,
before they get over us, they take a direction to the east or

to the west, or sometimes divide in two, go in part to one of those quarters, and in part to the other; as was truly the case in summer 1783, when, though the country round was continually harassed with tempests, and often from the south, yet we escaped them all, as appears by my journal of that summer.[1] The only way that I can at all account for this fact—for such it is—is that, on that quarter, between us and the sea, there are continual mountains, hill behind hill, such as Nore Hill, the Barnet, Butser Hill, and Portsdown, which somehow divert the storms, and give them a different direction. High promontaries, and elevated grounds, have always been observed to attract clouds and disarm them of their mischievous contents, which are discharged into the trees and summits as soon as they come in contact with those turbulent meteors; while the humble vales escape, because they are so far beneath them.

But, when I say I do not remember a thunder-storm from the south, I do not mean that we never have suffered from thunder-storms at all; for on June 5th, 1784, the thermometer in the morning being at 64°, and at noon at 70°, the barometer at $29 \cdot 6\frac{1}{2}°$ and the wind north, I observed a blue mist, smelling strongly of sulphur, hanging along our sloping woods, and seeming to indicate that thunder was at hand. I was called in about two in the afternoon, and so missed seeing the gathering of the clouds in the north; which they who were abroad assured me had something uncommon in its appearance. At about a quarter after two the storm began in the parish of Hartley, moving slowly from north to south: and from thence it came over Norton Farm, and so to Grange Farm, both in this parish. It began with vast drops of rain, which were soon succeeded by round hail, and then by convex pieces of ice, which measured three inches in girth. Had it been as extensive as it was violent, and of any continuance (for it was very short), it must have ravaged all the neighbourhood. In the parish of Hartley it did some damage to one farm; but Norton, which lay in the centre of the storm, was greatly injured; as was Grange, which lay next to it. It did but just reach to the middle of the village, where the hail broke my north windows, and all my garden-lights and handglasses, and many of my neighbours' windows. The extent of the storm was about two miles in length and one in breadth. We were just sitting down to dinner; but were

[1] Cowper alludes to this terrible summer of 1783 in his *Task* (Book ii.).

soon diverted from our repast by the clattering of tiles and the jingling of glass. There fell at the same time prodigious torrents of rain on the farms above-mentioned, which occasioned a flood as violent as it was sudden; doing great damage to the meadows and fallows, by deluging the one and washing away the soil of the other. The hollow land towards Alton was so torn and disordered as not to be passable till mended, rocks being removed that weighed two hundredweight. Those that saw the effect which the great hail had on ponds and pools say that the dashing of the water made an extraordinary appearance, the froth and spray standing up in the air three feet above the surface. The rushing and roaring of the hail, as it approached, was truly tremendous.

Though the clouds at South Lambeth, near London, were at that juncture thin and light, and no storm was in sight, nor within hearing, yet the air was strongly electric; for the bells of an electric machine at that place rang repeatedly, and fierce sparks were discharged.

When I first took the present work in hand I proposed to have added an *Annus Historico Naturalis*, or The Natural History of the Twelve Months of the Year; which would have comprised many incidents and occurrences that have not fallen in my way to be mentioned in my series of letters; but, as Mr. Aikin of Warrington has lately published somewhat of this sort, and as the length of my correspondence has sufficently put your patience to the test, I shall here take a respectful leave of you and natural history together, and am,

With all due deference and regard,

Your most obliged and most humble servant,

GIL. WHITE.

SELBORNE,
June 25th, 1787.

OBSERVATIONS ON NATURE.

GREAT SPECKLED DIVER, OR LOON.

As one of my neighbours was traversing Wolmer Forest from Bramshot across the moors, he found a large uncommon bird fluttering in the heath, but not wounded, which he brought home alive. On examination it proved to be *Colymbus glacialis, Linn.*, the great speckled diver or loon, which is most excellently described in Willughby's Ornithology.

Every part and proportion of this bird is so incomparably adapted to its mode of life, that in no instance do we see the wisdom of God in the creation to more advantage. The head is sharp and smaller than the part of the neck adjoining, in order that it may pierce the water; the wings are placed forward, and out of the centre of gravity, for a purpose which shall be noticed hereafter; the thighs quite at the podex, in order to facilitate diving; and the legs are quite flat, and as sharp backwards almost as the edge of a knife, that in striking they may easily cut the water; while the feet are palmated, and broad for swimming, yet so folded up when advanced forward to take a fresh stroke, as to be full as narrow as the shank. The two exterior toes of the feet are longest; the nails flat and broad, resembling the human, which give strength, and increase the power of swimming. The foot, when expanded, is not at right angles to the leg or body of the bird: but the exterior part inclining towards the head, forms an acute angle with the body; the intention being not to give motion in the line of the legs themselves, but by the combined impulse of both in an intermediate line, the line of the body.

Most people know, that have observed at all, that the swimming of birds is nothing more than a walking in the water, where one foot succeeds the other as on the land; yet no one, as far as I am aware, has remarked that diving fowls, while under water, impel and row themselves forward by a motion of their wings, as well as by the impulse of their feet: but such is really the case, as any person may easily be convinced, who will observe ducks when hunted by dogs in a clear pond

Nor do I know that any one has given a reason why the wings
of diving fowls are placed so forward: doubtless, not for the
purpose of promoting their speed in flying, since that position
certainly impedes it; but probably for the increase of their
motion under water, by the use of four oars instead of two;
yet were the wings and feet nearer together, as in land-birds,
they would, when in action, rather hinder than assist one
another.

This *Colymbus* was of considerable bulk, weighing only three
drachms short of three pounds avoirdupois. It measured in
length from the bill to the tail (which was very short) two
feet, and to the extremities of the toes four inches more; and
the breadth of the wings expanded was forty-two inches. A
person attempted to eat the body, but found it very strong
and rancid, as is the flesh of all birds living on fish. Divers
or loons, though bred in the most northerly parts of Europe,
yet are seen with us in very severe winters; and on the
Thames they are called sprat loons, because they prey much
on that sort of fish.

The legs of the *Colymbi* and *Mergi* are placed so very backward, and so out of all centre of gravity, that these birds
cannot walk at all. They are called by Linnæus *compedes*,
because they move on the ground as if shackled or fettered.

INSECTS IN GENERAL.

The day and night insects occupy the annuals alternately;
the *Papilios*, *Muscæ*, and *Apes*, are succeeded at the close of
day by *Phalænæ*, earwigs, woodlice, &c. In the dusk of the
evening, when beetles begin to buzz, partridges begin to call;
these two circumstances are exactly coincident.

Ivy is the last flower that supports the hymenopterous and
dipterous insects. On sunny days quite on to November they
swarm on trees covered with this plant; and when they disappear, probably retire under the shelter of its leaves, con-
cealing themselves between its fibres and the trees which it
entwines.[1]

[1] The ivy is haunted at night by swarms of moths and other insects. I have seen
an ivy bush, on a warm summer night, literally moving with the number of moths
which were feeding on it. The eyes of the larger ones glowed like sparks of fire.—W.

To this note, William Markwick, a contemporary of White, and a noted naturalist
in his day, adds the following remarks:—"This I have often observed, having seen
bees and other winged insects swarming about the flowers of the ivy, very late in the
autumn."

Spiders, woodlice, *Lepismæ* in cupboards and among sugar, some *Empedes*, gnats, flies of several species, some *Phalænæ* in hedges, earth-worms, &c., are stirring at all times when winters are mild; and are of great service to those soft-billed birds that never leave us.

On every sunny day the winter through, clouds of insects usually called gnats (I suppose tipulæ and empedes) appear sporting and dancing over the tops of the evergreen trees in the shrubbery, and striking about as if the business of generation was still going on. Hence it appears that these *Diptera* (which by their sizes appear to be of different species) are not subject to a torpid state in the winter, as most winged insects are. At night, and in frosty weather, and when it rains and blows, they seem to retire into those trees. They often are out in a fog.[1]

HUMMING IN THE AIR.

There is a natural occurrence to be met with upon the highest part of our down in hot summer days, which always amuses me much, without giving me any satisfaction with respect to the cause of it; and that is, a loud audible humming of bees in the air, though not one insect is to be seen. The sound is to be heard distinctly the whole common through, from the Money-dells to Mr. White's avenue gate. Any person would suppose that a large swarm of bees was in motion, and playing about over his head. This noise was heard last week, on June 28th.

> " Resounds the living surface of the ground,
> Nor undelightful is the ceaseless hum
> To him who muses ———— at noon."

> "Thick in yon stream of light a thousand ways.
> Upward and downward, thwarting and convolv'd,
> The quivering nations sport."—THOMSON'S SEASONS.

CHAFFERS.

Cockchaffers seldom abound oftener than once in three or four years; when they swarm they deface the trees and hedges. Whole woods of oaks are stripped bare by them.

[1] "This I have also seen, and have frequently observed swarms of little winged insects playing up and down in the air in the middle of winter, even when the ground has been covered with snow."—MARKWICK.

Chaffers are eaten by the turkey, the rook, and the house-sparrow.

The *Scarabœus solstitialis* first appears about June 26th: they are very punctual in their coming out every year. They are a small species, about half the size of the May-chaffer, and are known in some parts by the name of the fern-chaffer.[1]

PTINUS PECTINICORNIS.

Those maggots that make worm-holes in tables, chairs, bed-posts, etc., and destroy wooden furniture, especially where there is any sap, are the larvæ of the *Ptinus pectinicornis.* This insect, it is probable, deposits its eggs on the surface, and the worms eat their way in.

In their holes they turn into their pupæ state, and so come forth winged in July; eating their way through the valances or curtains of a bed, or any other furniture that happens to obstruct their passage.

They seem to be most inclined to breed in beech: hence beech will not make lasting utensils, or furniture. If their eggs are deposited on the surface, frequent rubbing will pre-serve wooden furniture.

BLATTA ORIENTALIS.—COCKROACH.

A neighbour complained that her house was overrun with a kind of black beetle, or, as she expressed herself, with a kind of black-bob, which swarmed in her kitchen when they got up in a morning before daybreak.

Soon after this account, I observed an unusual insect in one of my dark chimney closets, and find since, that in the night, they swarm also in my kitchen.   On examination I soon ascer-tained the species to be the *Blatta orientalis* of Linnæus, and the *Blatta molendinaria* of Mouffet.   The male is winged; the

---

[1] A singular circumstance relative to the cockchaffer, or, as it is called here, the May-bug, *Scarabœus melolontha*, happened this year (1800). My gardener, in digging some ground, found, about six inches under the surface, two of these insects alive and perfectly formed, so early as the 24th of March. When he brought them to me, they appeared to me as perfect, and as much alive as in the midst of summer, crawl-ing about as briskly as ever; yet I saw no more of this insect till the 22nd of May, when it began to make its appearance. How comes it, that though it was perfectly formed so early as the 24th of March, it did not show itself above ground till nearly two months afterwards?—MARKWICK.

female is not, but shows somewhat like the rudiments of wings, as if in the pupa state.

These insects belonged originally to the warmer parts of America, and were conveyed from thence by shipping to the East Indies; and by means of commerce begin to prevail in the more northern part of Europe, as Russia, Sweden, etc. How long they have abounded in England I cannot say; but have never observed them in my house till lately.

They love warmth, and haunt chimney closets and the backs of ovens. Poda says that these and house crickets will not associate together; but he is mistaken in that assertion, as Linnæus suspected he was. They are altogether night insects (*lucifugæ*), never coming forth till the rooms are dark and still, and escaping away nimbly at the approach of a candle. Their antennæ are remarkably long, slender, and flexile.

October 1790.—After the servants are gone to bed, the kitchen hearth swarms with young crickets, and young *Blattæ molendinariæ* of all sizes, from the most minute growth to their full proportions. They seem to live in a friendly manner together, and not to prey the one on the other.

August 1792.—After the destruction of many thousands of *Blattæ molendinariæ*, we find that at intervals a fresh detachment of old ones arrives, and particularly during this hot season; for the windows being left open in the evenings, the males come flying in at the casements from the neighbouring houses, which swarm with them. How the females, that seem to have no perfect wings that they can use, can contrive to get from house to house, does not so readily appear. These, like many insects, when they find their present abodes overstocked, have powers of migrating to fresh quarters. Since the *Blattæ* have been so much kept under, the crickets have greatly increased in number.

GRYLLUS DOMESTICUS.—HOUSE-CRICKET.

November.—After the servants are gone to bed, the kitchen hearth swarms with minute crickets not so large as fleas, which must have been lately hatched. So that these domestic insects, cherished by the influence of a constant large fire, regard not the season of the year, but produce their young at a time when their congeners are either dead, or laid up for the winter, to pass away the uncomfortable months in the profoundest slumbers, and a state of torpidity.

When house-crickets are out, and running about in a room in the night, if surprised by a candle, they give two or three shrill notes, as it were for a signal to their fellows, that they may escape to their crannies and lurking-holes, to avoid danger.

PHALÆNA QUERCUS.

Most of our oaks are naked of leaves, and even the Holt in general, having been ravaged by the caterpillars of a small *Phalæna* which is of a pale yellow colour. These insects, though a feeble race, yet, from their infinite numbers, are of wonderful effect, being able to destroy the foliage of whole forests and districts. At this season they leave their *aurelia*, and issue forth in their fly-state, swarming and covering the trees and hedges.

In a field at Greatham, I saw a flight of swifts busied in catching their prey near the ground; and found they were hawking after these *Phalænæ*. The *aurelia* of this moth is shining and as black as jet; and lies wrapped up in a leaf of the tree, which is rolled round it, and secured at the ends by a web, to prevent the maggot from falling out.[1]

EPHEMERA CAUDA BISETA.—MAY-FLY.

June 10th, 1771.—Myriads of May-flies appear for the first time on the Alresford stream. The air was crowded with them, and the surface of the water covered. Large trouts sucked them in as they lay struggling on the surface of the stream, unable to rise till their wings were dried.

This appearance reconciled me in some measure to the wonderful account that Scopoli gives of the quantities emerging from the rivers of Carniola. Their motions are very

---

[1] I suspect that the insect here meant is not the *Phalæna quercus*, but the *Phalæna viridata*, concerning which I find the following note in my "Naturalist's Calendar" for the year 1785:—

About this time, and for a few days last past, I observed the leaves of almost all the oak-trees in Denn Copse to be eaten and destroyed, and, on examining more narrowly, saw an infinite number of small beautiful pale green moths flying about the trees; the leaves of which that were not quite destroyed were curled up, and withinside were the *exuviæ* or remains of the *chrysalis*, from whence I suppose the moths had issued, and whose caterpillar had eaten the leaves.—MARKWICK.

peculiar, up and down for many yards almost in a perpendicular line.[1]

SPHYNX OCELLATA.

A vast insect appears after it is dusk, flying with a humming noise, and inserting its tongue into the bloom of the honey-suckle; it scarcely settles upon the plants, but feeds on the wing in the manner of humming birds.[2]

WILD BEE.

There is a sort of wild bee frequenting the garden-campion for the sake of its tomentum,[3] which probably it turns to some purpose in the business of nidification. It is very pleasant to see with what address it strips off the pubes, running from the top to the bottom of a branch, and shaving it bare with all the dexterity of a hoop-shaver. When it has got a vast bundle, almost as large as itself, it flies away, holding it secure between its chin and its fore legs.

There is a remarkable hill on the downs near Lewes in Sussex, known by the name of Mount Carburn, which overlooks that town, and affords a most engaging prospect of all the country round, besides several views of the sea. On the very summit of this exalted promontory, and amidst the trenches of its Danish camp, there haunts a species of wild bee, making its nest in the chalky soil. When people approach the place, these insects begin to be alarmed, and, with a sharp and hostile sound, dash and strike round the heads and faces of intruders. I have often been interrupted myself while contemplating the grandeur of the scenery around me, and have thought myself in danger of being stung.

[1] I once saw a swarm of these insects playing up and down over the surface of a pond in Denn Park, exactly in the manner described by this accurate naturalist. It was late in the evening of a warm summer's day when I observed them.—MARKWICK.

[2] I have frequently seen the large bee-moth, *Sphinx stellatarum*, inserting its long tongue or proboscis into the centre of flowers, and feeding on their nectar, without settling on them, but keeping constantly on the wing.—MARKWICK.

[3] *Tomentum*—The closely matted hair or downy nap covering the leaves or stems of some plants.

WASPS.

Wasps abound in woody wild districts far from neighbour-hoods; they feed on flowers, and catch flies and caterpillars to carry to their young. Wasps make their nests with the rasp-ings of sound timber; hornets, with what they gnaw from decayed: these particles of wood are kneaded up with a mix-ture of saliva from their bodies and moulded into combs.

When there is no fruit in the gardens, wasps eat flies, and suck the honey from flowers, from ivy blossoms and umbel-lated plants; they carry off also flesh from butcher's sham-bles.[1]

OESTRUS CURVICAUDA.

This insect lays its nits or eggs on horses' legs, flanks, &c., each on a single hair. The maggots, when hatched, do not enter the horses' skins, but fall to the ground. It seem to abound most in moist, moorish places, though sometimes seen in the uplands.

NOSE-FLY.

About the beginning of July, a species of fly (*Musca*) obtains, which proves very tormenting to horses, trying still to enter their nostrils and ears, and actually laying their eggs in the latter of those organs, or perhaps in both. When these abound, horses in woodland districts become very impatient at their work, continually tossing their heads, and rubbing their noses on each other, regardless of the driver, so that accidents often ensue. In the heat of the day, men are often obliged to desist from ploughing. Saddle-horses are also very troublesome at such seasons. Country people call this insect the nose-fly.[2]

[1] In the year 1775, wasps abounded so prodigiously in this neighbourhood, that, in the month of August, no less than seven or eight of their nests were ploughed up in one field: of which there were several instances, as I was informed.

In the spring, about the beginning of April, a single wasp is sometimes seen, which is of a larger size than usual; this I imagine is the queen or female wasp, the mother of the future swarm.—MARKWICK.

[2] Is not this insect the *Oestrus nasalis* of Linnæus, so well described by Mr. Clark in the third volume of the *Linnæan Transactions*, under the name of *Oestrus veter-inus*?—MARKWICK.

ICHNEUMON FLY.

I saw lately a small ichneumon fly attack a spider much larger than itself on a grass-walk. When the spider made any resistance, the ichneumon applied her tail to him, and stung him with great vehemence, so that he soon became dead and motionless. The ichneumon then running backward drew her prey very nimbly over the walk into the standing grass. This spider would be deposited in some hole where the ichneumon would lay some eggs; and as soon as the eggs were hatched, the carcase would afford ready food for the maggots.

Perhaps some eggs might be injected into the body of the spider, in the act of stinging. Some ichneumons deposit their eggs in the aurelia of moths and butterflies.[1]

BOMBYLIUS MEDIUS.

The *Bombylius medius* is much about in March and the beginning of April, and soon seems to retire. It is a hairy insect, like the humble-bee, but with only two wings, and a long straight beak, with which it sucks the early flowers. The female seems to lay its eggs as it poises on its wings, by striking its tail on the ground, and against the grass that stands in its way, in a quick manner, for several times together.[2]

MUSCÆ.—FLIES.

In the decline of the year, when the mornings and evenings become chilly, many species of flies (*Muscæ*) retire into houses, and swarm in the windows.

---

[1] In my "Naturalist's Calendar" for 1795, July 21st, I find the following note:—

It is not uncommon for some of the species of ichneumon flies to deposit their eggs in the chrysalis of a butterfly; some time ago I put two of the chrysales of a butterfly into a box, and covered it with gauze, to discover what species of butterfly they would produce; but instead of a butterfly, one of them produced a number of small ichneumon flies.

There are many instances of the great service these little insects are to mankind in reducing the number of noxious insects, by depositing their eggs in the soft bodies of their *larvæ*; but none more remarkable than that of the ichneumon *Tipulæ*, which pierces the tender bodies and deposits its eggs in the *larva* of the *Tipula tritici*, an insect which, when it abounds greatly, is very prejudicial to the grains of wheat. This operation I have frequently seen it perform with wonder and delight.—MARKWICK.

[2] I have often seen this insect fly with great velocity, stop on a sudden, hang in the air in a stationary position for some time, and then fly off again; but do not recollect having ever seen it strike its tail against the ground, or any other substance.—MARKWICK.

At first they are very brisk and alert; but as they grow more torpid, one cannot help observing that they move with difficulty, and are scarce able to lift their legs, which seem as if glued to the glass; and by degrees many do actually stick on till they die in the place.

It has been observed that divers flies, besides their sharp hooked nails, have also skinny palms or flaps to their feet, whereby they are enabled to stick on the glass and other smooth bodies, and to walk on ceilings with their backs downward, by means of the pressure of the atmosphere on those flaps; the weight of which they easily overcome in warm weather, when they are brisk and alert. But in the decline of the year, this resistance becomes too mighty for their diminished strength; and we see flies labouring along, and lugging their feet in windows as if they stuck to the glass, and it is with the utmost difficulty they can draw one foot after another, and disengage their hollow caps from the slippery surface.

Upon the same principle that flies stick and support themselves, do boys, by way of play, carry heavy weights by only a piece of wet leather at the end of a string clapped close on the surface of a stone.

TIPULÆ, OR EMPEDES.

May.—Millions of *Empedes*, or *Tipulæ*, come forth at the close of day, and swarm to such a degree as to fill the air. At this juncture they sport and copulate; as it grows more dark they retire. All day they hide in the hedges. As they rise in a cloud they appear like smoke.

I do not remember to have seen such swarms, except in the fens of the Isle of Ely. They appear most over grass grounds.

APHIDES.

On the 1st August, about half an hour after three in the afternoon, the people of Selborne were surprised by a shower of aphides which fell in these parts. They who were walking in the streets at that time found themselves covered with these insects, which settled also on the trees and gardens, and blackened all the vegetables where they alighted. These armies, no doubt, were then in a state of emigration, and shifting their quarters; and might perhaps come from the great hop-plantations of Kent or Sussex, the wind being that day at north. They were observed at the same time at Farnham, and all along the vale to Alton.

ANTS.

August 23rd.—Every ant-hill about this time is a strange hurry and confusion; and all the winged ants, agitated by some violent impulse, are leaving their homes, and, bent on emigration, swarm by myriads in the air, to the great emolument of the *Hirundines*, which fare luxuriously. Those that escape the swallows return no more to their nests, but looking out for fresh settlements, lay a foundation for future colonies. All the females at this time are pregnant; the males that escape being eaten, wander away and die.

October 2nd.—Flying-ants, male and female, usually swarm and migrate on hot sunny days in August and September: but this day a vast emigration took place in my garden, and myriads came forth, in appearance from the drain which goes under the fruit-wall, filling the air and the adjoining trees and shrubs with their numbers. The females were full of eggs. This late swarming is probably owing to the backward wet season. The day following, not one flying-ant was to be seen.

Horse-ants travel home to their nests laden with flies which they have caught, and the aureliæ of smaller ants, which they seize by violence.[1]

GLOW-WORMS.

By observing two glow-worms which were brought from the field to the bank in the garden, it appeared to us that these little creatures put out their lamps between eleven and twelve, and shine no more for the rest of the night.

[1] In my "Naturalist's Calendar" for the year 1777, on September 6th, I find the following note to the article Flying Ants:—

I saw a prodigious swarm of these ants flying about the top of some tall elm-trees (close by my house); some were continually dropping to the ground, as if from the trees, and others rising up from the ground; I imagine their life is short, for as soon as produced from the egg by the heat of the sun, they propagate their species, and soon after perish. They were black, somewhat like the small black ant, and had four wings. I saw also, at another place, a large sort, which were yellowish. On the 8th of September, 1785, I again observed the same circumstance of a vast number of these insects flying near the tops of the elms and dropping to the ground.

On the 2nd of March, 1777, I saw great numbers of ants come out of the ground.—MARKWICK.

Little glow-worms, attracted by the light of the candles, come into the parlour.

EARTH-WORMS.

Earth-worms make their casts most in mild weather, about March and April; they do not lie torpid in winter, but come forth when there is no frost; they travel about in rainy nights, as appears from their sinuous tracks on the soft muddy soil, perhaps in search of food.

When earth-worms lie out a-nights on the turf, though they extend their bodies a great way, they do not leave their holes, but keep the ends of their tails fixed therein, so that on the least alarm they can retire with precipitation under the earth. Whatever food falls within their reach when thus extended, they seem to be content with, such as blades of grass, straws, fallen leaves, the ends of which they often draw into their holes.

SNAILS AND SLUGS.

The shell-less snails called slugs are in motion all the winter in mild weather, and commit great depredations on garden plants, and much injure the green wheat, the loss of which is imputed to earth-worms; while the shelled snail, the φερεοικος,[1] does not come forth at all till about April 10th, and not only lays itself up pretty early in autumn, in places secure from frost, but also throws out round the mouth of its shell a thick operculum formed from its own saliva; so that it is perfectly secured and corked up, as it were, from all inclemencies. The cause why the slugs are able to endure the cold so much better than shell-snails is, that their bodies are covered with slime, as whales are with blubber.

Snails breed about midsummer; and soon after deposit their eggs in the mould by running their heads and bodies under ground. Hence the way to be rid of them is to kill as many as possible before they begin to breed.

Large, gray, shell-less cellar-snails lay themselves up about the same time with those that live abroad; hence it is plain that a defect of warmth is not the only cause that influences their retreat.

[1] The house-bearer.

A

COMPARATIVE VIEW

OF THE

NATURALIST'S CALENDAR,

AS KEPT AT

SELBORNE, IN HAMPSHIRE,

BY THE

REV. GILBERT WHITE, M.A.:

AND AT

CATSFIELD, NEAR BATTLE,

IN SUSSEX,

BY WILLIAM MARKWICK, ESQ., F.L.S.,

From the year 1768 to the year 1793.

N.B.—The dates in the following Calendars, when more than one, express the *earliest* and *latest* times in which the circumstance noted was observed.

240

A COMPARATIVE VIEW

OF

WHITE'S AND MARKWICK'S CALENDARS.

Of the abbreviations used, fl. signifies *flowering*; l. *leafing*;
and ap. the first *appearance*.

	WHITE.	MARKWICK.
Redbreast (sylvia rubecula) sings - -	Jan. 1—12 - {	Jan. 3—31, and again Oct. 6.
Larks (alauda arvensis) congregate -	Jan. 1—18 - -	Oct. 16, Feb. 9.
Nuthatch (sitta europæa) heard - -	Jan. 1—14 - -	Mar. 3, Apr. 10.
Winter aconite (helleborus hiemalis) fl. -	Jan. 1, Feb. 18 -	Feb. 28, Apr. 17.
Shell-less snail or slug (limax) ap. - -	Jan. 2 - -	Jan. 16, May 31.
Grey and } wagtail { (motacilla boarula)) White { ap. { (motacilla alba) ap. }	Jan. 2—11 - {	Jan. 24, Mar. 26. Dec. 12, Feb. 23.
Missel-thrush (turdus viscivorus) sings -	Jan. 2—14 - -	Feb. 19, Apr. 14.
Bearsfoot (helleborus fœtidus) fl. - -	Jan. 2, Feb. 14 -	Mar. 1, May 5.
Polyanthus (primula polyantha) fl. -	Jan. 2, Apr. 12 -	Jan. 1, Apr. 9.
Double daisy (bellis perennis plena) fl. -	Jan. 2, Feb. 1 -	Mar. 17, Apr. 29.
Mezereon (daphne mezereum) fl. -	Jan. 3, Feb. 16 -	Jan. 2, Apr. 4.
Pansy (viola tricolor) fl. - - - -	Jan. 3 - -	Jan. 1, May 10.
Red dead-nettle (lamium purpureum) fl.	Jan. 3—21 - -	Jan. 1, Apr. 5.
Groundsel (senecio vulgaris) fl. -	Jan. 3—15 - -	Jan. 1, Apr. 9.
Hazel (corylus avellana) fl. - -	Jan. 3, Feb. 28 -	Jan. 21, March 11.
Hepatica (anemone hepatica) fl. -	Jan. 4, Feb. 18 -	Jan. 17, Apr. 9.
Hedge-sparrow (sylvia modularis) sings -	Jan. 5—12 - -	Jan. 16, Mar. 13.
Common flies (musca domestica) seen in numbers - - - - - }	Jan. 5, Feb. 3 -	May 15.
Greater titmouse (parus major) sings -	Jan. 6, Feb. 6 -	Feb. 17, Mar. 17.
Thrush (turdus musicus) sings -	Jan. 6—22 - -	Jan. 15, Apr. 4.
Insects swarm under sunny hedges -	Jan. 6.	
Primrose (primula vulgaris) fl. -	Jan. 6, Apr. 7 -	Jan. 3, Mar. 22.
Bees (apis mellifica) ap. - - -	Jan. 6, Mar. 19 -	Jan. 31, Apr. 11; last [seen Dec. 30.
Gnats play about - - -	Jan. 6, Feb. 3.	
Chaffinches, male and female (fringilla cœlebs) seen in equal numbers - }	Jan. 6—11 - -	Dec. 2, Feb. 3.
Furze or gorse (ulex europæus) fl. -	Jan. 8—Feb. 1 -	Jan. 1, Mar. 27.
Wall-flower (cheiranthus cheiri; seu fruticulosus of Smith) fl. - - }	Jan. 8, Apr. 1 -	Feb. 21, May 9.
Stock (cheiranthus incanus) fl. -	Jan. 8—12 - -	Feb. 1, June 3.
Emberiza alba (bunting) in great flocks -	Jan. 9.	
Linnets (fringilla linota) congregate -	Jan. 9 - -	Jan. 11.
Lambs begin to fall - -	Jan. 9—11 - -	Jan. 6, Feb. 21.
Rooks (corvus frugilegus) resort to their nest-trees - - - - }	Jan. 10, Feb. 11	Jan. 23.

	WHITE.	MARKWICK.
Black hellebore (helleborus niger) fl. -	Jan. 10 - -	Apr. 27.
Snowdrop (galanthus nivalis) fl. -	Jan. 10, Feb. 5 -	Jan. 18, Mar. 1.
White dead-nettle (lamium album) fl. -	Jan. 13 - -	Mar. 23, May 10.
Trumpet honeysuckle fl. - - - -	Jan. 13.	
Common creeping crowfoot (ranunculus } repens) fl. - - - - -	Jan. 13 - -	Apr. 10, May 12.
House-sparrow (fringilla domestica) } chirps - - - - - -	Jan. 14 - -	Feb. 17, May 9.
Dandelion (leontodon taraxacum) fl. -	Jan. 16, Mar. 11	Feb. 1, Apr. 17.
Bat (vespertilio) ap. - - - - -	Jan. 16, Mar. 24 {	Feb. 6, June 1; last seen Nov. 20.
Spiders shoot their webs - - - -	Jan. 16.	
Butterfly ap. - - - - - -	Jan. 16 - {	Feb. 21, May 8; last seen Dec. 22.
Brambling (fringilla montifringilla) ap. -	Jan. 16 - -	Jan. 10—31.
Blackbird (turdus merula) whistles -	Jan. 17 - -	Feb. 15, May 13.
Wren (sylvia troglodytes) sings -	Jan. 17 - -	Feb. 7, June 12.
Earthworms lie out - - - - -	Jan. 18, Feb. 8.	
Crocus (crocus vernus) fl. - -	Jan. 13, Mar. 18	Jan. 20, Mar. 19.
Skylark (alauda arvensis) sings -	Jan. 21 - -	Jan. 12, Feb. 27; sings
Ivy casts its leaves - - - -	Jan. 22.	[till Nov. 13.
Helleborus hiemalis fl. - - -	Jan. 22—24 -	Feb. 28, Apr. 17.
Common dor or clock (scarabæus ster- } corarius) - - - - - -	Jan. 23 - {	Feb. 12, Apr. 12; last seen Nov. 24.
Peziza acetabulum ap. - - - -	Jan. 23.	
Helleborus virid fl. - - - -	Jan. 23, Mar. 5.	
Hazel (corylus avellana) fl. - -	Jan. 23, Feb. 1 -	Jan. 27, Mar. 11.
Woodlark (alauda arborea) sings -	Jan. 24, Feb. 21	Jan. 28, June 5.
Chaffinch (fringilla cœlebs) sings -	Jan. 24, Feb. 15	Jan. 21, Feb. 26.
Jack-daws begin to come to churches -	Jan. 25, Mar. 4.	
Yellow wagtail (motacilla flava) ap. -	Jan. 25, Apr. 14 {	Apr. 13, July 3; last seen Sept. 8.
Honeysuckle (lonicera periclymenum) l.	Jan. 25 - -	Jan. 1, Apr. 9.
Field or procumbent speedwell (veronica } agrestis) fl. - - - - -	Jan. 27, Mar. 15	Feb. 12, Mar. 29.
Nettle butterfly (papilio urticæ) ap. -	Jan. 27, Apr. 2 {	Mar. 5, Apr. 24; last seen June 6.
White wagtail (motacilla alba) chirps -	Jan. 28 - -	Mar. 16.
Shell-snail (helix nemoralis) ap. -	Jan. 28, Feb. 24	Apr. 2, June 11.
Earthworms engender - - -	Jan. 30.	
Barren strawberry (fragaria sterilis) fl. -	Feb. 1, Mar. 26 -	Jan. 13, Mar. 26.
Blue titmouse (parus cæruleus) chirps -	Feb. 1 - -	Apr. 27.
Brown wood-owls hoot - - -	Feb. 2.	
Hen (phasianus gallus) sits - -	Feb. 3 - -	March 8, hatches.
Marsh titmouse begins his two harsh } sharp notes - - - - -	Feb. 3.	
Gossamer floats - - - - -	Feb. 4, Apr. 1.	
Musca tenax ap. - - - -	Feb. 4, Apr. 8.	
Laurustine (viburnum tinus) fl. -	Feb. 5 - -	Jan 1, Apr. 5.
Butcher's broom (ruscus aculeatus) fl. -	Feb. 5 - -	Jan. 1, May 10.
Fox (canis vulpes) smells rank - -	Feb. 7 - -	May 19, young
Turkey-cocks strut and gobble -	Feb. 10.	[brought forth.
Yellow-hammer(emberiza citrinella)sings	Feb. 12 - -	Feb. 18, Apr. 28.
Brimstone butterfly (papilio rhamni) ap.	Feb. 13, Apr. 2 {	Feb. 13, Mar. 8; last seen Dec. 24.
Green-woodpecker (picus viridis) makes } a loud cry - - - - -	Feb. 13, Mar. 23	Jan. 1, Apr. 17.
Raven (corvus corax) builds - -	Feb. 14—17 {	April 1; has young ones June 1.
Yew-tree (taxus baccata) fl. - -	Feb. 14, Mar. 27	Feb. 2, Apr. 11.
Coltsfoot (tussilago farfara) fl. -	Feb. 15, Mar. 23	Feb. 18, Apr. 13.
Rooks (corvus frugilegus) build -	Feb. 16, Mar. 6 -	Feb. 28, Mar. 5.
Partridges (perdix cinerea) pair -	Feb. 17 - -	Feb. 16, Mar. 20.

	WHITE.	MARKWICK.
Peas (pisum sativum) sown - - -	Feb. 17, Mar. 8 -	Feb. 8, **Mar. 31.**
House-pigeon (columba domestica) has } young ones - - - - -	Feb. 18 - -	Feb. 8.
Field-crickets open their holes - -	Feb. 20, Mar. 30.	
Common flea (pulex irritans) ap. - -	Feb. 21—26.	
Pilewort (ficaria verna) fl. - -	Feb. 21, Apr. 13	Jan. 25, Mar. 26.
Goldfinch (fringilla carduelis) sings -	Feb. 21, Apr. 5 -	Feb. 28, May 5.
Viper (coluber berus) ap. - - -	Feb. 22, Mar. 26 {	Feb. 23, May 6; last seen Oct. 28.
Wood-louse (oniscus asellus) ap. -	Feb. 23, Apr. 1 -	Apr. 27, June 17.
Missel thrushes pair - - - -	Feb. 24.	
Daffodil (narcissus pseudonarcissus) fl. -	Feb. 24, Apr. 7 -	Feb. 26, Apr. 18.
Willow (salix alba) fl. - - -	Feb. 24, Apr. 2 -	Feb. 27, Apr. 11.
Frogs (rana temporaria) croak - -	Feb. 25 - -	Mar. 9, Apr. 20.
Sweet violet (viola odorata) fl. - -	Feb. 26, Mar. 31	Feb. 7, Apr. 5.
Phalæna tinea vestianella ap. - -	Feb. 26.	
Stone-curlew (otis œdicnemus) clamours	Feb. 27, Apr. 24	June 17.
Filbert (corylus sativus) fl. - -	Feb. 27 - -	Jan. 25, Mar. 26.
Ring-dove coos - - - - -	Feb. 27, Apr. 5 -	Mar. 2, Aug. 10.
Apricot-tree (prunus armeniaca) fl. -	Feb. - - -	Feb. 28, Apr. 5.
Toad (rana bufo) ap. - - - -	Feb. 28, Mar. 24	Mar. 15, July 1.
Frogs (rana temporaria) spawn -	Feb. 28, Mar. 22 {	Feb. 9, Apr. 10; tadpoles Mar. 19.
Ivy-leaved speedwell (veronica hederi- } folia) fl. - - - - -	Mar. 1, Apr. 2 -	Feb. 16, Apr. 10.
Peach (amygdalus persica) fl. - -	Mar. 2, Apr. 17 -	Mar. 4, Apr. 29.
Frog (rana temporaria) ap. - - -	Mar. 2, Apr. 6 -	Mar. 9.
Shepherd's purse (thlaspi bursa pastoris) } fl. - - - - -	Mar. 3 - -	Jan. 2, Apr. 16.
Pheasant (phasianus colchicus) crows -	March 3—29	Mar. 1, May 22.
Land-tortoise comes forth - -	Mar. 4, May 8.	
Lungwort (pulmonaria officinalis) fl. -	Mar. 4, Apr. 16 -	Mar. 2, May 19.
Podura fimetaria ap. - - - -	Mar. 4.	
Aranea scenica saliens ap. - - -	Mar. 4.	
Scolopendra forficata ap. - - -	Mar. 5—16.	
Wryneck (junx torquilla) ap. - -	Mar. 5, Apr. 25 {	Mar. 26, Apr. 23; last seen Sept. 14.
Goose (anas anser) sits on its eggs -	Mar. 5 - -	Mar. 21.
Duck (anas boschas) lays - - -	Mar. 5 - -	Mar. 28.
Dogs' violet (viola canina) fl. - -	Mar. 6, Apr. 18 -	Feb. 28, Apr. 22.
Peacock butterfly (papilio io) ap. -	Mar. 6 - {	Feb. 13, Apr. 20; last seen Dec. 25.
Trouts begin to rise - - - -	Mar. 7—14.	
Field beans (vicia faba) planted -	Mar. 8 - -	Apr.29, emerge.
Blood-worms appear in the water -	Mar. 8.	
Crow (corvus corone) builds - -	Mar. 10 - -	July1,hasyoung ones.
Oats (avena sativa) sown - - -	Mar. 10—18 -	Mar. 16, Apr. 13.
Golden-crowned wren (sylvia regulus) } sings - - - - -	Mar. 12, Apr. 30 {	Apr. 15, May 22; seen Dec. 23, Jan. 26.
Aspen (populus tremula) fl. - -	Mar. 12 - -	Feb. 26, Mar. 28.
Common elder (sambucus nigra) l. -	Mar. 13—20 -	Jan. 24, April 22.
Laurel (prunus laurocerasus) fl. -	Mar. 15, May 21	Apr. 2, May 27.
Chrysomela Gottingensis ap. - -	Mar. 15.	
Black ants (formica nigra) ap. - -	Mar. 15, Apr. 22	Mar. 2, May 18.
Ephemeræ bisetæ ap. - - -	Mar. 16.	
Gooseberry (ribes grossularia) l. -	Mar. 17, Apr. 11	Feb. 26, Apr. 9.
Common stitchwort (stellaria holostea) fl.	Mar. 17, May 19	Mar. 8, May 7.
Wood anemone (anemone nemorosa) fl. -	Mar. 17, Apr. 22	Feb. 27, Apr. 10.
Blackbird (turdus merula) lays - -	Mar. 17 - {	Apr 14; young ones May 19.
Raven (corvus corax) sits - - -	Mar. 17 - -	Apr. 1, builds.
Wheatear (sylvia œnanthe) ap. - -	Mar. 18—30 {	Mar. 13, May 23; last seen Oct. 26.

	WHITE.	MARKWICK.
Musk-wood crowfoot (adoxa moschatel-lina) fl. - - - - - -	Mar. 18, Apr. 13	Feb. 23, Apr. 28.
Willow-wren (sylvia trochilus) ap. - -	Mar. 19, Apr. 13	Mar. 30, May 16; sits May 27; last seen Oct. 23.
Fumaria bulbosa fl. - - - - -	Mar. 19.	
Elm (ulmus campestris) fl. - - -	Mar. 19, Apr. 4 -	Feb. 17, Apr. 25.
Turkey (meleagris gallopavo) lays - -	Mar. 19, Apr. 7	Mar. 18—25; sits Apr. 4; young ones Apr. 30.
House-pigeons (columba domestica) sit -	Mar. 20 - -	Ma. 20, young hatched.
Marsh-marigold (caltha palustris) fl. -	Mar. 20, Apr. 14	Mar. 22, May 8.
Buzz-fly (bombylius medius) ap. - -	Mar. 21, Apr. 28	Mar. 15, Apr. 30.
Sand-martin (hirundo riparia) ap. - -	Mar. 21, Apr. 12	Apr. 8, May 16; last seen Sept. 8.
Snake (coluber natrix) ap. - - -	Mar. 22—30	Mar. 3, Apr. 29; last seen Oct. 2.
Horse ant (formica herculeana) ap. -	Mar. 22, Apr. 18	Feb. 4, Mar. 26; last seen Nov. 12.
Greenfinch (loxia chloris) sings - -	Mar. 22, Apr. 22	Mar. 6, Apr. 26.
Ivy (hedera helix) berries ripe - -	Mar. 23, Apr. 14	Feb. 16, May 19.
Periwinkle (vinca minor) fl. - -	Mar. 25 - -	Feb. 6, May 7.
Spurge laurel (daphne laureola) fl. -	Mar. 25, Apr. 1 -	Apr. 12—22.
Swallow (hirundo rustica) ap. - -	Mar. 26, Apr. 20	Apr. 7—27; last seen Nov. 16.
Blackcap (sylvia atricapilla) heard -	Mar. 26, May 4	Apr. 14, May 18; seen Apr. 14, May 20; last seen Sept. 19.
Young ducks hatched - - -	Mar. 27 - -	Apr. 6, May 16.
Golden saxifrage (chrysosplenium oppo-sitifolium) fl. - - - -	Mar. 27, Apr. 9 -	Feb. 7, Mar. 27.
Martin (hirundo urbica) ap. - -	Mar. 28, May 1	Apr. 14, May 8; last seen Dec. 8.
Double hyacinth (hyacinthus orientalis) fl.	Mar. 29, Apr. 22	Mar. 13, Apr. 24.
Young geese (anas anser) - - -	Mar. 29 - -	Mar. 29, Apr. 19.
Wood-sorrel (oxalis acetosella) fl. -	Mar. 30, Apr. 22	Feb. 26, Apr. 26.
Ring-ousel (turdus torquatus) seen -	Mar. 30, Apr. 17	Oct. 11.
Barley (hordeum sativum) sown -	Mar. 31, Apr. 30	Apr. 12, May 20.
Nightingale (sylvia luscinia) sings -	Apr. 1, May 1	Apr. 5, July 4; last seen Aug. 29.
Ash (fraxinus excelsior) fl. - -	Apr. 1, May 4 -	Mar. 16, May 8.
Spiders' webs on the surface of the ground	Apr. 1.	
Chequered daffodil (fritillaria meleagris) fl.	Apr. 2—24 - -	Apr. 15, May 1.
Julus terrestris ap. - - - -	Apr. 2.	
Cowslip (primula veris) fl. - -	Apr. 3—24 - -	Mar. 3, May 17.
Ground-ivy (glecoma hederacea) fl. -	Apr. 3—15 - -	Mar. 2, Apr. 16.
Snipe pipes - - - - -	Apr. 3.	
Box-tree (buxus sempervirens) fl. -	Apr. 3 - -	Mar. 27, May 8.
Elm (ulmus campestris) l.ˡⁱ - -	Apr. 3 - -	Apr. 2, May 19.
Gooseberry (ribes grossularia) fl. -	Apr. 3—14 - -	Mar. 21, May 1.
Currant (ribes hortense) fl. - -	Apr. 3—5 - -	Mar. 24, Apr. 28.
Pear-tree (pyrus communis) fl. - -	Apr. 3, May 29 -	Mar. 30, Apr. 30.
Lacerta vulgaris (newt or eft) ap. -	Apr. 4 -	Feb. 17, Apr. 15; last seen Oct. 9.
Dogs' mercury (mercurialis perennis) fl. -	Apr. 5—19 - -	Jan. 20, Apr. 16.
Wych elm (ulmus glabra seu montana of Smith) fl. - - - - -	Apr. 5 - -	Apr. 19, May 10.
Ladysmock (cardamine pratensis) fl. -	Apr. 6—20 - -	Feb. 21, Apr. 26.
Cuckoo (cuculus canorus) heard - -	Apr. 7—26 -	Apr. 15, May 3; last heard June 28.
Black-thorn (prunus spinosa) fl. -	Apr. May 10 -	Mar. 16, May 8.
Death-watch (termes pulsatorius) beats -	Apr. 7 -	Mar. 28, May 28.
Gudgeon spawns - - - - -	Apr. 7.	

	WHITE.	MARKWICK.
Redstart (sylvia phænicurus) ap. - -	Apr. 8—28 - {	Apr. 5; sings Apr. 25; last seen Sept. 30.
Crown imperial (fritillaria imperialis) fl.	Apr. 8—24 - -	Apr. 1, May 13.
Titlark (alauda pratensis) sings - -	Apr. 9—19 - {	Apr. 14—29; sits June 16—17.
Beech (fagus sylvatica) l. - - - -	Apr. 10, May 8 -	Apr. 24, May 25.
Shell-snail (helix nemoralis) comes out in troops - - - -	Apr. 11, May 9 -	May 17, June 11 ap.
Middle yellow wren ap. - - - -	Apr. 11.	
Swift (hirundo apus) ap. - - - -	Apr. 13, May 7 -	Apr. 28, May 19.
Stinging-fly (conops calcitrans) ap. -	Apr. 14, May 17.	
Whitlow-grass (draba verna) fl. - -	Apr. 14 - -	Jan. 15, Mar. 24.
Larch-tree (pinus-larix rubra) l. -	Apr. 14 - -	Apr. 1, May 9.
Whitethroat (sylvia cinerea) ap. - -	Apr. 14, May 14 {	Apr. 14, May 5; sings May 3—10; last seen Sept. 23.
Red ant (formica rubra) ap. - - -	Apr. 14 - -	Apr. 9, June 26.
Mole cricket (gryllus gryllotalpa) churs -	Apr. 14.	
Second willow or laughing wren ap. -	Apr. 14—19—23.	
Red rattle (pedicularis sylvatica) fl. -	Apr. 15—19 -	Apr. 10, June 4.
Common flesh-fly (musca carnaria) ap. -	Apr. 15.	
Lady-cow (coccinella bipunctata) ap. -	Apr. 16.	
Grasshopper lark (alauda locustæ voce) ap. - - - - - -	Apr. 16—30.	
Willow wren, its shivering note heard -	Apr. 17, May 7 -	Apr. 28, May 14.
Middle willow wren (regulus non cristatus medius) ap. - - -	Apr. 17—27.	
Wild cherry (prunus cerasus) fl. - -	Apr. 18, May 12	Mar. 30, May 10.
Garden cherry (prunus cerasus) fl. -	Apr. 18, May 11	Mar. 25, May 6.
Plum (prunus domestica) fl. - - -	Apr. 18, May 5 -	Mar. 24, May 6.
Harebell (hyacinthus non-scriptus seu scilla nutans of Smith) fl. -	Apr. 19—25 -	Mar. 27, May 8.
Turtle (columba turtur) coos - - -	Apr. 20—27 -	May 14, Aug. 10, seen.
Hawthorn (cratægus seu mespilus oxycantha of Smith) fl. -	Apr. 20, June 11	Apr. 19, May 26.
Male fool's orchis (orchis mascula) fl. -	Apr. 21 - -	Mar. 29, May 13.
Blue-flesh fly (musca vomitoria) ap. -	Apr. 21, May 23.	
Black snail or slug (limax ater) abounds -	Apr. 22 - -	Feb. 1, Oct. 24 ap.
Apple-tree (pyrus malus sativus) fl. -	Apr. 22, May 25	Apr. 11, May 26.
Large bat ap. - - - - - -	Apr. 22, June 11.	
Strawberry, wild wood (fragaria vesca sylv.) fl. - - - - -	Apr. 23—29 -	Apr. 8—9.
Sauce alone (erysimum alliaria) fl. -	Apr. 23 - -	Mar. 31, May 8.
Wild or bird cherry (prunus avium) fl. -	Apr. 24 - -	Mar. 30, May 10.
Apis hypnorum ap. - - - - -	Apr. 24.	
Musca meridiana ap. - - - -	Apr. 24, May 28.	
Wolf-fly (asilus) ap. - - - -	Apr. 25.	
Cabbage butterfly (papilio brassicæ) ap. -	Apr. 28, May 20	Apr. 29, June 10.
Dragon-fly (libellula) ap. - - -	Apr. 30, May 21 {	Apr. 18, May 13; last seen Nov. 10.
Sycamore (acer pseudoplatanus) fl. -	Apr. 30, June 6 - May 1.	Apr. 20, June 4.
Bombylius minor ap. - - - -	May 1.	
Glow-worm (lampyris noctiluca) shines -	May 1, June 11 -	June 19, Sept. 28.
Fern-owl or goatsucker (caprimulgus europæus) ap. - - -	May 1—26 - -	May 16, Sept. 14.
Common bugle (ajuga reptans) fl. -	May 1 - -	Mar. 27, May 10.
Field crickets (gryllus campestris) crink	May 2—24.	
Chaffer or May-bug (scarabæus melolontha) ap. - - - -	May 2—26 -	May 2, July 7.
Honeysuckle (lonicera periclymenum) fl.	May 3—30 -	Apr. 24, June 21.
Toothwort (lathræa squamaria) fl. -	May 4—12.	
Shell-snails copulate - - - -	May 4, June 17.	
Sedge warbler (sylvia salicaria) sings -	May 4 - -	June 2—30.

	WHITE.	MARKWICK.
Mealy-tree (viburnum lantana) fl. - -	May 5—17 - -	Apr. 25, May 22.
Fly - catcher (stoparola muscicapa grisola) ap. - - - - -	May 10—30 -	Apr. 29, May 21.
Apis longicornis ap. - - - - - -	May 10, June 9.	
Sedge warbler (sylvia salicaria) ap. -	May 11—13 -	Aug. 2.
Oak (quercus robur) fl. - - - -	May 13—15 -	Apr. 29, June 4.
Admiral butterfly (papilio atalanta) ap. -	May 13.	
Orange-tip (papilio cardamines) ap. -	May 14 - -	Mar. 30, May 19.
Beech (fagus sylvatica) fl. - - -	May 15—26 -	Apr. 23, May 28.
Common maple (acer campestre) fl. -	May 16 - -	Apr. 24, May 27.
Barberry-tree (berberis vulgaris) fl. -	May 17—26 -	Apr. 28, June 4.
Wood argus butterfly (papilio ægeria) ap.	May 17.	
Orange lily (lilium bulbiferum) fl. - -	May 18, June 11	June 14, July 22.
Burnet moth (sphinx filipendulæ) ap. -	May 18, June 13	May 24, June 26.
Walnut (juglans regia) l. - - -	May 18 - -	Apr. 10, June 1.
Laburnum (cytisus laburnum) fl. - -	May 18, June 5 -	May 1, June 23.
Forest fly (hippobosca equina) ap. -	May 18, June 9.	
Saintfoin (hedysarum onobrychis) fl. -	May 19, June 8 -	May 21, July 28.
Peony (pæonia officinalis) fl. - -	May 20, June 15	Apr. 18, May 26.
Horsechestnut (æsculus hippocastanum) fl. - - - - - - - -	May 21, June 9 -	Apr. 19, June 7.
Lilac (syringa vulgaris) fl. - -	May 21 -	Apr. 15, May 30.
Columbine (aquilegia vulgaris) fl. -	May 21—27 -	May 6, June 13.
Medlar (mespilus germanica) fl. -	May 21, June 20	Apr. 8, June 19.
Tormentil (tormentilla erecta seu offici- nalis of Smith) fl. - - - -	May 21 - -	Apr. 17, June 11.
Lily of the valley (convallaria majalis) fl.	May 22 - -	Apr. 27, June 13.
Bees (apis mellifica) swarm - - -	May 22, July 22	May 12, June 23.
Woodroof (asperula odorata) fl. -	May 22—25 -	Apr. 14, June 4.
Wasp, female (vespa vulgaris), ap. -	May 23 - {	Apr. 2, June 4; last seen Nov. 2.
Mountain ash (sorbus seu pyrus aucu- paria of Smith) fl. - - - -	May 23, June 8 -	Apr. 20, June 8.
Bird's-nest orchis (ophrys nidus avis) fl. -	May 24, June 11	May 18, June 12.
White-beam tree (cratægus seu pyrus aria of Smith) fl. - - - -	May 24, June 4 -	May 3.
Milkwort (polygala vulgaris) fl. -	May 24, June 7 -	Apr. 13, June 2.
Dwarf cistus (cistus helianthemum) fl. -	May 25 - -	May 4, Aug. 8.
Gelder rose (viburnum opulus) fl. -	May 26 - -	May 10, June 8.
Common elder (sambucus nigra) fl. -	May 26, June 25	May 6, June 17.
Cantharis noctiluca ap. - - -	May 26.	
Apis longicornis bores holes in walks -	May 27, June 9.	
Mulberry-tree (morus nigra) l. -	May 27, June 13	May 20, June 11.
Wild service-tree (cratægus seu pyrus torminalis of Smith) fl. - - -	May 27 - -	May 13, June 19.
Sanicle (sanicula europæa) fl. - -	May 27, June 13	Apr. 23, June 4.
Avens (geum urbanum) fl. - -	May 28 - -	May 9, June 11.
Female fool's orchis (orchis morio) fl. -	May 28 - -	Apr. 17, May 20.
Ragged Robin (lychnis flos cuculi) fl. -	May 29, June 1 -	May 12, June 8.
Burnet (poterium sanguisorba) fl. -	May 29 - -	Apr. 30, Aug. 7.
Foxglove (digitalis purpurea) fl. -	May 30, June 22	May 23, June 15.
Corn-flag (gladiolus communis) fl. -	May 30, June 20	June 9, July 8.
Serapias longifolia fl. - - -	May 30, June 13.	
Raspberry (rubus idæus) fl. - -	May 30, June 31	May 10, June 16.
Herb Robert (geranium Robertianum) fl.	May 30 - -	Mar. 7, May 16.
Figwort (scrophularia nodosa) fl. -	May 31 - -	May 12, June 20.
Gromwell (lithospermum officinale) fl. -	May 31 - -	May 10—24.
Wood spurge (euphorbia amygdaloides) fl.	June 1 - -	Mar. 23, May 13.
Ramsons (allium ursinum) fl. - -	June 1 - -	Apr. 21, June 4.
Mouse-ear scorpion grass (myosotis scor- pioides) fl. - - - - - -	June 1 - -	Apr. 11, June 1.
Grasshopper (gryllus grossus) ap. - -	June 1—14- {	Mar. 25, July 6; last seen Nov. 3.

	WHITE.	MARKWICK.
Rose (rosa hortensis) fl. - - - -	June 1—21 - -	June 7, July 1.
Mouse-ear hawkweed (hieracium pilosella) fl. - - - - - -	June 1, July 16 -	Apr. 19, June 12.
Buckbean (menyanthes trifoliata) fl. -	June 1 - -	Apr. 20, June 8.
Rose-chaffer (scarabæus auratus) ap. -	June 2—8 - -	Apr. 18, Aug. 4.
Sheep (ovis aries) shorn - - - -	June 2—23- -	May 23, June 17.
Water-flag (iris pseudo-acorus) fl. -	June 2 - -	May 8, June 9.
Cultivated rye (secale cereale) fl. -	June 2 - -	May 27.
Hounds tongue (cynoglossum officinale) fl. - - - - - -	June 2 - -	May 11, June 7.
Helleborine (serapias latifolia) fl. -	June 2, Aug. 6 -	July 22, Sept. 6.
Green-gold fly (musca cæsar) ap. -	June 2.	
Argus butterfly (papilio moera) ap. -	June 2.	
Spearwort (ranunculus flammula) fl.	June 3 - -	Apr. 25, June 13.
Birdsfoot trefoil (lotus corniculatus) fl. -	June 3 - -	Apr. 10, June 3.
Fraxinella, or white dittany (dictamus albus) fl. - - - - - -	June 3—11- -	June 9, July 24.
Phryganea nigra ap. - - - - -	June 3.	
Angler's May-fly (ephemera vulg.) ap.	June 3—14.	
Ladies' finger (anthyllis vulneraria) fl.	June 4 - -	June 1, Aug. 16.
Bee-orchis (ophrys apifera) fl. - -	June 4, July 4.	
Pink (dianthus deltoides) fl. - - -	June 5—19- -	May 26, July 6.
Mock orange (philadelphus coronarius) fl.	June 5 - -	May 16, June 23.
Libellula virgo ap. - - - - -	June 5—20.	
Vine (vitis vinifera) fl. - - -	June 7, July 30 -	June 18, July 29.
Portugal laurel (prunus lusitanicus) fl. -	June 8, July 1 -	June 3, July 16.
Purple-spotted martagon (lilium martagon) fl. - - - - - -	June 8—25- -	June 18, July 19.
Meadow cranes-bill (geranium pratense) fl. - - - - - -	June 8, Aug. 1.	
Black bryony (tamus communis) fl. -	June 8 - -	May 15, June 21.
Field pea (pisum sativum arvense) fl.	June 9 - -	May 15, June 21.
Bladder campion (cucubalus behen seu silene inflata of Smith) fl. - -	June 9 - -	May 4, July 13.
Bryony (brionia alba) fl. - - -	June 9 - -	May 13, Aug. 17.
Hedge-nettle (stachys sylvatica) fl. -	June 10 - -	May 28, June 24.
Bittersweet (solanum dulcamara) fl. -	June 11 - -	May 15, June 20.
Walnut (juglans regia) fl. - - -	June 12 - -	Apr. 18, June 1.
Phallus impudicus ap. - - - -	June 12, July 23.	
Rosebay willow-herb (epilobium angustifolium) fl. - - - - - -	June 12 - -	June 4, July 28.
Wheat (triticum hybernum) fl. - -	June 13, July 22	June 4—30.
Comfrey (symphytum officinale) fl. -	June 13 - -	May 4, June 23.
Yellow pimpernel (lysimachia nemorum) fl. - - - - - -	June 13—30 -	Apr. 10, June 12.
Tremella nostoc ap. - - - - -	June 15, Aug. 24.	
Buckthorn (rhamnus catharticus) fl. -	June 16 - -	May 25.
Cuckow-spit insect (cicadia spumaria) ap.	June 16 - -	June 2—21.
Dog-rose (rosa canina) fl. - - -	June 17, 18 -	May 24, June 21.
Puff-ball (lycoperdon bovista) ap. -	June 17, Sept. 3	May 6, Aug. 19.
Mullein (verbascum thapsus) fl. - -	June 18 - -	June 10, July 22.
Viper's bugloss (echium anglicum seu vulgare of Smith) fl. - - - -	June 19 - -	May 27, July 3.
Meadow hay cut - - - - -	June 19, July 20	June 13, July 7.
Stag-beetle (lucanus cervus) ap. - -	June 19 - -	June 14—21.
Borage (borago officinalis) fl. - -	June 20 - -	Apr. 22, July 26.
Spindle-tree (euonymus europæus) fl.	June 20 - -	May 11, June 25.
Musk thistle (carduus nutans) fl. - -	June 20, July 4 -	June 4, July 25.
Dogwood (cornus sanguinea) fl. - -	June 21 - -	May 28, June 27.
Field scabious (scabiosa arvensis) fl. -	June 21 - -	June 16, Aug. 14.
Marsh thistle (carduus palustris) fl. -	June 21—27 -	May 15, June 19.
Dropwort (spiræa filipendula) fl. -	June 22, July 9 -	May 8, Sept. 3.
Great wild valerian (valeriana officinalis) fl.	June 22, July 7 -	May 22, July 21.

	WHITE.	MARKWICK.
Quail (perdix coturnix) calls - - -	June 22, July 4 -	July23;seenSept.1–18.
Mountain willow-herb (epilobium montanum) fl. - - - -	June 22 -	June 5—21.
Thistle upon thistle (carduus crispus) fl.	June 23—29 -	May 22, July 22.
Cow-parsnip (heracleum sphondylium) fl.	June 23 -	May 27, July 12.
Earth-nut (bunium bulbocastanum seu flexuosum of Smith) fl. - - -	June 23 -	May 4—31.
Young frogs migrate - - - -	June 23, Aug. 2.	
Œstrus curvicauda ap. - - -	June 24.	
Vervain (verbena officinalis) fl. -	June 24 -	June 10, July 17.
Corn poppy (papaver rhoeas) fl. -	June 24 -	Apr. 30, July 15.
Self-heal (prunella vulgaris) fl. -	June 24 -	June 7—23.
Agrimony (agrimonia eupatoria) fl. -	June 24—29 -	June 7, July 9.
Great horse-fly (tabanus bovinus) ap. -	June 24, Aug. 2.	
Greater knapweed (centaurea scabiosa) fl.	June 25 -	June 7, Aug. 14.
Mushroom (agaricus campestris) ap. -	June 26, Aug. 30	Apr. 16, Aug. 16.
Common mallow (malva sylvestris) fl. -	June 26 -	May 27, July 13.
Dwarf mallow (malva rotundifolia) fl. -	June 26 -	May 12, July 20.
St. John's wort (hypericum perforatum) fl.	June 26 -	June 15, July 12.
Broom-rape (orobanche major) fl. -	June 27, July 4 -	May 9, July 25.
Henbane (hyoscyamus niger) fl. -	June 27 -	May 13, June 19.
Goats-beard (tragopogon pratense) fl. -	June 27 -	June 5—14.
Deadly nightshade (atropa belladonna) fl.	June 27 -	May 22, Aug. 14.
Truffles begin to be found - -	June 28, July 29.	
Young partridges fly - - -	June 28, July 31	July 8—28.
Lime-tree (tilia europæa) fl. - -	June 28, July 31	June 12, July 30.
Spearthistle (carduus lanceolatus) fl.	June 28, July 12	June 27, July 18.
Meadow-sweet (spiræa ulmaria) fl. -	June 28 -	June 16, July 24.
Greenweed (genista tinctoria) fl. -	June 28 -	June 4, July 24.
Wild thyme (thymus serpyllum) fl. -	June 28 -	June 6, July 19.
Stachys germanica fl. - - -	June 29, July 20.	
Day-lily (hemerocallis flava) fl. -	June 29, July 4 -	May 29, June 9.
Jasmine (jasminum officinale) fl. -	June 29, July 30	June 27, July 21.
Holly-oak (alcea rosea) fl. - - -	June 29, Aug. 4 -	July 4, Sept. 7.
Monotropa hypopithys fl. - - -	June 29, July 23.	
Ladies' bedstraw (galium verum) fl. -	June 29 -	June 22, Aug. 3.
Galium palustre fl. - - - -	June 29.	
Nipplewort (lapsana communis) fl. -	June 29 -	May 30, July 24.
Welted thistle (carduus acanthoides) fl. -	June 29.	
Sneezewort (achillea ptarmica) fl. -	June 30 -	June 22, Aug. 3.
Musk mallow (malva moschata) fl. -	June 30 -	June 9, July 14
Pimpernel (anagallis arvensis) fl. -	June 30 -	May 4, June 22.
Hoary beetle (scarabæus solstit.) ap. -	June 30, July 17.	
Corn saw-wort (serratula arvensis seu carduus arvensis of Smith) fl. -	July 1 -	June 15, July 15.
Pheasant's eye (adonis annua seu autumnalis of Smith) fl. - - - -	July 1 -	April 11, July 15.
Red eyebright (euphrasia seu bartsia odontites of Smith) fl. - - -	July 2 -	June 20, Aug. 10.
Thorough wax (bupleurum rotundifol.) fl.	July 2.	
Cockle (agrostemma githago) fl. -	July 2 -	May 14, July 25.
Ivy-leaved wild lettuce (prenanthes muralis) fl. - - - - -	July 2 -	June 2, July 25.
Feverfew (matricaria seu pyrethrum parthenium of Smith) fl. - - -	July 2 -	June 19, July 24.
Wall pepper (sedum acre) fl. - -	July 3 -	June 8, July 12.
Privet (ligustrum vulgare) fl. - -	July 3 -	June 3, July 13.
Common toadflax (antirrhinum linaria) fl.	July 3 -	June 21, Aug. 3.
Perennial wild flax (linum perenne) fl. -	July 4 -	Apr. 21, July 6.
Whortleberries (vaccinium ulig.) ripe -	July 4—24.	
Yellow base rocket (reseda lutea) fl. -	July 5 -	July 19.
Blue-bottle (centaurea cyanus) fl. -	July 5 -	May 15, Oct. 14.
Dwarf carline thistle (carduus acaulis) fl.	July 5—12 -	June 30, Aug. 4.

	WHITE.	MARKWICK.
Bull-rush, or cat's-tail (typha latifolia) fl.	July 6 - -	June 29, July 21.
Spiked willow-herb (lythrum salicaria) fl.	July 6 - -	June 24, Aug. 17.
Black mullein (verbascum niger) fl. -	July 6.	
Chrysanthemum coronarium fl. -	July 6 - -	May 28, July 28.
Marigolds (calendula officinalis) fl. -	July 6—9 - -	Apr. 20, July 16.
Little field madder (sherardia arvensis) fl.	July 7 - -	Jan 11, June 6.
Calamint (melissa seu thymus calamintha of Smith) fl. - - - -	July 7 - -	July 21.
Black horehound (ballota nigra) fl. -	July 7 - -	June 16, Sept 12.
Wood betony (betonica officinalis) fl. -	July 8—19 - -	June 10, July 15.
Round-leaved bell-flower (campanula rotundifolia) fl. - - - -	July 8 - -	June 12, July 29.
All-good (chenopodium bonus henricus) fl.	July 8 - -	Apr. 21, June 15.
Wild-carrot (daucus carota) fl. -	July 8 - -	June 7, July 14.
Indian cress (epopæolum majus) fl. -	July 8—20 - -	June 11, July 25.
Cat-mint (nepata cataria) fl. - -	July 9.	
Cow-wheat (melampyrum sylvaticum seu pratense of Smith) fl. - -	July 9 - -	May 2, June 22.
Crosswort (valantia cruciata seu galium cruciatum of Smith) fl. - - -	July 9 - -	Apr. 10, May 28.
Cranberries ripe - - - -	July 9—27.	
Tufted vetch (vicia cracca) fl. - -	July 10 - -	May 31, July 8.
Wood vetch (vicia sylvatica) fl. -	July 10.	
Little throat-wort (campanula glomerata) fl. - - - - -	July 11 - -	July 28, Aug. 18.
Sheep's scabious (jasione montana) fl. -	July 11 - -	June 10, July 25.
Pastinaca sylvestris fl. - - -	July 12.	
White lily (lilium candidum) fl. -	July 12 - -	June 21, July 22.
Hemlock (conium maculatum) fl. -	July 13 - -	June 4, July 20.
Caucalis anthriscus, fl. - - -	July 13.	
Flying ants ap. - - - -	July 13—Aug. 11	Aug. 29, Sept. 19.
Moneywort (lysimachia nummularia) fl. -	July 13 - -	June 14, Aug. 16.
Scarlet martagon (lilium chalcedonicum) fl. - - - - -	July 14—Aug. 4	June 21, Aug. 6.
Lesser stitchwort (stellaria graminea) fl.	July 14 - -	May 8, June 23.
Fool's parsley (æthusa cynapium) fl. -	July 14 - -	June 9, Aug. 9.
Dwarf elder (sambucus ebulus) fl. -	July 14—29.	
Swallows and martins congregate -	July 14, Aug. 29	Aug. 12, Sept. 8.
Potato (solanum tuberosum) fl. -	July 14 - -	June 3, July 12.
Angelica sylvestris fl. - - -	July 15.	
Digitalis ferruginea fl. - - -	July 15—25.	
Ragwort (senecio jacobæa) fl. - -	July 15 - -	June 22, July 13.
Golden rod (solidago virgaurea) fl. -	July 15 - -	July 7, Aug. 29.
Star thistle (centaurea calcitrapa) fl.	July 16 - -	July 16, Aug. 16.
Tree primrose (œnothera biennis) fl.	July 16 - -	June 12, July 18.
Peas (pisum sativum) cut - - -	July 17, Aug. 14	July 13, Aug. 15.
Galega officinalis fl. - - - -	July 17.	
Apricots (prunus armeniaca) ripe -	July 17, Aug. 21	July 5, Aug. 16.
Clown's allheal (stachys palustris) fl. -	July 17 - -	June 12, July 14.
Branching willow-herb (epilobium ramosum) fl. - - - - -	July 17.	
Rye-harvest begins - - -	July 17, Aug. 7.	
Yellow centaury (chlora perfoliata) fl. -	July 18, Aug. 15	June 15, Aug. 13.
Yellow vetchling (lathyrus aphaca) fl.	July 18.	
Enchanter's nightshade (circæa lutetiana) fl. - - - - -	July 18 - -	June 20, July 27.
Water hemp agrimony (eupatorium cannabinum) fl. - - - -	July 18 - -	July 4, Aug. 6.
Giant throatwort (campanula trachelium) fl. - - - - -	July 19 - -	July 13, Aug. 14.
Eyebright (euphrasia officinalis) fl. - -	July 19 - -	May 28, July 19.
Hops (humulus lupulus) fl. - -	July 19, Aug. 10	July 20, Aug. 17.
Poultry moult - - - - -	July 19.	

	WHITE.	MARKWICK.
Dodder (cuscuta europæa seu epithymum of Smith) fl. - - - -	July 20 - -	July 9, Aug. 7.
Lesser centaury (gentiana seu chironia centaurium of Smith) fl.	July 20 - -	June 3, July 19.
Creeping water parsnep (sium nodiflorum) fl. - - - - -	July 20 - -	July 10, Sept. 11.
Common spurrey (spergula arvensis) fl. -	July 21 - -	Apr. 10, July 16.
Wild clover (trifolium pratense) fl. -	July 21 - -	May 2, June 7.
Buckwheat (polygonum fagopyrum) fl. -	July 21 - -	June 27, July 10.
Wheat harvest begins - - -	July 21, Aug. 23	July 11, Aug. 26.
Great burr-reed (sparganium erectum) fl.	July 22 - -	June 10, July 23.
Marsh St. John's-wort (hypericum elodes) fl. - - - - -	July 22—31	June 16, Aug 10.
Sun-dew (drosera rotundifolia) fl. -	July 22 - -	Aug. 1.
March cinquefoil (comarum palustre) fl.	July 22 - -	May 27, July 12.
Wild cherries ripe - - - -	July 22.	
Lancashire asphodel (anthericum ossifragum) fl. - - - - -	July 22 - -	June 31, July 29.
Hooded willow-herb (scutellaria galericulata) fl. - - - - -	July 23 - -	June 2, July 31.
Water dropwort (œnanthe fistulosa) fl. -	July 23.	
Horehound (marrubium vulgare) fl. -	July 23.	
Seseli caruifolium fl. - - - -	July 24.	
Water plantain (alisma plantago) fl. -	July 24 - -	May 1, July 31.
Alopecurus myosuroides fl. - -	July 25.	
Virgin's bower (clematis vitalba) fl. -	July 25, Aug. 9 -	July 13, Aug. 14.
Bees kill the drones - - - -	July 25.	
Teasel (dipsacus sylvestris) fl. - -	July 26 - -	July 16, Aug. 3.
Wild marjoram (origanum vulgare) fl.	July 26 - -	July 17, Aug. 29.
Swifts (hirundo apus) begin to depart	July 27—29	Aug. 5.
Small wild teasel (dipsacus pilosus) fl.	July 28, 29.	
Wood sage (teucrium scorodonia) fl.	July 28 - -	June 17, July 24.
Everlasting pea (lathyrus latifolius) fl. -	July 28 - -	June 20, July 30.
Trailing St. John's-wort (hypericum humifusum) fl. - - - - -	July 29 - -	May 20, June 22.
White hellebore (veratrum album) fl.	July 30 - -	July 18—22.
Camomile (anthemis nobilis) fl. -	July 30 - -	June 21, Aug. 20.
Lesser field scabious (scabiosa columbaria) fl. - - - - -	July 30 - -	July 13, Aug. 9.
Sun-flower (helianthus multiflorus) fl.	July 31, Aug. 6 -	July 4, Aug. 22.
Yellow loosestrife (lysimachia vulgaris) fl.	July 31 - -	July 2, Aug. 7.
Swift (hirundo apus) last seen - -	July 31, Aug. 27	Aug. 11.
Oats (avena sativa) cut - - -	Aug. 1—16-	July 26, Aug. 19.
Barley (hordeum sativum) cut- - -	Aug. 1—26-	July 27, Sept. 4.
Lesser hooded willow-herb (scutellaria minor) fl. - - - - -	Aug. 1 - -	Aug. 8, Sept. 7.
Middle fleabane (inula disinterica) fl. -	Aug. 2 - -	July 7, Aug. 3.
Apis manicata ap. - - - -	Aug. 2.	
Swallow-tailed butterfly (papilio machaon) ap. - - - - -	Aug. 2 - {	Apr. 20, June 7; last seen Aug. 28.
Whame or burrel-fly (œstrus bovis) lays eggs on horses - - - -	Aug. 3—19.	
Sow thistle (sonchus arvensis) fl. -	Aug. 3 - -	June 17, July 21.
Plantain fritillary (papilio cinxia) ap. -	Aug. 3.	
Yellow succory (picris hieracioides) fl. -	Aug. 4 - -	June 6—25.
Musca mystacea ap. - - - -		
Canterbury bells (campanula medium) fl.	Aug. 5 - -	June 5, Aug. 11.
Mentha longifolia fl. - - - -	Aug. 5.	
Carline thistle (carlina vulgaris) fl. -	Aug. 7 - -	July 21, Aug. 18.
Venetian sumach (rhus cotinus) fl. -	Aug. 7 - -	June 5, July 20.
Ptinus pectinicornis ap. - - -	Aug. 7.	
Burdock (arctium lappa) fl. - -	Aug. 8 - -	June 17, Aug. 4.
Fell-wort (gentiana amarella) fl. - -	Aug. 8, Sept. 3.	

	WHITE.	MARKWICK.
Wormwood (artemisia absinthium) fl. -	Aug. 8 - -	July 22, Aug. 21.
Mugwort (artemisia vulgaris) fl. -	Aug. 8 - -	July 9, Aug. 10.
St. Barnaby's thistle (centauria solstit.) fl.	Aug. 10.	
Meadow saffron (colchicum autumnale) fl.	Aug. 10, Sept. 13	Aug. 15, Sept. 29.
Michaelmas daisy (aster tradescantia) fl.	Aug. 12, Sept. 27	Aug. 11, Oct. 8.
Meadow rue (thalictrum flavum) fl. -	Aug. 14.	
Sea holly (eryngium maritimum) fl. -	Aug. 14.	
China aster (aster chinensis) fl. -	Aug. 14, Sept. 28	Aug. 6, Oct. 2.
Boletus albus ap. - - -	Aug. 14 - -	May 10.
Less Venus looking-glass (campanula hybrida) fl. - - -	Aug. 15 - -	May 14.
Carthamus tinctorius fl. - - -	Aug. 15.	
Goldfinch (fringilla carduelis) young broods ap. - - -	Aug. 15 - -	June 15.
Lapwings (tringa vanellus) congregate -	Aug. 15, Sept. 12	Sept. 25, Feb. 4.
Black-eyed marble butterfly (papilio semele) ap. - - -	Aug. 15.	
Birds reassume their spring notes -	Aug. 16.	
Devil's bit (scabiosa succisa) fl. -	Aug. 17 - -	June 22, Aug. 23.
Thistle-down floats - - - -	Aug. 17, Sept. 10.	
Ploughman's spikenard (conyza squarrosa) fl. - - -	Aug. 18.	
Autumnal dandelion (leontodon autumnale) fl. - - -	Aug. 18 - -	July 25.
Flies about in windows - - -	Aug. 18.	
Linnets (fringilla linota) congregate -	Aug. 18, Nov. 1-	Aug. 22, Nov. 8.
Bulls make their shrill autumnal noise -	Aug. 20.	
Aster amellus fl. - - - -	Aug. 22.	
Balsam (impatiens balsamina) fl. -	Aug. 23 - -	May 22, July 26.
Milk thistle (carduus marinus) fl. -	Aug. 24 - -	Apr. 21, July 18.
Hop-picking begins - - -	Aug. 24, Sept. 17	Sept. 1—15.
Beech (fagus sylvatica) turns yellow -	Aug. 24, Sept. 22	Sept. 5—29.
Soapwort (saponaria officinalis) fl. -	Aug. 25 - -	July 19, Aug. 23.
Ladies' traces (ophrys spiralis) fl. -	Aug. 27, Sept. 12	Aug. 18, Sept. 18.
Small golden black-spotted butterfly (papilio phlæas) ap. - - -	Aug. 29.	
Swallow (hirundo rustica) sings -	Aug. 29 - -	Apr. 11, Aug. 20.
Althæa frutex (hibiscus syriacus) fl. -	Aug. 30, Sept. 2	July 20, Sept. 28.
Great fritillary (papilio paphia) ap. -	Aug. 30.	
Willow red under-wing moth (phalæna pacta) ap. - - - -	Aug. 31.	
Stone curlew (otis œdicnemus) clamours -	Sept. 1, Nov. 7 -	June 17.
Phalæna russula ap. - - -	Sept. 1.	
Grapes ripen - - - -	Sept. 4, Oct. 24 -	Aug. 31, Nov. 4.
Wood-owls hoot- - - -	Sept. 4, Nov. 9.	
Saffron butterfly (papilio hyale) ap. -	Sept. 4 - -	Aug. 5, Sept. 26.
Ring-ousel appears on its autumnal visit	Sept. 4—30.	
Flycatcher (muscicapa grisola, last seen -	Sept. 6—29	Sept. 4—30.
Beans (vicia faba) cut - - -	Sept. 11 - -	Aug. 9, Oct. 14.
Ivy (hedera helix) fl. - - -	Sept. 12, Oct. 2 -	Sept. 18, Oct. 28.
Stares (starlings) congregate - -	Sept. 12, Nov. 1	June 4, Mar. 21.
Wild honeysuckle fl. a second time -	Sept. 24.	
Woodlark sings - - - -	Sept. 28, Oct. 24.	
Woodcock (scolopax rusticola) returns -	Sept. 29, Nov. 11 {	Oct. 1, Nov. 1; young ones April 28; last seen April.
Strawberry-tree (arbutus unedo) fl. -	Oct. 1 - -	May 21, Dec. 10.
Wheat sown - - - -	Oct. 3, Nov. 9	Sept. 23, Oct. 19.
Swallows last seen. (N.B. The house-martin the latest) - - -	Oct. 4, Nov. 5 -	Nov. 16.
Redwing (turdus iliacus) comes -	Oct. 10, Nov. 10 {	Oct. 1, Dec. 18; sings Feb. 10, Mar. 21; last seen April 13.

* Misprint for Lady's tresses, so-called because the flower imitates a plait of hair. It has a beautiful scent.

	WHITE.	MARKWICK.
Fieldfare (turdus pilaris) returns - -	Oct. 12, Nov. 23 {	Oct. 13, Nov. 18; last seen May 1.
Gossamer fills the air - - - -	Oct. 15—27.	
Chinese hollyoak (alcea rosea) fl. - -	Oct. 19 - -	July 7, Aug. 21.
Hen chaffinches congregate - - -	Oct. 20, Dec. 31.	
Wood-pigeons come - - - - -	Oct. 23, Dec. 27.	
Royston crow (curvus cornix) returns -	Oct. 23, Nov. 29 {	Oct. 13, Nov. 17; last seen April 15.
Snipe (scolopax gallinago) returns - -	Oct. 25, Nov. 20 {	Sept. 29, Nov. 11; last seen April 14.
Tortoise begins to bury himself - -	Oct. 27, Nov. 26.	
Rooks (corvus frugilegus) return to their nest-trees }	Oct. 31, Dec. 25 -	June 29, Oct. 20.
Bucks grunt - - - - - -	Nov. 1.	
Primrose (primula vulgaris) fl. - -	Nov. 10 - -	Oct. 7, Dec. 30.
Green whistling plover ap. - - -	Nov. 13, 14.	
Helvella mitra ap. - - - - -	Nov. 16.	
Greenfinches flock - - - - -	Nov. 27.	
Hepatica fl. - - - - - -	Nov. 30, Dec. 29	Feb. 19.
Furze (ulex europæus) fl. - - -	Dec. 4—21 - -	Dec. 16—31.
Polyanthus (primula polyanthus) fl. -	Dec. 7—16 - -	Dec. 31.
Young lambs dropped - - - -	Dec. 11—27 -	Dec. 12, Feb. 21.
Moles work in throwing up hillocks -	Dec. 12—23.	
Helleborus fœtidus fl. - - - -	Dec. 14—30.	
Daisy (bellis perennis) fl. - - -	Dec. 15 - -	Dec. 26—31.
Wall-flower (cheiranthus cheiri seu fruticulosus of Smith) fl. - - - }	Dec. 15 - -	Nov. 5.
Mezereon fl. - - - - - -	Dec. 15.	
Snowdrop fl. - - - - - -	Dec. 29.	

In sese vertitur annus.[1]

[1] The years return upon themselves.